Not too far north of the atomic proving grounds, a new blast shook the entertainment world when NOEL COWARD appeared in Las Vegas and overnight became America's #1 nightclub performer. Prior to this debut Coward had been known to American audiences only as a playwright, author, actor, director, composer, brilliant wit . . . and legend.

Mr. Coward made another spectacular debut in the fall of 1955, this time before an American audience of many millions, when he appeared, with Mary Martin, in the first of three big TV shows.

Now he is introduced to the widest audience of American readers in this collection of his best stories, short plays and songs.

NOEL

SHORT STORIES,
SHORT PLAYS
AND SONGS BY

COWARD

INTRODUCED AND EDITED BY
GILBERT MILLSTEIN

A DELL FIRST EDITION

Published by DELL PUBLISHING COMPANY, INC.
261 Fifth Avenue, New York 16, N. Y.

Library of Congress Catalog Card No. 55-11760

Cover design by Edward Sorel

Photograph of Noel Coward by Mark Swain

Designed and produced by
Western Printing and Lithographing Company

Printed in U. S. A.

TABLE OF CONTENTS

★

INTRODUCTION

NOEL COWARD is a British playwright, actor, composer, director and nightclub performer of such ferocious chic that he has frequently been mistaken, principally by others, for a mere exquisite, a condition he regards as a historical deception, like the Cardiff Giant. In this connection, he was once reported to have ended the run of a production simply because it had failed to sell out every night. When it was pointed out to him that the enterprise *had*, after all, been making money, Coward is said to have replied, with metrical hauteur, "I shall go first class. I shall go third class. But I shall not go second class." Some years later, upon having this reported to him, Coward responded with a remarkably reflective flow of profanity, to which he added, in flat prose, "I *love* to go second class." He went on to say that he thought himself ham enough to be roused by half-empty houses into giving an even more stimulating performance and that he had closed the show (it was a New York revival of six of his nine short plays, "Tonight At 8:30") on the ground that extended runs made him nervous: He had suffered a severe breakdown after playing in "The Vortex" for two years. In any case, three days before the closing, in the airless hours between a matinee and an evening performance, he was discovered minutely rehearsing a number of scenes with his co-star, the late Gertrude Lawrence, who, like others of his intimates, invariably referred to Coward as "The Master."

Coward is, in fact, a kind of agreeably sardonic, knowledgeably tailored Proteus, who has managed to hide a voracious professional appetite beneath an appearance of delighted dilettantism. (An intimate friend of his once

observed that while "Noel is inclined to be annoyed by
financial details, in business, he's just about as vague as
United States Steel.") Between the years 1910, when, at
the age of 10, he made his first professional stage appearance (at a guinea and a half a week) as Prince Mussel
in a gummous thing for children known as "The Goldfish,"
and 1955, when he made his American nightclub debut
in Las Vegas, creating a smash hit (at $30,000 a week),
Coward has worked unceasingly and often at terrifying
speed. He has, of course, been highly gratified by and well
paid for his work and professes to be unimpressed by the
haste with which it was accomplished.

This haste, he has written, "seemed to excite gossip-
writers inordinately, although why the public should care
whether a play takes three days or three years to write I
shall never understand. Perhaps they don't." Of his first
play, which he turned out in his late teens, Coward has
set down that ". . . Conception was only removed from
achievement by the actual time required for putting the
words on paper (and) it was completed inside a week.
It was entitled 'The Last Trick' and was a melodrama in
four acts." He "manufactured" for Gilbert Miller, as he
puts it, "I'll Leave It To You" within a few weeks. "Hay
Fever" took him three days and was conceived in an
English garden. He wrote the entire second act of "Bitter
Sweet," songs and all, in a hospital bed the night before
he was scheduled to be operated on, inelegantly enough,
for hemorrhoids. ". . . In the morning," he has said, "consciousness that I had accomplished a considerable job of
work upheld me throughout the routine indignities that
I had to endure." One of his greatest successes, "Blithe
Spirit," was written in six days. ". . . Disdaining archness
and false modesty," he wrote of it, "I will admit that I
knew it was witty, I knew it was well constructed, and I
also knew that it would be a success," to which he added,
with what he terms a "detached pride . . . not to be confused with boastfulness," that "Beyond a few typograph-
ical errors I made no corrections, and only two lines of

the original script were ultimately cut."

Altogether, Coward has written forty-five dramas, comedies and revues, some of them of consequence; roughly fourscore songs, several dozen of pleasing durability; three volumes of autobiography, two of short stories and one of parody, which got him involved in a lawsuit from which he extricated himself by settling with the aggrieved. (The parody was called "The Spangled Unicorn," and Coward had illustrated it with photographs of people who, he had been assured by a bookdealer in Marseilles who had sold him the pictures, were long since dead. One was not, or was at least alive enough to sue.) He has sung, danced and performed in dozens of his own and other plays and he has written, directed and appeared in motion pictures. In the fall of 1955, with Mary Martin, for whom he wrote the play, "Pacific 1860," some years ago, Coward made the first of three American television appearances, for which the Columbia Broadcasting System paid him about half a million dollars, a sum Coward thinks of as "lovely." ("Lovely," as employed by him, appears to be a mildly ironic blanket endorsement, applying equally to large amounts of money and other pleasing incidents, and is often modified by him, depending on the degree of pleasure, by the words "utterly" or "simply.")

Miss Martin's relationship with Coward, although more recent than Coward's relationship, say, with Alfred Lunt and Lynn Fontanne, Miss Lawrence, or the producer and director, John C. Wilson, who handled Coward's American theatrical affairs for better than two decades, is about as indicative as anything else of his unquestionably bravura involvement with the theatre, people and life in general, possibly in that order. ("I think he's got out of life just what he wanted," his American attorney, David Holtzmann, has said. "Fame may very well be the least of it. It's the satisfaction of doing a professional job. The only snobbery he recognizes is the snobbery of the intellect. And as for the theatre, why, the tides of his affection flow over show people. Those are the ones he loves.")

Miss Martin recalled not long ago that her first intimation of Coward's mortality had come to her in a movie theatre in her home town, Weatherford, Tex., in 1935. "I saw him in 'The Soundrel,'" she said, "and, gosh, I went for him hook, line and sinker. I had a fabulous thing about this man. He was the epitome of sophistication."

A number of years later, having come to New York and made her first triumph singing "My Heart Belongs to Daddy," in the musical comedy, "Leave It to Me," she was sitting in a nightclub called "Leon & Eddie's," which has since become a parking lot, when a slim, correct man materialized at her table in the half light. "He kissed me on the forehead," Miss Martin recalled, "and said, 'I've never seen anything so exciting in my life, my dear. You were absolutely wonderful, wonderful,' and walked away. Someone said to me, 'Do you know who that was? That was Noel Coward.' That was the clincher. I didn't actually meet him until he came backstage at 'One Touch of Venus' and introduced himself to me—to *me*, can you imagine? Then, when I was in 'Lute Song,' he sent me a cable saying, 'Would you be interested if I wrote a play for you?' I was so upset I had to have a cigarette. I don't smoke. It was the dream of my life ever to work with this man.

"The play was 'Pacific 1860.' The night before the dress rehearsal we had a fight over a bow on a dress and a big hat he wanted me to wear. It wasn't my style. Oh, there were other things, too, but that was the focal point, in a way. It got so silly and out of proportion we both had hysterics before it was all over. I'd never had hysterics before. I'd never been able to give way to emotions even when I should have on stage. It got bigger and bigger and bigger and our friendship went . . ." She slowly stretched her arms wide. "This was the biggest hurt I ever had in my life or ever hope to have again. I would wake up in the night truly sobbing because of the terrible break with this man. I'd write him long letters, think of telephone calls, cables, anything to make it up. But I tore up the letters and I didn't make the calls. One night, a couple of years later, I was playing in 'South Pacific' and an enormous box of flowers came backstage. In it there was a card, and it said, 'Mary, may I come back?' He had been out front seeing the show." Miss Martin paused, overcome for the moment in poignant reminiscence. "When he came back to my dressing room," she went on, finally, "he knelt and kissed my hand and said, 'I can't stand it. You can't stand it. It's all too silly. I've been miserable for two years. How asinine can people get?' He made me a bigger person."

The passage with Miss Martin is characteristic of the flair, both instinctive and acquired, with which Coward's whole life has been, so to speak, stage-managed. At the age of 6 he was sent to a day school kept by a Miss Willington. "I didn't care for her," he has written. "On one occasion when she had been irritating me over some little question of English grammar I bit her arm right through to the bone, an action which I have never for an instant regretted." When he was 9 he made the acquaintance of several small girls and "forced them to act a tragedy that I had written, but they were very silly and during the performance forgot their lines and sniggered, so I hit the eldest one on the head with a wooden spade, the whole affair thus ending in tears and a furious quarrel between the mothers involved." One night during the Twenties, he was sitting in a London restaurant with a young man and two girls when an elderly woman with dyed hair and a fevered manner came dancing by with a gigolo. "Look at the old hag," one of the girls said. Coward rose from his seat, cut in on the gigolo, kissed the woman and said, quite loudly, "Darling, how are you?" The woman was the mother of the young man in his party.

When he first became a celebrity, it was Coward's insouciant habit to sit in a box at his opening nights and conspicuously open congratulatory telegrams. When his play, "Home Chat," aroused a remarkable hostility in an opening-night audience, a member of which shouted at him, "We expected a better play," Coward answered, "So did I," and added that he had also expected better manners. After the opening of "Sirocco," another angry failure, he was spat on as he left the theatre and commented equably later that "the next day I had to send my evening coat to the cleaners." It is utterly characteristic of him that he should have sung "Mad Dogs and Englishmen" to both Winston Churchill and Franklin D. Roosevelt, although not, however, to Dwight Eisenhower, with whom he talked politics in North Africa. Having been offered the job of setting up a propaganda office in Paris during the second World War, he found it quite natural to drop in on Churchill and ask his advice in the matter. "Get into a warship and see some action!" Churchill trumpeted. "Go and sing to them when the guns are firing—that's your job!" "With, I think commendable restraint," Coward wrote of that interview, "I bit back the retort that if the morale of the Royal Navy was at such low ebb that the troops were unable to go into action without me singing 'Mad Dogs and Englishmen' to them, we were in trouble at the outset and that, although theoretically, 'Singing when the guns are firing' sounds extremely gallant, it is, in reality, impracticable, because during a naval battle all ship's companies are at action stations and the only place for me to sing would be in the wardroom by myself."

Nevertheless, in the end Coward wound up doing pretty much what Churchill had told him to do, singing to thousands of troops in the Middle East, the Far East and elsewhere. He also wrote, co-directed and starred in what is undoubtedly one of the finest war pictures ever made, "In Which We Serve." (In the first World War, Coward was drafted. He fell on his head while training and "ended [his] inglorious career as a soldier in an advanced state of neurasthenia . . ." He later noted that psychoanalysts believed this to be "self-engendered and the outward manifestation of inner conflict; that the concussion and coma . . . was in reality a form of hysteria induced by a subconscious . . . urge to break away from the rigours of unfamiliar army routine." He has been at pains to point out that the urge was "far from subconscious" and that the fall on his head was motivated "by an unsubconscious wooden slat which tripped me up.")

By and large, everywhere he has gone in the world—which is most of it, since he is of a notoriously inquiring disposition—Coward has gone trailing great clouds of charm behind him, followed by thunders of "Noel" and "Darling," and taking tea, martinis (champagne, he says, gives him acid) or Coca-Cola impartially as the occasion demanded. More than two decades ago, the British playwright and critic, St. John Ervine, spoke of Coward as "one of the three most widely celebrated young men of our time, the others being the Prince of Wales and Colonel Lindbergh." He went on to say that "Whatever our opinion of his work may be, we cannot ignore Mr. Coward: he is a figure of his age, a faithful representative of a part of the spirit of his time." In 1933 young lady students of the Katherine Gibbs School, a business school, without explanation named him the "ideal employer," and in 1935 the senior class at Princeton University voted him a greater playwright (135 votes) than either Shakespeare (107) or O'Neill (79).

"A great many of the people he meets, he likes very much," John C. Wilson observed recently, "and the ones he doesn't, he pretends he does. The point is, he's always charming. He fends off bores by being absolutely enchanting and then ushering them to the door and they never know they weren't expected. I've never seen him with his defenses down. They may have been down, but he certainly never showed it. His reaction to situations which would be normally disastrous is to pull himself together and be bright as a button. His reaction to adversity is always up. And so it is with people—the only way one can tell his close friends from casual acquaintances is that he spends more time with his friends. There's no other way."

Coward has been neither astonished nor unduly edified by the revelation of his humanity, and his estimate of himself, while on the whole favorable, is cool, proud and disenchanted. "The general illusion that success automatically transfers ordinary human beings into monsters of egotism has, in my case, been shattered," he noted. "I am neither conceited, overbearing, rude, nor insulting to waiters. People often refer to me as being 'simple' and 'surprisingly human.' All of which is superficially gratifying but, on closer analysis, quite idiotic. Conceit is more often than not an outward manifestation of an inward sense of inferiority. Stupid people are frequently conceited because they are subconsciously frightened of being found out; scared that some perceptive eye will pierce through their façade and discover the timid confusion behind it. As a general rule, the most uppish people I have met have been those who have never achieved anything whatsoever.

"I am neither stupid nor scared, and my sense of my own importance to the world is relatively small. On the other hand, my sense of my importance to myself is tremendous. I am all I have, to work with, to play with, to suffer and to enjoy. It is not the eyes of others that I am wary of, but my own. I do not intend to let myself down more than I can possibly help, and I find that the fewer illusions that I have about me or the world around me, the better company I am for myself." He appears to be irritated only—and in a charming way, of course—by the legend of Noel Coward. "All that was important for monotonous future reference," he once wrote, "was the created image—the talented, neurotic, sophisticated playboy. In later years this imaginary, rather tiresome figure suffered occasional eclipses, but they were of short duration. 'Calvalcade,' 'Bitter Sweet,' 'This Happy Breed,' 'Brief Encounter,' and 'In Which We Serve' scratched a little gloss off the legend, but not enough to damage it irreparably. It still exists today in 1952, with the slight modification that I am now an ageing playboy, still witty, still brittle, and still sophisticated, although the sophistication is alas, no longer up-to-date, no longer valid. It is a depressing thought to be a shrill relic at the age of fifty-two, but there is still a little time left, and I may yet snap out of it."

Neither the shrill relic nor anyone else would have been prepared to predict that Coward would be singing "I'll See You Again," "I'll Follow My Secret Heart" or a naughty parody of Cole Porter's "Let's Do It" in Las Vegas in the late spring of 1955, although at an early age, upon being taken to church he was "unimpressed by everything except the music to which I danced immediately in the aisle before anyone could stop me, and, upon being hoisted back into the pew, fell into such an ungovernable rage that I had to be taken home." (Coward was born on Dec. 16, 1899, in Teddington, a suburb of London, the son of an employee of a music-publishing firm, and of the daughter of a naval officer who played the piano and had a taste for the theatre. His schooling was fragmentary and marked by bold truancies.) His manifestation in Las Vegas was the work of a rough-hewn but imaginative man named Joe Glaser, a New York booking agent, whose greatest previous triumph had been the rehabilitation and enrichment of Louis Armstrong, the trumpet player, and whose principal reading matter consists of Variety and The Billboard, the Good Books of show business.

Glaser sent an advance man to sound Coward out in London on the notion of performing in a nightclub in Las Vegas (Coward had already been playing the exclusive Café de Paris for several seasons) and then turned up in London himself to close the deal, succumbing at the same time, without a struggle, to Coward's charm. "I been around some important people, but never like him, which I can verify and prove," Glaser has since said. "I knew I could get along with him. I enjoyed him and he enjoyed me. I just acted natural and the more natural I acted, the better he liked it. He says right away, 'There's something peculiar about you I like. When were you born?' I said Dec. 17. He started to laugh like hell. It was the day after him. He said, 'We're both Sagitarrius or whatever you call it.' " Glaser now signs all letters, telegrams and cables to

Coward "Your greatest admirer and pal."

Upon the conclusion of his opening show in Las Vegas, Coward rushed backstage to await an admiring crush of Hollywood visitors who agreed loudly among themselves that he had brought to Las Vegas what they called "class." In a quiet interval between congratulations, the actor, David Niven, remarked thoughtfully to an acquaintance, "You know, I once wrote a novel—a bad one—in which I spoke of opening nights and what I called the 'eddies of mass insincerity' that accompany them. Nothing like that here. Listen to the joyful screams of the mad pack."

GILBERT MILLSTEIN

SHORT STORIES

★

STOP ME IF YOU'VE HEARD IT

"PLEASE GOD," she whispered to herself. "Don't let it be the one about the Englishman and the Scotsman and the American in the railway carriage, nor the one about the old lady and the parrot, nor the one about the couple arriving at the seaside hotel on their honeymoon night! I'll settle for any of the others, but please, please, merciful God, not one of those three—I can't bear it. If it's one of those three, particularly the Englishman and the Scotsman and the American in the railway carriage, I shall go mad —I shall do something awful—I'll shriek—I'll make a hideous scene—I'll bash his head in with a bottle——."

Her husband, sitting opposite to her at the table, cleared his throat. Her whole body became rigid at the sound. With a great effort she took a cigarette out of a little blue enamel pot in front of her and lit it. Some of the general conversation at the table died away into polite attentiveness. She was aware, wretchedly aware, of the quick, resigned glance that Louis Bennet exchanged with Susan Lake. She looked at her host, Carroll Davis, leaning forward politely, his good-looking face blank. Carroll was kind; Carroll understood; his manners were dictated by his heart—he wouldn't hurt Budge's feelings for the world; he would listen appreciatively and laugh at the right moments, saving his loudest, most convincing laugh for the point at the end, and Budge would never know, never remotely suspect for an instant, that he hadn't been amused.

The others would laugh too, of course, but there would be an undertone of malice—their alert, cruel minds would be silently communicating with one another. "Poor Budge," they would be saying, "the kiss of death on every party—he never knows when to stop. In the old days he used to be funny on the stage, but now he's even lost that. Why does Carroll ask him? Obviously, for Marty's sake— she *must* know how awful he is. She *must* realise, deep down, that she's married to the most monumental cracking bore. Why doesn't she leave him? Why doesn't she at least come to parties without him? She knows we're all old friends—she knows we love her. Why the hell doesn't she leave that aggressive, over-eager little megalomaniac at home?"

Marty drew deeply at her cigarette. Jane and Shirley and Bobby Peek were still talking and laughing at the other end of the table. They had not noticed—yet. They were still unaware of doom. Budge shot them a quick, resentful look and cleared his throat again. They glanced up, and the light went out of their faces. Shirley stubbed out her cigarette, put her head back, and closed her eyes. Marty felt an insane desire to lean forward and slap her face violently. "Listen, you languid, supercilious bitch, Budge Ripley's going to tell a story. Sit up and listen, and mind your manners! He was telling stories—amusing people— millions of people—making them laugh until they cried, making them forget their troubles—making them happy— before you were born. All right, all right—he may be a bore now—he may have lost his touch, but mind your manners—lean forward, look interested, whatever you feel—bitch—spoiled, supercilious bitch."

"Stop me if you've heard it." Budge's voice grated in the silence. He caught her eye, and, painting an encouraging smile on her face, she leaned forward. No more than a split second could have passed before he began, but in that split second the years of her life with him rolled out before her—jerkily and confused in memory, like a panorama she had been taken to see at Earl's Court when she was a child.

She had been getting on quite well twenty years ago when she had first met him—chorus and understudy and small parts here and there. She had never been pretty, but there was something about her that people liked, a comic quality of personality. Carroll had always asked her to his grandest parties regardless of the fact that she was really small fry in the theatre compared with his other guests. She had had wit always, a realistic, unaffected Cockney humour, quick as a whip but without malice. It was at one of Carroll's parties, in this same house, that Budge had first noticed her. It was in this same house three years later, after she had slept with him hundreds of times, that he had told her that his divorce was through and that they could get married. Seventeen years ago that was. They had moved into Number 18—she had been so proud, so grateful, and he had been so sweet. No more stage work for her, no more prancing on and off for finales and opening choruses. She ran the house fairly well, went to all Budge's first nights in a box or stalls; stood with him afterwards in the dressing room while people came rushing in to say how marvellous he was. "Funnier than ever." "I laughed until I was sick." "Nobody like you, Budge, the comic genius of the age—your inventiveness—your pathos too—only really great comedians have that particular quality, that subtle balance between grave and gay——"

They gave parties at Number 18—gay and amusing, lasting sometimes until dawn. Several years of happiness passed—several years of excitement and success and occasional holidays in the South of France. Then, insidiously, the rot began to set in—very gradually at first, so gradually, indeed, that it was a long time before she even suspected it. A strange rot, composed of circumstances, small, psychological maladjustments, mutual irritations, sudden outbursts of temper; the subtle cause of it all still obscure, still buried deep.

It was about then that he began to be unfaithful to her—nothing serious—just an occasional roll in the hay with someone who took his fancy. Marty found out about this almost immediately, and it hurt her immeasurably. She reasoned with herself, of course; she exerted every ounce of common sense and self-control, and succeeded bleakly in so far that she said nothing and did nothing, but from then on everything was different. There was no security any more, and no peace of mind. It was not that she cared so desperately about him popping into bed every now and then with someone else—only a fool, married happily for years to a famous star, would make a fuss about that. It was something deeper, something that bewildered and gnawed at her, something more important that she knew to exist but somehow could not identify.

It was later—quite a long while later—that the truth suddenly became clear to her, that the answer to this riddle, which had tortured her for so long, suddenly flashed onto her consciousness with all the blatant clarity of a neon light—a neon light sign flashing on and off with hideous monotony one vulgar, piteous word, jealousy. Budge was jealous of her. He was jealous of her wit, her gaiety, her friends. She could have slept with other men as much as she liked, and he would have forgiven her; she could have drunk herself into a coma every night, and he would have been loving and concerned and understanding; but because she was herself, because people of all kinds found her good company, because she could, without effort, embroider an ordinary anecdote with genuine humour and infectious gaiety and be loved and welcomed for it—this he could never forgive; for this, she realised in that blinding flash of revelation, he would hate her until the day he died.

"Stop me if you've heard it!" That idiotic, insincere phrase—that false, unconvincing opening gambit—as though people ever had the courage to stop anyone however many times they'd heard it! Human beings could be brave—incredibly brave about many things. They could fly in jet-propelled planes; fling themselves from the sky in parachutes; hurl themselves fully clothed into turbulent seas to rescue drowning children; crawl on their mortal stomachs through bullet-spattered mud and take pins out of unexploded bombs or shells or whatever they were, but no one, no one in the whole twisting, agonised world was brave enough to say loudly and clearly, "Yes, I have heard it. It is dull and unfunny; it bores the liver and lights out of me. I have heard it over and over again, and if I have to hear it once more in any of the years that lie between me and the grave, I'll plunge a fork into your silly throat—I'll pull out your clacking tongue with my nails."

Marty suddenly caught sight of her hands. One was resting on the table; the other was holding her cigarette; both were trembling. She looked miserably round the table. They were all listening with exaggerated courtesy. Shirley was looking down, her long, scarlet-tipped fingers scratching about among the bread crumbs by her plate, making them into little patterns, a circle with one larger one in the middle, then a triangle. Budge's voice grated on. The Englishman, the Scotsman, and the American, "I say you know," "Och aye," "Gee." Marty stared across the years at his face. There it was, aged a little, but not much changed since she had loved it so; the same kindly, rather protuberant blue eyes, the fleshy nose, the straw-coloured hair, the wide comedian's mouth. His head was bent forward eagerly. He was talking a trifle too quickly because somewhere writhing deep inside him was a suspicion that his audience was not wholly with him, he hadn't quite got them. He finished the Scotsman's bit. Bobby Peek laughed, and Marty could have flung her arms round his neck and hugged him for it.

Budge's eyes shone with pleasure—"Gee, Buddy!" There was quite a loud laugh at the end of the story.

Carroll's kindness triumphed over his wisdom. "That was wonderful, Budge," he said. "Nobody can tell a story like you!"

Marty's heart died in her. She made a swift, instinctive movement to get up from the table. Budge looked at her, and his eyes hardened. She sat still as death, chained to her chair. He cleared his throat again.

"Marty half getting up like that reminded me of a good one," he said. "Do you know the one about the shy lady at the dinner party who wanted to go to the telephone?"

There was a polite murmur round the table. Shirley took her compact out of her bag and scrutinised her face in the little mirror. Louis Bennet coughed and exchanged another meaning glance with Susan. Budge pushed back his chair, recrossed his legs, and started. . . .

Marty stared down into her lap. There was some gold embroidery on her dress and it seemed to be expanding and changing into curious shapes because her eyes were filled with tears.

A hundred years later they were driving home. It was very late and the streets were almost empty. Budge was bunched up in his corner, sulky and silent. Marty stared at the back of Gordon's neck. Gordon drove well, but he was inclined to take risks. As a rule she was nervous and made him go slowly, but tonight she didn't care; she wouldn't have minded if he had driven at sixty miles an hour, careering along Oxford Street, crashing all the lights.

They arrived at Number 18 still in silence. Budge said good night to Gordon, and they went into the house. Rose had left the drink tray on the dining-room table and a plate of curly-looking sandwiches.

Budge poured himself out a whisky and soda. "I'm going on up," he said. "I'm tired."

Suddenly something seemed to crack inside Marty's head and she started to laugh. There was an ugly note in the laugh which she recognised, but she had neither the strength nor the will to do anything about it.

"You must be," she said. "Oh, my God, you certainly must be!"

Budge stopped at the door and turned and looked at her.

"And what exactly do you mean by that?" he asked.

"Don't you know?" she said, and her voice sounded shrill and hysterical. "Don't you really know? Haven't you got the faintest idea?"

Budge's already red face flushed, and he advanced two steps towards her. "What's the matter with you?"

Marty backed away from him, still laughing miserably.

"This is a good one," she said. "Stop me if you've heard it. Stop me if you've heard it or not, because if you don't you'll never forgive me and I shall never forgive myself."

Budge frowned. "Are you drunk?"

Marty shook her head dumbly. She felt the tears starting and tried to wipe them away with the back of her hand. Budge came closer to her and looked carefully into her face. There was no more anger in his eyes, only bewilderment. She tried to look away, to escape from that puzzled, anxious face. She backed farther and, feeling the edge of a chair under her knees, sank down into it.

"What's the matter?" Budge persisted. "You're not ill or anything, are you? Is it anything to do with me? What have I done?"

He put his hand on her arm. She felt the warmth of it through her sleeve. Suddenly her hysteria evaporated. She felt utterly exhausted, but no longer wild, no longer shrill and nerve-strained and cruel. She put her hand up, and pressed his more firmly onto her arm. Then she gave a little giggle, not a very convincing one really, but good enough.

"You may well ask what you've done," she said. "You may well ask if it's anything to do with you——"

Her voice broke, and, bringing her face against his stomach, she started crying thoroughly and satisfyingly.

Budge remained silent, but his other hand smoothed her hair away from her forehead. After a moment or two she controlled herself a bit and pushed him gently away.

"You've given me a miserable evening," she said huskily. "You never took your eyes off Shirley Dale from the beginning of supper to the end. You then behave like a sulky little boy all the way home in the car, and, to round the whole thing off, you help yourself to a drink without even asking if I want one and tell me you're tired! You're an inconsiderate, lecherous little pig and I can't imagine why I ever let you lead me to the Registry Office."

She rose to her feet and put her arms round him tightly.

She felt his body relax.

He gave a complacent chuckle. "Of all the bloody fools," he said. The warmth was back in his voice, the crisis had passed, and the truth was stamped down again deep into the ground.

He led her over to the table and mixed her a drink. "Shirley Dale, indeed—you must be out of your mind!"

She stood there with one arm still around him, sipping her drink. Nothing more was said until he had switched off the lights and they had gone upstairs. They talked ordinarily while they undressed; the familiarity of the bedroom seemed over-eager to put their hearts at ease.

Later on, after he had attacked his teeth in the bathroom with his customary violence, sprinkled himself with Floris 127, and put on his pyjamas, he came over and sat on the edge of her bed.

She smiled and reached out and patted his hand. Then gently, almost timidly, as though she were not quite sure of her ground, she pulled him towards her. "I've got something to tell you," she said. "Stop me if you've heard it."

★

CHEAP EXCURSION

JIMMY SAID, "Good night, Miss Reed," as she passed him in the passage. He did it ordinarily, no overtones or undertones, not the slightest indication of any secret knowledge between them, not even a glint in his eye, nothing beyond the correct subservience of an assistant stage-manager to a star. She answered him vaguely, that well-known gracious smile, and went on to the stage door, her heart pounding violently as though someone had sprung at her out of the dark.

In the car, she sat very still with her hands folded in her lap, vainly hoping that this very stillness, this stern outward quietness might help to empty her mind. Presently she gave up and watched herself carefully taking a cigarette out of her case and lighting it. "I am Diana Reed. *The* Diana Reed, lighting a cigarette. I am Diana Reed driving home in my expensive car to my expensive flat—I am tired after my performance and as I have a matinee to-morrow it is sane and sensible for me to go straight home to bed after the show. I am having supper with Jimmy to-morrow night and probably Friday night, too—there are hundreds of other nights and there is no reason whatsoever for me to feel lonely and agonised and without peace. I am Diana Reed—I am celebrated, successful, sought after—my play is a hit—my notices were excellent—except the *Sunday Times*. I am Diana Reed, famous, nearing forty and desperate. I am in love, not perhaps really in love like I was with Tony, nor even Pierre Chabron, but that was different, because it lasted such a little time and was foreign and mixed up with being abroad and everything, but I am in love all right and it's different again, it's always different and always difficult, and I wish to God I could be happy with it and give up to it, but there's too much to remember and too much to be careful of and too many people wanting to find out about it and gossip and smear it with their dirty fingers."

She let down the window and flicked her cigarette on to the pavement. It fell at the feet of a man in a mackintosh and a bowler hat, he looked up quickly and she drew herself back guiltily into the corner of the car. When she let herself into her flat and switched on the lights in the sitting-room its smug tidy emptiness seemed to jeer at her. It was a charming room. The furniture was good, plain and luxuriously simple in line. There was the small "Utrillo" that Tony had given her so many years ago—it had been in her flat in Cavendish Street for ages, and she had even taken it on tour with her. That sharp sunny little street with the pinkish-white walls and neat row of plane trees making shadows across the road. The only other picture in the room was a Marie Laurencin of a woman in a sort of turban. It was quite small and framed in glass. That she had bought herself a couple of years ago when she was in Paris with Barbara and Nicky. Nicky said it looked like a very pale peach with currants in it.

She pitched her hat on to the sofa where it lay looking apologetic, almost cringing, and went over and opened the window. Outside it was very quiet, only dark roof tops and an occasional light here and there, but there was a glow in the sky over Oxford Street, and she could hear the noise of traffic far away muffled by the houses and squares in between. Just round the corner in George Street she heard a taxi stop, the slam of its door and the sharp ping as the driver shut off the motor. It might so easily be Jimmy, knowing that she was coming home alone, knowing how happy it would make her if he just came along for ten minutes to say good night. The taxi with a grind of its gears started up and drove away, she could hear it for quite a while until there was silence again. It might still be Jimmy, he wouldn't be so extravagant as to keep a taxi waiting—he might at this very moment be coming up in the lift. In a few seconds she would hear the lift doors opening and then the front-door bell. She listened, holding her breath. He might, of course, come up the stairs in order not to be seen by the liftman. Jimmy was nothing if not cautious. She waited, holding on to the window-sill tight to prevent herself from going to the front door. There was no sound, and presently her tension relaxed and, after rather a disdainful glance at herself in the glass over the mantelpiece, she went and opened the front door anyhow. The landing was deserted. When she came back into the room again she discovered, to her great irritation, that she was trembling.

She sat on a chair by the door, bolt upright, like somebody in a dentist's waiting-room. It wouldn't have surprised her if a bright, professionally smiling nurse had suddenly appeared and announced that Doctor Martin was ready for her. Again she folded her hands in her lap. Someone had once told her that if you sat still as death with your hands relaxed, all the vitality ran out of the ends of your fingers and your nerves stopped being strained and tied up in knots. The frigidaire in the kitchen suddenly gave a little click and started whirring. She stared at various things in the room, as though by concentrating, identifying herself with them she could become part of them and not feel so alone. The pickled wood Steinway with a pile of highly-coloured American tunes on it; the low table in front of the fire with last week's *Sketch* and *Bystander,* and the week before last's *New Yorker,* symmetrically arranged with this morning's *Daily Telegraph* folded neatly on top; the Chinese horse on the mantelpiece, very aloof and graceful with its front hoof raised as though it were just about to stamp on something small and insignificant. Nicky had said it was "Ming" and Eileen had sworn it was "Sung" because she had once been to China on a cruise and became superior at the mention of anything remotely oriental.

There had been quite a scene about it culminating in Martha saying loudly that she'd settle for it being "Gong" or "Pong" if only everybody would bloody well shut up arguing and give her a drink.

Diana remembered how Jimmy had laughed, he was sitting on the floor next to Barbara. She looked at the empty space in front of the fireplace and saw him clearly, laughing, with his head thrown back and the firelight shining on his hair. That was during rehearsals, before anything had happened, before the opening night in Manchester and the fatal supper party at the Midland, when he had come over from his party at the other end of the French restaurant to tell her about the rehearsal for cuts the next afternoon. She remembered asking him to sit down and have a glass of champagne, and how politely he had accepted with a rather quizzical smile, almost an air of resignation. Then the long discussion about Duse and Bernhardt, and Jonathan getting excited and banging the table, and Jimmy sitting exactly opposite her where she could watch him out of the corner of her eye, listening intently to the conversation and twiddling the stem of his wine-glass. They had all been dressed, of course. Jonathan and Mary had come up from London especially for the first night, also Violet and Dick and Maureen. Jimmy was wearing a grey flannel suit and a blue shirt and navy blue tie; occasionally the corners of his mouth twitched as though he were secretly amused, but didn't want to betray it. Then he had caught her looking at him, raised his eyebrows just for the fraction of a second and, with the most disarming friendliness, patted her hand. "You gave a brilliant performance to-night," he said. "I felt very proud to be there." That was the moment. That was the spark being struck. If she had had any sense she'd have run like a stag, but instead of running, instead of recognising danger, there she had sat idiotically smiling, warmed and attracted. Not content with having had a successful first night and having given a good performance, not satisfied with the fact that her friends, her close intimate friends had trailed all the way from London to enjoy her triumph with her, she had had to reach out greedily for something more. Well, God knows she'd got it all right. Here it was, all the fun of the fair. The fruits of those few weeks of determined fascination. She remembered, with a slight shudder, how very much at her best she had been, how swiftly she had responded to her new audience, this nice-looking, physically attractive young man at least ten years younger than herself. How wittily she had joined in the general conversation. She remembered Jonathan laughing until he cried at the way she had described the dress re-hearsal of *Lady from the East*, when the Japanese bridge had broken in the middle of her love scene. All the time, through all the laughter, through all the easy intimate jokes, she had had her eye on Jimmy, watching for his re-sponse, drawing him into the circle, appraising him, not-ing his slim wrists, the way he put his head on one side when he asked a question, his eyes, his thick eyelashes, his wide square shoulders. She remembered saying "good night" to him with the others as they all went up in the lift together. Her suite was on the second floor, so she got out first. He was up on the top floor somewhere, sharing a room with Bob Harley, one of the small-part actors. She remembered, also, looking at herself in the glass in her bathroom and wondering, while she creamed her face, how attractive she was to him really, or how much of it was star glamour and position. Even then, so early in the business, she had begun to doubt. It was inevitable, of course, that doubt, particularly with someone younger than herself, more particularly still when that someone was assistant stage-manager and general understudy. A few days after that, she had boldly asked him to supper in her suite. She remembered at the time being inwardly horri-fied at such flagrant indiscretion; however, no one had found out or even suspected. He accepted with alacrity, arrived a little late, having had a bath and changed his suit, and that was that.

Suddenly, the telephone bell rang. Diana jumped, and with a sigh of indescribable relief went into her bedroom to answer it. Nobody but Jimmy knew that she was coming

home early—nobody else would dream of finding her in
at this time of night. She sat on the edge of the bed just
in order to let it ring once more, just to give herself time
to control the foolish happiness in her voice. Then she
lifted the receiver and said "Hallo," in exactly the right
tone of politeness only slightly touched with irritation.
She heard Martha's voice at the other end, and the sud-
denness of the disappointment robbed her of all feeling
for a moment. She sat there rigid and cold with a dead
heart. "My God," Martha was saying, "you could knock
me down with a crowbar, I couldn't be more surprised. I
rang up Jonathan and Barbara and Nicky, and finally the
Savoy Grill—this is only a forlorn hope—I never thought
for a moment you'd be in." Diana muttered something
about being tired and having a matinee to-morrow, her
voice sounded false and toneless. Martha went on. "I don't
want to be a bore, darling, but Helen and Jack have arrived from New York, and they're leaving on Saturday
for Paris, and they've been trying all day to get seats for
your show, and the nearest they could get was the four-
teenth row, and I wondered if you could do anything
about the house seats." With a great effort Diana said: "Of
course, darling, I'll fix it with the box-office to-morrow."
"You're an angel—here are Helen and Jack, they want to
say 'Hullo'." There was a slight pause, then Helen's husky
Southern voice: "Darling—"

Diana put her feet up and lay back on the bed, this was
going to be a long business. She was in command of herself
again, she had been a fool to imagine it was Jimmy, anyhow; he never telephoned unless she asked him to, that
was one of the most maddening aspects of his good behaviour. Good behaviour to Jimmy was almost a religion.
Excepting when they were alone together, he never for an
instant betrayed by the flicker of an eyelash that they
were anything more than casual acquaintances. There was
no servility in his manner, no pandering to her stardom.
On the contrary the brief words he had occasion to speak
to her in public were, if anything, a trifle brusque, per-

fectly polite, of course, but definitely without warmth. Helen's voice went on. She and Jack had had a terrible trip on the *Queen Mary*, and Jack had been sick as a dog for three whole days. Presently Jack came to the telephone and took up the conversation where Helen had left off. Diana lay still, giving a confident, assured performance, laughing gaily, dismissing her present success with just enough disarming professional modesty to be becoming. "But, Jack dear, it's a marvellous part—nobody could go far wrong in a part like that. You wait until you see it— you'll see exactly what I mean. Not only that, but the cast's good too, Ronnie's superb. I think it's the best performance he's given since *The Lights Are Low*, and, of course, he's heaven to play with. He does a little bit of business with the breakfast-tray at the beginning of the third act that's absolutely magical. I won't tell you what it is, because it would spoil it for you, but just watch out for it—— No, dear, I can't have supper to-morrow night— I've a date with some drearies that I've already put off twice—no, really, I couldn't again—how about lunch on Friday? You'd better come here and bring old Martha too—all right—it's lovely to hear your voice again. The seats will be in your name in the box-office to-morrow night. Come back-stage afterwards, anyhow, even if you've hated it—good-bye!"

Diana put down the telephone and lit a cigarette, then she wrote on the pad by the bed: "Reminder fix house seats, Jack and Helen." Next to the writing-pad was a thermos jug of Ovaltine left for her by Dora. She looked at it irritably and then poured some out and sipped it.

Jimmy had probably gone straight home. He generally did. He wasn't a great one for going out, and didn't seem to have many friends except, of course, Elsie Lumley, who'd been in repertory with him, but that was all over now and she was safely married, or was she? Elsie Lumley, judging from what she knew of her, was the type that would be reluctant to let any old love die, married or not married. Elsie Lumley! Pretty, perhaps rather over-vivacious, certainly talented. She'd be a star in a year or two if she behaved herself. The picture of Elsie and Jimmy together was unbearable—even though it all happened years ago—it *had* happened and had gone on for quite a long while, too. Elsie lying in his arms, pulling his head down to her mouth, running her fingers through his hair—— Diana put down the cup of Ovaltine with a bang that spilt a lot of it into the saucer. She felt sick, as though something were dragging her heart down into her stomach. If Jimmy had gone straight home he'd be in his flat now, in bed probably, reading. There really wasn't any valid reason in the world why she shouldn't ring him up. If he didn't answer, he was out, and there was nothing else to do about it. If he was in, even if he had dropped off to sleep, he wouldn't really mind her just ringing up to say "Good night."

She put out her hand to dial his number, then withdrew it again. It would be awful if someone else was there and answered the telephone, not that it was very likely, he only had a bed-sitting-room, but still he might have asked Bob Harley or Walter Grayson home for a drink. If Walter Grayson heard her voice on the telephone it would be all over the theatre by to-morrow evening. He was one of those born theatrical gossips, amusing certainly, and quite a good actor, but definitely dangerous. She could, of course, disguise her voice. Just that twang of refined cockney that she had used in *The Short Year*. She put out her hand again, and again withdrew it. "I'll have another cigarette and by the time I've smoked it, I shall decide whether to ring him up or not." She hoisted herself up on the pillow and lit a cigarette, methodically and with pleasure. The ache had left her heart and she felt happier—unaccountably so, really; nothing had happened except the possibility of action, of lifting the receiver and dialing a number, of hearing his voice—rather sleepy, probably—saying: "Hallo, who is it?" She puffed at her cigarette luxuriously watching the smoke curl up into the air. It was blue when it spiralled up from the end of the cigarette and grey when she blew it out of her mouth. It might, of course, irritate him being rung up, he might think she was being indiscreet or tiresome or even trying to check up on him: trying to find out whether he'd gone straight home, and whether he was alone or not.

How horrible if she rang up and he wasn't alone: if she heard his voice say, just as he was lifting the receiver: "Don't move, darling, it's probably a wrong number," something ordinary like that, so simple and so ordinary, implying everything, giving the whole game away. After all, he was young and good-looking, and they had neither of them vowed any vows of fidelity. It really wouldn't be so surprising if he indulged in a little fun on the side every now and then. Conducting a secret liaison with the star of the theatre in which you work must be a bit of a strain from time to time. A little undemanding, light, casual love with somebody else might be a relief.

Diana crushed out her cigarette angrily, her hands were shaking and she felt sick again. She swung her legs off the bed and, sitting on the edge of it, dialed his number viciously, as though she had found him out already; caught him red-handed. She listened to the ringing tone, it rang in twos—brrr-brrr—brrr-brrr. The telephone was next to his bed, that she knew, because once when she had dropped him home he had asked her in to see his hovel. It was a bed-sitting-room on the ground floor in one of those small, old-fashioned streets that run down to the river from John Street, Adelphi . . . brr-brr—brr-brrr—she might have dialed the wrong number. She hung up and then redialed it, again the ringing tone, depressing and monotonous. He was out—he was out somewhere—but where could he possibly be? One more chance, she'll call the operator and ask her to give the number a special ring, just in case there had been a mistake.

The operator was most obliging, but after a few minutes her voice, detached and impersonal, announced that there was no reply from the number and that should she call again later? Diana said no, it didn't matter, she'd call in the morning. She replaced the receiver slowly, wearily, as though it were too heavy to hold any longer, then she buried her face in her hands.

Presently she got up again and began to walk up and down the room. The bed, rumpled where she had lain on it, but turned down, with her nightdress laid out, ready to get into, tortured her with the thought of the hours she would lie awake in it. Even medinal, if she were stupid enough to take a couple of tablets before a matinee, wouldn't be any use to-night. That was what was so wonderful about being in love, it made you so happy! She laughed bitterly aloud and then caught herself laughing bitterly aloud and, just for a second, really laughed. Just a grain of humour left after all. She stopped in front of a long glass and addressed herself in a whisper, but with clear, precise enunciation as though she were trying to explain something to an idiot child. "I don't care," she said, "I don't care if it's cheap or humiliating or unwise or undignified or mad, I'm going to do it, so there. I'm going to do it now, and if I have to wait all night in the street I shall see him, do you understand? I shall see him before I go to sleep, I don't mind if it's only for a moment, I shall see him. If the play closes to-morrow night. If I'm the scandal of London. If the stars fall out of the sky. If the world comes to an end! I shall see him before I go to sleep to-night. If he's alone or with somebody else. If he's drunk, sober or doped, I intend to see him. If he is in and his lights are out I shall bang on the window until I wake him and if, when I wake him, he's in bed with man, woman or child, I shall at least know. Beyond arguments and excuses I shall *know*. I don't care how foolish and neurotic I may appear to him. I don't care how high my position is, or how much I trail my pride in the dust. What's position anyway, and what's pride? To hell with them. I'm in love and I'm desperately unhappy. I know there's no reason to be unhappy, no cause for jealousy and that I should be ashamed of myself at my age, or at any age, for being so uncontrolled and for allowing this God-

damned passion or obsession or whatever it is to conquer
me, but there it is. It can't be helped. No more fighting—
no more efforts to behave beautifully. I'm going to see him
—I'm going now—and if he is unkind or angry and turns
away from me I shall lie down in the gutter and howl."

She picked up her hat from the sofa in the sitting-room,
turned out all the lights, glanced in her bag to see if she
had her keys all right and enough money for a taxi, and
went out on to the landing, shutting the door furtively
behind her. She debated for a moment whether to ring for
the lift or slip down the stairs, finally deciding on the latter
as it would be better on the whole if the liftman didn't see
her. He lived in the basement and there was little chance
of him catching her unless by bad luck she happened to
coincide with any of the other tenants coming in. She
got out into the street unobserved and set off briskly in
the direction of Orchard Street. It was a fine night, fortunately, but there had been rain earlier on and the roads
were shining under the lights. She waited on the corner
of Orchard Street and Portman Square for a taxi that
came lolling towards her from the direction of Great Cumberland Place. She told the driver to stop just opposite
the Little Theatre in John Street, Adelphi, and got in.
The cab smelt musty and someone had been smoking a
pipe in it. On the seat beside her something white caught
her eye; she turned it over gingerly with her gloved hand,
and discovered that it was a programme of her own play,
with a large photograph of herself on the cover. She looked
at the photograph critically. The cab was rattling along
Oxford Street now, and the light was bright enough. The
photograph had been taken a year ago in a Molyneux
sports dress and small hat. It was a three-quarter length
and she was sitting on the edge of a sofa, her profile half
turned away from the camera. She looked young in it,
although the poise of the head was assured, perhaps a
trifle too assured. She looked a little hard too, she thought,
a little ruthless. She wondered if she was, really. If this
journey she was making now, this unwise, neurotic ex-

cursion, merely boiled down to being an unregenerate determination to get what she wanted, when she wanted it, at no matter what price. She thought it over calmly, this business of being determined. After all, it was largely that, plus undoubted talent and personality, that got her where she was to-day. She wondered if she were popular in the theatre. She knew the stage-hands liked her, of course, they were easy; just remembering to say "thank you," when any of them held open a door for her or "good evening," when she passed them on the stage was enough— they were certainly easy because their manners were good, and so were hers; but the rest of the company—not Ronnie, naturally, he was in more or less the same position as herself; the others, little Cynthia French, for instance, the ingenue, did she hate her bitterly in secret? Did she envy her and wish her to fail? Was all that wide-eyed, faintly servile eagerness to please, merely masking an implacable ambition, a sweet, strong, female loathing? She thought not on the whole, Cynthia was far too timid a creature, unless, of course, she was a considerably finer actress off the stage than she was on. Walter Grayson, she knew, liked her all right. She'd known him for years, they'd been in several plays together. Lottie Carnegie was certainly waspish at moments, but only with that innate defensiveness of an elderly actress who hadn't quite achieved what she originally set out to achieve. There were several of them about, old-timers without any longer much hope left of becoming stars, but with enough successful work behind them to assure their getting good character parts. They all had their little mannerisms and peculiarities and private fortresses of pride. Lottie was all right really, in fact as far as she, Diana, was concerned she was all sweetness and light, but, of course, that might be because she hated Ronnie. Once, years ago apparently, he had been instrumental in having her turned down for a part for which he considered her unsuitable. The others liked her well enough, she thought, at least she hoped they did; it was horrid not to be liked; but she hadn't any illusions as to what would happen if she made a false step. This affair with Jimmy, for example. If that became known in the theatre the whole of London would be buzzing with it. She winced at the thought. That would be horrible. Once more, by the light of a street lamp at the bottom of the Haymarket, she looked at the photograph. She wondered if she had looked like that to the man with the pipe to whom the programme had belonged; whether he had taken his wife with him or his mistress; whether they'd liked the play and cried dutifully in the last act, or been bored and disappointed and wished they'd gone to a musical comedy. How surprised they'd be if they knew that the next person to step into the taxi after they'd left was Diana Reed, Diana Reed herself, the same woman they had so recently been applauding, as she bowed and smiled at them in that shimmering silver evening gown—that reminded her to tell Dora at the matinee to-morrow that the paillettes where her cloak fastened were getting tarnished and that she must either ring up the shop or see if Mrs. Blake could deal with it in the wardrobe.

The taxi drew up with a jerk opposite the Little Theatre. Diana got out and paid the driver. He said: "Good night, Miss," and drove away down the hill, leaving her on the edge of the kerb feeling rather dazed, almost forgetting what she was there for. The urgency that had propelled her out of her flat and into that taxi seemed to have evaporated somewhere between Oxford Street and here. Perhaps it was the photograph on the programme, the reminder of herself as others saw her, as she should be, poised and well-dressed with head held high, not in contempt, nothing supercilious about it, but secure and dignified, above the arena. Those people who had taken that taxi, who had been to the play—how shocked they'd be if they could see her now, not just standing alone in a dark street, that wouldn't of course shock them particularly, merely surprise them; but if they could know, by some horrid clairvoyance, why she was here. If, just for an instant, they could see into her mind. Diana Reed, that smooth, gracious creature whose stage loves and joys and sorrows they had so often enjoyed, furtively loitering about in the middle of the night in the hopes of spending a few minutes with a comparatively insignificant young man whom she liked going to bed with. Diana resolutely turned in the opposite direction from Jimmy's street and walked round by the side of the Tivoli into the Strand. Surely it was a little more than that? Surely she was being unnecessarily hard on herself. There was a sweetness about Jimmy, a quality apart from his damned sex appeal. To begin with, he was well-bred, a gentleman. (What a weak, nauseating alibi, as though that could possibly matter one way or the other and yet, of course, it did.) His very gentleness, his strict code of behaviour. His fear, so much stronger even than hers, that anyone should discover their secret. Also he was intelligent, infinitely more knowledgable and better read than she. All that surely made a difference, surely justified her behaviour a little bit? She walked along the Strand towards Fleet Street, as though she were hurrying to keep an important appointment. There were still a lot of people about and on the other side of the street two drunken men were happily staggering along with their arms round each other's necks, singing "Ramona." Suddenly to her horror she saw Violet Cassel and Donald Ross approaching her, they had obviously been supping at the Savoy and decided to walk a little before taking a cab. With an instinctive gesture she jammed her hat down over her eyes and darted into Heppell's, so quickly that she collided with a woman who was just coming out and nearly knocked her down. The woman said, "Christ, a fugitive from a chain gang?" and waving aside Diana's apologies, went unsteadily into the street. Diana, faced with the enquiring stare of the man behind the counter and slightly unhinged by her encounter in the doorway, and the fact that Donald and Violet were at that moment passing the shop, racked her brains for something to buy. Her eyes lighted on a bottle of emerald green liquid labelled "Ess Viotto for the

hands." "I should like that," she said, pointing to it. The
man, without looking at her again, wrapped it up and
handed it to her. She paid for it and went out of the shop.
Violet and Donald were crossing over further down. She
walked slowly back the way she had come. An empty taxi
cruising along close to the kerb passed her and almost
stopped. She hailed it, gave the driver her address, got in
and sank thankfully back on to the seat. "A fugitive from
a chain gang." She smiled and closed her eyes for a moment. "What an escape!" She felt utterly exhausted as if
she had passed through a tremendous crisis, she was safe,
safe as houses, safe from herself and humiliation and in-
dignity. No more of such foolishness. She wondered whether or not she had replaced the stopper in the thermos.
She hoped she had, because the prospect of sitting up,
snug in bed, with a mind at peace and a cup of Ovaltine
seemed heavenly. She opened her eyes as the taxi was
turning into Lower Regent Street and looked out of the
window. A man in a camel-hair coat and a soft brown hat
was waiting on the corner to cross the road. Jimmy! She
leant forward hurriedly and tried to slide the glass window back in order to tell the driver to stop, but it wouldn't
budge. She rapped on the glass violently. The driver
looked round in surprise and drew into the kerb. She was
out on the pavement in a second, fumbling in her bag.
"I've forgotten something," she said breathlessly. "Here"—
she gave him a half a crown and turned and ran towards
Jimmy. He had crossed over by now and was just turning
into Cockspur Street. She had to wait a moment before
crossing because two cars came by and then a bus. When
she got round the corner she could still see him just passing the lower entrance to the Carlton. She put on a great
spurt and caught up with him just as he was about to
cross the Haymarket. He turned his head slightly just as
she was about to clutch at his sleeve. He was a pleasant-
looking young man with fair hair and a little moustache.
Diana stopped dead in her tracks and watched him cross
the road, a stream of traffic went by and he was lost to

view. She stood there trying to get her breath and controlling an overpowering desire to burst into tears. She stamped her foot hard as though by so doing she could crush her agonising, bitter disappointment into the ground.

A passing policeman looked at her suspiciously, so she moved miserably across the road and walked on towards Trafalgar Square, past the windows of the shipping agencies filled with smooth models of ocean liners. She stopped at one of them for a moment and rested her forehead against the cold glass, staring at a white steamer with two yellow funnels; its decks meticulously scrubbed and its paintwork shining in the light from the street lamps. Then, pulling herself together, she set off firmly in the direction of the Adelphi. No use dithering about any more. She had, in leaving the flat in the first place, obeyed an irresistible, but perfectly understandable impulse to see Jimmy. Since then, she had hesitated and vacillated and tormented herself into a state bordering on hysteria. No more of that, it was stupid, worse than stupid, this nerve-racking conflict between reason and emotion was insane. Reason had done its best and failed. No reason in the world could now woo her into going back to that empty flat without seeing Jimmy. Fate had ranged itself against reason. If Fate hadn't dressed that idiotic young man with a moustache in Jimmy's camel-hair coat and Jimmy's hat, all would have been well. If Fate had arbitrarily decided, as it apparently had, that she was to make a fool of herself, then make a fool of herself she would. Jimmy was probably fast asleep by now and would be furious at being awakened. She was, very possibly, by this lamentable, silly behaviour, about to wreck something precious, something which, in future years, she might have been able to look back upon with a certain wistful nostalgia. Now of course, after she had observed Jimmy's irritation and thinly-veiled disgust, after he had kissed her and comforted her and packed her off home in a taxi, she would have to face one fact clearly and bravely and that fact would be that a love affair, just another love affair, was ended. Not a violent break or a quarrel or anything like that, just a gentle, painful decline, something to be glossed over and forgotten. By the time she had reached the top of Jimmy's street there were tears in her eyes.

She walked along the pavement on tip-toe. His windows were dark, she peered into them over the area railings. His curtains were not drawn, his room was empty. She walked over the road to where there was a street lamp and looked at her wrist-watch. Ten past two. She stood there leaning against a railing, not far from the lamp, for several minutes. There were no lights in any of the houses except one on the corner. On the top floor, a little square of yellow blind with a shadow occasionally moving behind it. On her left, beyond the end of the road which was a cul-de-sac, were the trees of the gardens along the embankment; they rustled slightly in the damp breeze. Now and then she heard the noise of a train rumbling hollowly over Charing Cross bridge, and occasionally the mournful hoot of a tug on the river. Where on earth could he be at this hour of the morning? He hated going out, or at least so he always said. He didn't drink much either. He wouldn't be sitting up with a lot of cronies just drinking. He was very responsible about his job too and in addition to a matinee to-morrow there was an under-study rehearsal at eleven— she knew that because she had happened to notice it on the board. He couldn't have gone home to his parents; they lived on the Isle of Wight. She sauntered slowly up to the corner of John Street and looked up and down it. No taxi in sight, nothing, only a cat stalking along by the railings. She stooped down and said "Puss, puss" to it but it ignored her and disappeared down some steps. Suddenly a taxi turned into the lower end of the street. Diana took to her heels and ran. Supposing it were Jimmy coming home with somebody—supposing he looked out and saw her standing on the pavement, watching him. Panic seized her. On the left, on the opposite side of the road from the house where he lived, was a dark archway. She dived into it and pressed herself flat against the wall. The taxi turned into the street and drew up. She peeped round the corner and saw a fat man and a woman in evening dress get out of it and let themselves into one of the houses. When the taxi had backed and driven away she emerged from the archway. "I'll walk," she said to herself out loud. "I'll walk up and down this street twenty times and if he hasn't come by then I'll—I'll walk up and down it another twenty times." She started walking and laughing at herself at the same time, quite genuine laughter; she listened to it and it didn't sound in the least hysterical. I'm feeling better, she thought, none of it matters nearly as much as I think it does, I've been making mountains out of molehills. I'm enjoying this really, it's an adventure. There's something strange and exciting in being out alone in the city at dead of night, I must do it more often. She laughed again at the picture of herself solemnly setting out two or three times a week on solitary nocturnal jaunts. After about the fifteenth time she had turned and retraced her steps, she met Jimmy face to face at the corner. He stopped in amazement and said, "My God—Diana—what on earth—"

She held out to him the parcel she'd been holding.

"I've brought you a present," she said with a little giggle. "It's Ess Viotto—for the hands!"

★

AUNT TITTIE

ONCE UPON A TIME in a small fishing village in Cornwall there lived a devout and angry clergyman named Clement Shore. He was an ex-missionary and had a face almost entirely encircled by whiskers, like a frilled ham. His wife, Mary, was small and weary, and gave birth to three daughters, Christina, Titania, and lastly Amanda, with whose birth she struggled too long and sadly, and died, exhausted by the effort. Amanda was my mother. On Christmas day 1881, Grandfather Clement himself died and my Aunt Christina then aged sixteen, having arranged for what furniture there was to be sold, and the lease of the house taken over, travelled to London with several tin trunks, a fox terrier named Roland and her two younger sisters aged respectively thirteen and eleven. They were met, dismally, at Paddington by their father's spinster sister Ernesta, a grey woman of about fifty, who led them, without protest, to Lupus Street, Pimlico, where with a certain grim efficiency she ran a lodging house for bachelors. Once installed they automatically became insignificant but important cog-wheels in the smooth running machinery of the house, which was very high and respectable. The three of them shared a small bedroom with Roland, from whom they refused to be parted, and lived two years of polite slavery until in the spring of 1883 Christina suddenly married James Rogers, Ernesta Shore's first-floor-front tenant, and went with him to a small house in Camberwell, taking with her Titania and Amanda.

James Rogers was a good man and a piano tuner at the time of his marriage, later he developed into a travelling agent for his firm, so that during my childhood in the house I didn't see much of him, but he was mild tempered and kind when he did happen to be at home and only drank occasionally, and then without exuberance.

Aunt Christina was formidable, even when young, and ruled him firmly until the day of his death. She was less successful however with Aunt Titania and my mother. Aunt Titania stayed the course for about a year and then eloped to Manchester with a young music hall comedian, Jumbo Potter, with whom she lived in sin for three years to the bitter shame of Aunt Christina. At the end of this liaison she went on to the stage herself in company with three other girls. They called themselves "The Four Rosebuds" and danced and sang through the music halls of England. Meanwhile my mother, Amanda, continued to live in Camberwell, helping with the housework and behaving very well until 1888, when Titania reappeared in London, swathed in the glamour of the theatre, and invited her to a theatrical supper party at the Monico. Amanda climbed out of her bedroom window and over the yard fence in order to get there and never returned. Titania on being questioned later by Christina stated that the last she'd seen of Amanda, she was seated on the knee of an Argentine with a paper fireman's cap on her head, blowing a squeaker. Titania's recollections were naturally somewhat vague as she had been drinking a good deal and left the party early on the strength of an unpremeditated reunion with Jumbo Potter. Christina anxiously pursued her enquiries, but could discover nothing about the Argentine; nobody knew his name, he had apparently drifted into the party, entirely uninvited. Finally when two days had elapsed and she was about to go to the police, a telegram arrived from Amanda saying that she was at Ostend and that it was lovely and that nobody was to worry about her and that she was writing. A few weeks later she did write, briefly, this time from Brussels, she said she was staying with a friend, Madame Vaudrin, who was very nice and there were lots of other girls in the house, and it was all great fun, and nobody was to worry about her as she was very, very happy.

For five years after that, neither Titania nor Christina heard from her at all until suddenly, just before Christmas 1893, she appeared at Christina's house in Camberwell in a carriage and pair. She was dressed superbly and caused a great sensation in the neighborhood. Christina received her coldly but finally melted when Amanda offered to pay off all the instalments on the new drawing-room set and gave her a cheque for twenty-five pounds as well. Titania by this time had married Jumbo Potter and Amanda gave a family Christmas dinner party at the Grosvenor Hotel where she was staying, and as a *bonne bouche* at the end of the meal, produced an Indian Prince who gave everybody jewellery. She stayed in London for six weeks and then went to Paris, still with her Prince, and spent a riotous month or two, until finally she accompanied him to Marseilles where he took ship for India leaving her sobbing picturesquely on the dock with a cabochon emerald and a return ticket for Paris. It was while she was on the platform awaiting the Paris train that she met my father, Sir Douglas Kane-Jones. He was a prosperous-looking man of about fifty, returning on leave from Delhi to visit his wife and family in Exeter. However he postponed his home-coming for three weeks in order to enjoy Paris with Amanda. Finally they parted, apparently without much heart-break, he for England, and she for Warsaw, whither she had been invited by a Russian girl she had met in Brussels, Nadia Kolenska. Nadia had been living luxuriously in Warsaw for a year as the guest of a young attaché to the French Embassy. Upon arrival in Warsaw, Amanda was provided with a charming suite of rooms and several admirers, and was enjoying herself greatly when to her profound irritation, she discovered she was going to have a child.

She and Nadia, I believe, did everything they could think of to get rid of it but without success, and so Amanda decided to continue to enjoy life for as long as she could and then return to England. Unfortunately, however, she left it rather late, and on a frozen morning in January, I was born in a railway carriage somewhere between Warsaw and Berlin. The reason for my abrupt arrival several weeks earlier than was expected was the sudden jolting of the train while my mother was on her way back from the lavatory to her compartment. She fell violently over a valise that someone had left in the corridor, and two hours later, much to everyone's embarrassment and discomfort, I was born and laid in the luggage rack wrapped in a plaid travelling rug.

A week later Aunt Christina arrived in Berlin in response to a telegram, just in time to see my mother die in a hospital ward. With her usual prompt efficiency she collected all my mother's personal effects, which were considerable, and having ascertained that there were no savings in any bank, took me back to England with her and ensconced me in her own bedroom in her new house, Number 17, Cranberry Avenue, Kennington.

2

My life until my Uncle James Rogers' death in 1904 was as eventful for me as it is for most children who are learning to walk and talk and become aware of things. A few incidents remain in my memory. Notably, a meeting with my Aunt Titania when I was about three. She smelt strongly of scent and her hair was bright yellow. She bounced me gaily on her knee until I was sick, after which, she seemed to lose interest in me. I remember also, when I was a little older, my Uncle Jim came into my room late at night. I awoke just in time to see him go over to the mantelpiece and throw two green china vases onto the floor. I cried a lot because I was frightened, Aunt Christina cried too and finally soothed me to sleep again by singing hymns softly and saying prayers.

When I was five I was sent to a kindergarten on weekdays, and a Sunday School on Sunday afternoons. A Miss Brace kept the kindergarten. She wore shirt blouses with puffed sleeves, and tartan skirts. Her hair was done up over a pad. Twice a week we had drawing lessons and were allowed to use coloured chalks. I didn't care for any of the other children, and disliked the little girls particularly because they used to squabble during playtime, and pull each other's hair, and cry at the least thing.

I enjoyed the Sunday School much more because we used to stand in a circle and sing hymns, and the teacher had a large illustrated Bible which had a picture of God the Father throwing a hen out of Heaven, and another one of Jesus, with his apostles, sitting at a large table and eating india-rubber rolls. Everybody had beards and white nightgowns, and looked very funny.

When I was nine, Uncle Jim died. All the blinds in the house were pulled down, and we walked about softly as though he were only asleep and we were afraid of waking him. Iris, the servant, who had only been with us for two weeks, trailed up and down the stairs miserably with woebegone tears streaking her face. Perhaps she cried as a natural compliment to bereavement, however remote from herself, or perhaps she was merely frightened. Even the cat seemed depressed and lay under the sofa for hours at a time in a sort of coma. Aunt Christina took me in to see Uncle Jim lying in bed covered with a sheet up to his chin, his eyes were closed, and his face was yellow like tallow, his nose looked as though someone had pinched it. Aunt Christina walked firmly up to the bed, and having straightened the end of the sheet, bent down and kissed him on the forehead so suddenly that I'm sure he would have jumped if he had been alive. Then she looked across at me and said that his spirit had gone to heaven. Outside in the street a barrel organ was playing and there were some children yelling a little way off, but these sounds seemed faint and unreal as though I were listening to them from inside a box.

I went to the funeral with Aunt Christina and Aunt Titania in a closed carriage which smelt strongly of horses and leather. On the way Aunt Titania wanted to smoke a cigarette but Aunt Christina was very angry and wouldn't let her. I sat with my back to the horse and watched them arguing about it, sitting side by side joggling slightly as the carriage wheels bumped over the road. Finally Aunt Christina sniffed loudly and shut her mouth in a thin line and refused to say another word, whereupon Aunt Titania leaned a little forward and looked grandly out of the window until we reached the Cemetery. I stood under a tree with her while the actual burial was going on and she gave me some peppermints out of her muff. When we got home again we all had tea and Iris made some dripping toast, but the atmosphere was strained. After tea I went down to the kitchen to help Iris with the washing up and we listened to the voices upstairs getting angrier and angrier until finally the front door slammed so loudly that all the crockery shook on the dresser. Presently we heard Aunt Christina playing hymns and I didn't see Aunt Titania again for many years.

Soon after this I went to a day school in Stockwell, it wasn't very far away and I used to go there in a 'bus and walk home. There was an enormous horse chestnut tree just inside the school gate and we used to collect the chestnuts and put them on strings and play conkers. They were rich shiny brown when we first picked them up, like the piano in our front room, but afterwards the shine wore off and they weren't nearly so nice. I hated the Headmaster who was stout and had a very hearty laugh. He insisted on everybody playing football and used to keep goal himself, shouting loudly as he jumped about. One of the under masters was freckled and kind and used to pinch my behind in the locker room when I was changing. Much as I disliked school, I disliked coming home in the evenings still more, my heart used to sink as I stood outside the front door and watched Aunt Christina wobbling towards me through the coloured glass. She generally let me in without saying a word and I used to go straight upstairs to my bedroom and read and do my home-work until supper time, because Iris left at six and there was

nobody to talk to. Aunt Christina always said grace before and after meals, and regularly, when we'd cleared
away the supper things and piled them up in the kitchen,
she used to play hymns and make me sing them with her.
Sundays were particularly awful because I had to go to
Church morning and evening, as well as to Sunday School
in the afternoons. The Vicar was very skinny and while
I listened to his throaty voice screeching out the sermon
I used to amuse myself by counting how many times his
Adam's Apple bobbed up and down behind his white
collar. The woman who always sat next to us had bad
feet and the whole pew smelt of her.

I used to ask Aunt Christina about my mother but all
she'd say was that Satan had got her because she was
wicked, and whenever I asked about my father she said
he was dead and that she had never known him.

At the beginning of 1906 when I was eleven, things
became even gloomier. Aunt Christina bought a whole
lot of modeling wax and made a figure of Jesus lying
down, then she put red ink on it to look like blood, but
it soaked in. It wasn't a very good figure anyhow; the face
was horrid and the arms much too long, but she used to
kiss it and croon over it. Once she tried to make me kiss
it but I wouldn't, so she turned me out into the yard. I
stayed all night in the shed and caught cold. After that she
wouldn't speak to me for days, I was unhappy and made
plans about running away, but I hadn't any money and
there was nowhere to run.

One evening in April, I came home from school and
she was in bed with a terrible headache; the next morning when I went in to her room, she was gasping and
saying she couldn't breathe, so I ran out and fetched a
doctor. He said she had pneumonia and that we must
have a nurse, so we did, and the nurse rattled about the
house and clicked her tongue against her teeth a good
deal and washed everything she could. Three days later
Mr. Wendell, the Vicar, came and stayed up in Aunt
Christina's room for a time, and a short while after he'd

gone the nurse came running downstairs and said I was to fetch the doctor. Just as I was leaving the house to fetch him, I met him at the gate on his way in. He went upstairs quickly and an hour later he and the nurse came down and told me that my aunt had passed away.

He asked me for Aunt Titania's address, so we looked through Aunt Christina's davenport and found it and sent her a telegram. Late that afternoon Uncle Jumbo Potter arrived and interviewed the nurse, and then took me round to the doctor's house, and he talked to him for ages while I sat in the waiting-room, and looked at the people who had come to be cured; one little boy with a bandage round his head was whimpering and his mother tried to comfort him by telling him stories. Presently Uncle Jumbo came out and took me home with him in a cab. He lived in rooms near Victoria Station. He told me that Aunt Titania wasn't living with him any more and that she was in Paris singing at a place called the Café Bardac, and that he was going to send me to her the next day. That night I went with him to Shoreditch where he was doing his turn at the Empire. I sat in his dressing-room and watched him make up and then he took me down onto the stage and let me stand at the side with the stage manager. Uncle Jumbo was a great favourite and the audience cheered and clapped the moment he walked on to the stage. He wore a very small bowler hat and loose trousers and had a large red false nose. His songs were very quick indeed until it came to the chorus, when he slowed down and let the audience join in too. The last thing he did was a dance in which his trousers kept nearly falling off all the time. At the end he had to go before the curtain and make a speech before they'd let him go. He took me upstairs with him and undressed, still very out of breath. He sat down quite naked and smoked a cigarette, and I watched the hair on his chest glistening with sweat as he breathed. He asked me if I liked his turn and I said I loved it and he said, "Damned hard lot down here, can't get a bloody smile out of 'em, pardon me." After he'd taken his makeup off and powdered his face and dressed we went to a bar just opposite the Theatre and he drank beer with two gentlemen and a woman with a white fur, then we went home first in a tram and then a 'bus. I went to sleep in the 'bus. When we got to his rooms he gave me a glass of soda water and made up a bed for me on the sofa.

The next morning Uncle Jumbo took me back to Aunt Christina's house. The nurse was still there, and Mrs. Harrison from next door, who kissed me a lot and told me to be a brave little man and asked me if I would like to come upstairs and see my dear Auntie, but Uncle Jumbo wouldn't let me, he said he didn't hold with kids looking at corpses because it was morbid. He helped me pack my clothes and then we got a cab and drove back to his rooms. In the afternoon he went out and left me alone and I amused myself by looking at some magazines and a large album of photographs and press cuttings about Aunt Titania and Uncle Jumbo. When he came back he had a friend with him, Mrs. Rice, who he said would take me to the station, as the train went at eight o'clock and he would be in the Theatre. Mrs. Rice was pretty and laughed a lot. We all made toast, and had tea round the fire. Mrs. Rice sat on Uncle's knee for a little and he winked at me playfully over her shoulder and said, "You tell your Aunt Tittie how pretty Mrs. Rice is, won't you?" whereupon she got up and said, "Leave off, Jumbo, you ought to be ashamed" and looked quite cross for a minute. Uncle Jumbo went off to the Theatre at 5.30; he gave me five pounds and my ticket and said he had telegraphed to Aunt Tittie to meet me at the station. He kissed me quite affectionately and said, "Fancy me being fatherly!" Then he laughed loudly, tickled Mrs. Rice under the arms, and went down the stairs whistling. When he'd gone Mrs. Rice and I went back and sat by the fire. She asked me a lot of questions about Aunt Titania but as I hadn't seen her since Uncle Jim's funeral I couldn't answer them very well. After a while she went to the cupboard and

poured herself a whisky and soda, and while she was sipping it she told me all about her husband who used to
beat her and one night he tied her to the bed in their
rooms in Huddersfield and kept on throwing the wet
sponge at her until her nightgown was soaking wet and
the landlady came in and stopped him. She said she'd met
Uncle Jumbo in Blackpool in the summer and that they
used to go out after the show and sit on the sand dunes in
the moonlight, and then her husband found out and there
was an awful row, and Jumbo knocked her husband down
on the pier and brought her to London on the Sunday
and she hadn't seen her husband since, but she believed
he was still on tour in *Miss Mittens* and hoped to God
he'd stay in it and not come worrying her. She had several
more whiskies and sodas before it was time to go and
showed me a scar on her thigh where a collie bit her during her honeymoon in Llandudno. I looked at it politely
and then she pulled her skirts down and said I was a bad
boy and how old was I anyhow? I said I was eleven and
she laughed and asked me if it made me feel naughty to
see a pretty girl's bare leg. I said no and she said "Get
along with you. I must put some powder on my nose."
After a minute she came out of the bedroom, put her
hat on and said we must go. We took a cab to the station
on account of my trunk and Mrs. Rice told the porter to
register through to Paris. She bought me some buns and
chocolate and two magazines and put me in the train and
waited to tell the guard to keep his eye on me before she
kissed me and said good-bye. I waved to her all the way
up the platform until she was out of sight and then sat
back in my corner feeling very grown up and excited and
waiting for the train to start.

That journey to Paris was momentous for me. I was
alone and free for the first time, my going was in no way
saddened by memories of people I'd left behind. I had
left no one behind whom I could possibly miss; my school
friendships were casual and I had definitely grown to
hate poor Aunt Christina during the last few years of her

life. I pressed my face against the cold glass of the carriage window and searched for country shapes in the darkness, trees and hills and hedges, and felt as though I should burst with joy. There were two other people in the carriage with me; a man and a woman who slept, sitting up, with their mouths open. When we reached Newhaven, the guard came and led me to the gangway of the ship and gave me in charge of one of the men on board who offered me a ham sandwich and showed me a place in the saloon where I could put my feet up and go to sleep, but I couldn't begin to sleep until the ship started although I was dead tired, so I went up on deck and watched the lights of the town receding, and the red and green harbour lamps reflected in the water and I looked up at the clouds scurrying across the moon, and, suddenly, like a blow in the face, loneliness struck me down. I was chilled through and through with it—I wondered what I should do if when I got to Paris Aunt Titania was dead too. I tried very hard not to cry but it was no use, I had a pretty bad fit of hysteria and everyone crowded round me and patted me and tried to comfort me with eatables, until finally one kind woman took me in charge completely and gave me some brandy which made me choke but pulled me together. Then she put me to sleep in her private cabin and I didn't wake up until we got to Dieppe. I was all right from then on, the woman's name was Roylat and she was on her way to Ceylon to visit her son who was a rubber planter. I had some tea with her in the station buffet at Dieppe and travelled with her to Paris, sleeping most of the way.

When we arrived at Gare St. Lazare Aunt Titania was waiting at the barrier wearing a sealskin coat and a bright red hat with a veil floating from it. I said good-bye to Mrs. Roylat who kissed me, bowed to Aunt Titania and disappeared after her luggage. Aunt Titania and I had to go and sit in the Customs room for three-quarters of an hour until my trunk came in. She was pleased to see me but very cross with Jumbo for having sent me by night instead of day. She said it was damned thoughtless of him because he knew perfectly well that she never got to bed before four o'clock in the morning and to have to get up again at six-thirty was too much of a good thing; then she hugged me and said it wasn't my fault and that we were going to have jolly times together.

At last, when the Customs man had marked my trunk, we got a cab and drove out into Paris. It had been raining and the streets were wet and shiny. The shutters on most of the shops were just being put up and waiters in their vests and trousers were polishing the tables outside the cafés. We drove across the river and along the quai Voltaire with the trees all glistening and freshly green; our cab horse nearly fell down on the slippery road as we turned up the rue Bonaparte. Aunt Tittie talked all the way about everything she'd been doing and her contract at the Café Bardac which they'd renewed for another month. She asked me if Aunt Christina had left me any money and I said I didn't know, but I gave her a letter that Jumbo had told me to give her. She pursed up her lips when she read it and then said, "It looks like I shall have to find a job for you, duckie, you'd better come along with me and see Monsieur Claude but there's no hurry, we'll talk about that later on." Finally the cab drew up before a very high house, and a little man in a shirt and trousers ran out and helped the driver down with my trunk. Aunt Tittie said something to him in French and took me up four flights of dark stairs and opened the door into a sitting-room which had a large bedroom opening out of it on one side with a feather mattress on the bed that looked like a pink balloon, and a tiny room on the other side which she said I was to have. There were lots of coloured bows on the furniture and hundreds of photographs, lots of them fixed to the blue-striped wallpaper with ordinary pins. There was a small alcove in her bedroom with a wash-hand stand in it and a gas ring, and on the sitting-room table was a tray with some dirty glasses on it and a saucer full of cigarette-ends. Aunt Tittie took off her hat and coat and threw

them on the sofa, then she ran her fingers through her hair
and said, "Well, here we are. Home Sweet Home with a
vengeance." Then she went out onto the landing and
screamed: "Louise!" very loudly and came in again and
sat down. "We'll have some coffee and rolls," she said,
"then we'll go to bed until lunch time, how does that suit
you?" I said it suited me very well and we lapsed into
silence until Louise came. Louise was about seventeen
with a pallid face, a dirty pink dress turned up under an
apron, and green felt slippers, her hair was bristling with
curlpapers. Aunt Tittie had a long conversation with her
in French and then the little man came clambering upstairs with my trunk and put it in my room. Then Louise
and he both disappeared and I was left alone again with
Aunt Tittie. I felt rather strange and oddly enough a little
homesick, not really homesickness for that dreary house
in Kennington, but a longing for something familiar.
Aunt Tittie must have sensed that I wasn't feeling too
happy because she put her arm round me and hugged me.
"It's funny, isn't it?" she said, "you arriving suddenly like
this? You must tell me all about poor Aunt Christina and
what you've been learning at school and everything, and
you haven't got any cause to worry about anything because
you're going to be company for me and I shall love having
you here." Then she held me close to her for a moment
and surprisingly burst out crying, she fumbled for her
handkerchief in her belt and went into the bedroom and
shut the door. I didn't know what to do quite, so I started
to unpack my trunk. Presently Louise returned with a
tray of coffee and rolls and butter; she plumped it down
on the table and screamed something at Aunt Tittie
through the door and went out again. I sat at the table
and waited until Aunt Tittie came out of the bedroom in
a long blue quilted satin dressing-gown, with her hair
down. She looked quite cheerful again. "I can't think
what made me burst out like that," she said as she seated
herself at the table. "It came over me all of a sudden about
you being all alone in the world and your poor mother

dying in childbirth and now Christina. We're the only ones left out of the whole lot and that's a fact. Two lumps?" She poured out coffee for us both and talked volubly all the time, a stream of scattered remarks, beginnings of stories, references to people I'd never heard of, all jumbled together incoherently, but somehow all seeming to fit into a sort of pattern.

She must have been about forty then, her hair had been re-dyed so often that it was entirely metallic, as bright as new brass fire-irons. Her face was pretty with a slightly retroussé nose and wide-set blue-grey eyes, her mouth was generous and large and gay when she laughed. She talked of Jumbo a good deal, irritably, but with underlying tenderness. I suspect that she always loved him more than anyone else. She asked me if I'd seen Mrs. Rice and said that she was sorry for any man that got tangled up with a clinging vine of that sort. After breakfast, and when she'd smoked two or three cigarettes, she said she was going to bed until one o'clock and that I could do what I liked, but that she strongly advised me to go to bed too as I was probably more tired after my journey than I thought I was.

I went into my little room and when I'd finished unpacking I sat and looked out of the window for a while. It was at the back of the house looking down into a courtyard, the sun was shining into the rooms on the other side of the court, in one of them I saw an old woman in a blue dressing-gown working a sewing machine, the whirr of it sounded very loud, and every now and then there was the noise of rattling crockery far down on the ground floor, and somebody singing.

There were lots of grey roofs and chimney-pots and several birds flying about and perching on the telegraph wires, which stretched right across into the next street and then were hidden by a tall many-windowed building that looked like some sort of factory. I felt very drowsy and quite happy so I went and lay down on the bed and the next thing I knew was that it was lunch time and Aunt

Tittie was shaking me gently and telling me to get up. She was still in her dressing-gown, but her head was done up in a towel because she'd just washed her hair.

We had hot chicken and vegetables and salad for lunch and fresh crusty bread and coffee. When we'd finished, Aunt Tittie stretched herself out on the sofa and then moved her legs so as to make room for me on the end of it.

"Now we'd better talk a bit," she said. "I had a good think while I was washing my head and if you'll listen carefully I'll tell you just how things stand and then we'll decide what's best to be done." I settled myself more comfortably and handed her the matches off the table which she was reaching out for. "To begin with," she said, "I haven't got any money except what I earn, but we can both live on that if we're careful anyhow for a bit, until you start to make a little on your own. I know I ought to send you to school really but I can't, it's none too easy living in this damned town, because you've got to look smart and have nice clothes otherwise nobody will take any notice of you. Now I've got an idea which I'll have to talk over with Mattie Gibbons, she's my partner. We do a parasol dance, and then she does her skipping rope specialty which is fine, then I sing a ballad, one verse and chorus in English and the second verse and chorus in French and then we do a number together called 'How would you like a rose like me?' and go round to all the tables giving the men paper roses out of a basket. My idea was that you should be dressed up as a little dandy with a silk hat and a cane and gloves, you know the sort of thing, and flirt with us during the parasol dance and bring on our props for us all through the act. If Mattie agrees we'll ask Monsieur Claude about it. I think he'll say yes because he's a bit keen on me if you know what I mean and you ought to get about fifteen francs a week which would be a help to begin with. Would you like that?"

I said eagerly that I'd love it better than anything in the world and flung my arms round her neck and kissed her and she said, "Here wait a minute, it isn't settled yet, we've got to talk to Mattie and Monsieur Claude and arrange hundreds of things. I shall have to tell you a whole lot you're really too young to know, before I let you loose in the Café Bardac; to start with how much do you know?" This was rather a difficult question to answer so I sat looking at her without saying anything. "You know about men and women having babies and all that, don't you?" she said with an obvious effort.

I said "Yes," and blushed.

"Well, that's a good start anyway," she said. "Now then—" she stopped short and blushed herself, and then giggled nervously, "Oh, my God, I don't know how the hell to begin and that's a fact, well—" she pulled herself together. "Take the plunge, that's always been my motto, so here goes." She crushed out her cigarette and sat up and spoke very fast. "Now listen, Julian, it's a strange world, and it's not a bit of good pretending it isn't. You're only a kid and you ought to have a nice home and go to a nice school and learn history and geography and what not and get to know all about everything gradually, so it wouldn't be a shock to you, but as it happens you haven't got a nice home, you haven't got a home at all, you're alone except for me and Christ knows I'm no Fairy Godmother, but I've got to tell you everything I can so that you don't go and get upset by things and led away through not realising what it's all about. To begin with, dear, you're a bastard, which sounds awful but isn't so bad really, it only means that your mother wasn't married to your father, they just had an affair and that was that, no obligations on either side and then you were born and your mother died and nobody knew who your father was anyhow except by rumour and what Nadia Kolenska, who was your mother's friend, wrote to your Aunt Christina. You were brought up on the money that your mother's jewels fetched when your Aunt Christina sold them, and now she's dead too and here you are, alone in Paris with your Aunt Tittie, who's not a 'good' woman by any manner of means, but she's all you got so you'd better make

the best of her." Here she leant back and the cushion fell
over the end of the sofa onto the floor, so I picked it up
and put it behind her head and sat down again.

"When I say I'm not a good woman," she went on, "I
mean I'm not what your Aunt Christina would call good.
I take life as I find it and get as much as I can out of it. I
always have been like that, it's me all over and I can't
help it, tho' many's the row I've had with Christina because she never would see that what was good for her
wasn't necessarily good for me. I'm more like your mother
I think really, only not quite so reckless.

"Now if you're going to live with me here, there's a lot
of goings on you'll have to open your eyes to wide and
then shut 'em tight and not worry, and you mustn't be
upset by Mattie's swearing, her flow of language is something fierce when she gets going, but she's a really good
friend and you'll like her. As far as the Café Bardac goes
you'll have to look out and not be surprised by anything,
it's none too refined there after one in the morning. People
of all sorts and sizes come and drink at the bar, and sometimes there's a fight and you'll get a good laugh every now
and again to see the way those old tarts shriek and yell and
carry on. You know what tarts are, don't you?"

I said I wasn't sure, but I thought I did.

"Well," she continued, "they're women who have affairs
with men professionally, if you know what I mean. They
take 'em home and cuddle up with 'em and the men pay
them for it, though when you've had a look at some of
them you'll wonder how the hell they get as much as fourpence. But they're quite decent sorts, most of them. Then
there are young men who dance around and get paid by
the women, they're called 'macros' and aren't much use to
anyone except that they dance well and keep the rich old
American ladies happy. Then there are lots of boys and
young men who make up their faces like women, they're
tarts too, only male ones as you might say. Heaps of men
like cuddling up with them much better than women,
though I should think personally it must feel rather silly,

but after all that's their look-out and no business of mine.
They're awfully funny sometimes, you'd die laughing to
see them have a row. They scream and slap one another.
There's one at the Bardac called Birdie, always in trouble
that one, but he's awfully sweet so long as he doesn't get
drunk. If any of the old men ever come up and ask you
to drink or go out with them don't you do it, and if they
catch hold of you and start getting familiar just wriggle
away politely and come and tell me. I'll let 'em have it all
right. It's a queer world and no mistake, and you'd much
better get to know all you can about it as soon as may be
and then you can stand on your own feet and not give a
damn for anyone."

   She finished up with rather a rush and then looked at
me anxiously. I felt slightly bewildered but I said I'd try
to remember all she'd told me and not be surprised at anything whatever happened; then we talked about other
things. She asked me to tell her all the details of Aunt
Christina's death which I did and she sighed and shook
her head sadly and looked for a moment as if she were going to cry, but fortunately just then there was a loud banging on the door and Mattie Gibbons came in. She was
shorter and plumper than Aunt Tittie and very dark, she
had a grey dress with grey laced-up boots which showed
when she sat down, and a bright green blouse with a small
diamond watch pinned on it, her hat was grey felt with a
blue bird on it. She was very nice to me and shook hands
politely and said she didn't know I was going to be such a
big boy. She had a deep husky voice, and I liked her at
once.

   Aunt Tittie said they wanted to talk privately for a
while and would I like to go for a walk. I said I would,
and after she'd warned me about looking to the left first
when crossing the road, and told me to mark well the
number of the house and street so that I wouldn't get lost,
she kissed me and waved me out of the door. I felt my way
carefully down the dark stairs and when I got to the front
door it wouldn't open. After I'd struggled with it for a

long time, a woman put her head out of a door and
screamed something at me and then there was a click and
the door opened of its own accord. The street was very
narrow and filled with traffic. I walked down it slowly
looking into all the shop windows; pastry-cooks with the
most beautiful-looking cakes I'd ever seen; several artists'
shops with easels and paints and boxes of coloured pastels,
and wooden jointed figures in strange positions; and a toy
shop with hundreds of cheap toys jumbled up in cardboard
boxes. There were also grocers and greengrocers and one
big shop filled with old furniture and china. This was on
the corner and half of it faced the river. I crossed over
carefully and walked along the other side past all the little
boxes on the parapet filled with books and coloured prints
and thousands of back numbers of magazines, very tattered
and dusty and tied together in bundles with string.

There were lots of people fingering the books and hurrying along the pavement, nearly all the men had long
beards and some of them went into round iron places
covered with advertisements on the outside, and then came
out again doing up their trousers. I was very puzzled by
this so I peeped into one of them and saw what it was.
After that it amused me a lot, looking at the different
kinds of feet standing round underneath.

I crossed over a bridge and leant on the stone rail, the
water was very green and there were several steamers puffing up and down, occasionally a larger one would come
along and its funnel would bend in half as it went under
the bridge. The river divided a little way further up, leaving an island in the middle with houses on it coming out
almost into a point, and there were trees everywhere all
along the edges. Everything looked much clearer and
cleaner than London and the shadows of the houses
stretched right across the road, sharp and definite.

I felt excited and adventurous and went across to the
other side and walked for a long way under the trees;
every now and then a noisy yellow tram came along. The
lines were more like railway lines than tram lines and grass

was growing between them. By the time I got back to the house the sun was setting and all the windows along the quai looked as though they were on fire.

That evening Mattie came round at about nine o'clock and we all three of us went and had dinner at a café. Our table was right on the pavement and there was a little red-shaded lamp on it. Mattie and Aunt Tittie were very gay and talked very fast in French to the people that they knew and in English to each other and to me. Aunt Tittie told me what lots of things were in French and said I'd better learn to speak it as quickly as I could as it was very useful. They had had a long talk about me being a "dandy" in their turn and Mattie was pleased with the idea; they said they'd take me that night to the Café Bardac with them and interview Monsieur Claude right away.

After dinner we walked along the boulevard to another café where we had coffee in glasses and they had brandy as well, then we went home and Aunt Tittie made me lie down for an hour while she dressed. She said that as I was going to be up late I'd better get as much rest as possible. At about half-past eleven Mattie called for us, she and Aunt Tittie were both in sparkling evening dresses and cloaks and then we all got into a cab and drove a long way through brightly lighted streets. In the cab Aunt Tittie gave me a latch-key and some money and made me repeat the address over and over again, and said that I should always have to come home by myself, even when I was actually acting in the turn with them, because they generally had to stay on and talk to people sometimes nearly all night. She told me how much the cab would cost and then very slowly and clearly what I was to say to the driver. When I repeated it she and Mattie both laughed and said I spoke French like a native. Mattie said she wondered if it was all right to let me wander about Paris alone at night, and Aunt Tittie said I was very sensible for my age and that it was much better for me to get used to managing for myself and learn independence.

When we arrived at the Café Bardac nobody was there but a lot of waiters and a man behind the bar. We all went upstairs and sat in a small dressing-room which Mattie and Aunt Tittie shared. Their dresses were hanging up on pegs and there were two chairs, two mirrors on a shelf, and a very small wash-basin in the corner with a jug without a handle standing on the floor by the side of it.

Mattie took a bottle out of the cupboard and they both had a drink. Presently Aunt Tittie went downstairs to see Monsieur Claude and left me to talk to Mattie.

Mattie asked me if I didn't feel strange and I said yes but that I was enjoying it. She said, "It's a bloody awful life this really, you know, but it has its funny moments. This café's not so bad as some I've been in. I was dancing with a troupe in Antwerp once and they made us dress in a lavatory on the third floor, and the smell was enough to knock you down I give you my word; this is a little peep at Paradise compared to that and no error!"

Then she took out the bottle again and had another swig and said would I like a taste. I said "yes" and she said "My God, here I go corrupting you already," but she let me have a sip and laughed when I made a face. "It's raw gin, ducks, and don't let anybody ever tell you it's water, but it does make you feel fine, all ready to go out and fight someone, and believe me or believe me not you need that feeling in this Pavilion d'Amour!"

Aunt Tittie came back, looking very pleased and said Monsieur Claude wanted to see me, so down we went onto the next floor into a little room with a desk in it and a lot of photographs of naked women stuck on the walls. Monsieur Claude was fat and excitable; he kissed me on both cheeks and then held me by the shoulders and pushed me away from him and looked at me carefully, talking all the time very quickly in French. Then he whispered a lot to Aunt Tittie, gave her a smacking kiss on the lips and ushered us out into the passage. Just as I went through the door he fumbled in his pocket and gave me three francs. Aunt Tittie was frightfully pleased and said didn't I think he was a dear. "Kind as can be, you know, of course, he gets a bit excited now and again but he's never downright nasty except when he's had a couple, which isn't often, thank God."

We went upstairs to the dressing room again and told Mattie all about it. I was to get ten francs a week to begin with and fifteen later on if I was good. Mattie said the mean old bastard might have come across with a bit more but Aunt Tittie reminded her that after all he did have to think of his business. We all three went downstairs after a little while. Aunt Tittie introduced me to the barman. He spoke English and gave me a high stool to sit on in a corner behind the bar where I could watch all the people. I sat there for ages until my eyes prickled with the smoke. Every now and then Mattie or Aunt Tittie would come and see if I was all right, then they came down dressed as shepherdesses with bare legs and after they'd had a little port at the bar they did their parasol dance. Nobody seemed to watch it very much, but they all applauded and cheered when it was finished. I watched their turn all through and then felt so tired that I decided to go home, so I went upstairs to the dressing room to fetch my hat. I knocked and went in thinking Aunt Tittie and Mattie were downstairs, but they weren't, at least Aunt Tittie wasn't. She was in there with Monsieur Claude. She was sitting on his knee with hardly any clothes on at all and he was kissing her. They both had their eyes closed and neither of them saw me, so I closed the door again very quietly and went out without my hat. I got a cab quite easily and he drove me home and when I paid him, had a long conversation with me which I didn't understand, so I bowed and said *bon soir* and he drove away.

I lay in bed for a long while without sleeping. I felt strange, as though none of the things that were happening to me were real. I wondered whether Aunt Tittie liked being kissed by fat Monsieur Claude, and then all the faces of the people I'd seen at the café seemed to go across my eyes very fast until they were all blurred and I fell asleep.

I woke up just for a second in the early morning; a cold grey light was showing through the shutters and I heard Aunt Tittie's voice in the next room. Then her bedroom door slammed and I turned over and went to sleep again.

3

When I first appeared with Aunt Titania and Mattie Gibbons at the Café Bardac in Paris, I had a great personal success; all the tarts made a tremendous fuss of me and said I was *très gentil* and *très beau gars* and gave me sweet cakes, and Monsieur Claude raised my salary from ten francs to fifteen francs a week, quite soon. When the engagement came to an end Mattie and Aunt Tittie had a row and parted company. I think the row somehow concerned Monsieur Claude and it was terrible while it lasted. Aunt Tittie cried a lot and said Mattie was a dirty double-faced bitch and Mattie just sat there laughing until Aunt Tittie completely lost control and threw a vermouth bottle at her, which missed her and went flying through the open door into my bedroom and broke the looking-glass over my wash-basin. After that Mattie stopped laughing and chased Aunt Tittie around the table, swearing loudly. They were both drunk and I got rather frightened so I ran outside and sat on the stairs with my fingers in my ears. Presently Mattie came rushing out and fell over me; she smacked my face and went on downstairs screaming. I heard her wrestling with the front door and swearing at it, finally she got it open and slammed it behind her so hard that a large bit of plaster fell off the ceiling into a slop pail on the landing. When I went back into the sitting-room Aunt Tittie was lying on the sofa crying; her hair was down and her nose was bleeding, making stains all down the front of her dress. When I came in she got up and stumbled into her bedroom where I heard her being very sick. I shut my door and locked it and opened the shutters to see what the day looked like. It was raining

hard and the gutters were gurgling loudly so I went back
to bed and slept.

Soon after this Aunt Tittie and I packed up everything
and went to Ostend. We appeared at a Café Concert in
a side street which led down to the Plage. Aunt Tittie did
three songs and I learnt a speech in French to introduce
her. Everybody used to laugh and clap when I came on
with my silk hat and cane and white gloves. Aunt Tittie
thought it would be a good thing if I wore a monocle,
but I couldn't keep it in my eye until we stuck it in with
spirit gum, then it was a great success. We stayed there for
six weeks and I used to play about on the Plage during
the day.

We lived in a cheap hotel kept by a very thin woman
called Madame Blücher; she was half German and sometimes made chocolate cakes with whipped cream on them
which were delicious. She had a lot of sons and used to
show me photographs of them. One was a sailor and he
was photographed holding an anchor and sticking his
chest out. He had the biggest behind I've ever seen.

When we'd finished our engagement in Ostend we went
to Brussels and were out of work for nearly five weeks. We
used to go and sit in the waiting-room of an agent's office
with lots of other people wanting a job. The walls were
plastered with posters of celebrated stars very vividly coloured and there was a signed photograph of Sarah Bernhardt looking like a sheep in white lace.

We had to move out of the hotel we were in and go to
a still cheaper one. Aunt Tittie got more and more depressed, but one day she met an Austrian officer in some
café or other and came home late looking much more
cheerful. He was very handsome and took us both to dinner at an open-air restaurant one night; he joked with
me a lot and pinched my ear which hurt, but I pretended
I liked it. After dinner he put me in a cab and told it to
go to the hotel, and gave me the money to pay it, but I
stopped the driver when we'd got round the corner and
paid him a little and walked home; it was further than I

thought but I was three francs to the good. About a week after this Aunt Tittie got a contract to go to Antwerp for three weeks. After that we went to Amsterdam and then back again to Brussels, where we stayed for two months and played for some part of the time at the Mercedes Music-hall.

It was strange at first, doing our turn on an actual stage, but I liked it much better. It wasn't really a proper theatre because most of the audience sat at tables, but it had footlights and scenery and a drop curtain.

Aunt Tittie taught me a song which I did dressed as a pierrot while she changed her dress. It was called "Keep Off the Grass" and was out of a musical comedy in England. Nobody seemed to pay very much attention to it but I enjoyed doing it enormously.

After this we got a long contract and travelled all over France playing a week in each place, ending up with Lyons and Nice and Marseilles and then we went over to Algiers where we stayed for three weeks. There was a conjuror on the bill with us who took a great fancy to me. He asked me to have supper with him one night and we sat in a café with lots of Arabs wearing fezzes. I think he was half an Arab himself. Then he went for a drive along by the sea and he said I was "very nice boy" and "very pretty and had naughty eyes." He held my hand for a little and I knew what was coming so I said I felt very sick and started retching. He took me back to the hotel at once. His turn came on after ours and I always used to wait and watch it; he did card tricks and shot pigeons out of a gun and then to finish up he used to walk down to the front of the stage and say very solemnly, "Mesdames, Messieurs, maintenant je vous monterai un experiment très, très difficile, un experience de vie," whereupon he would take off his coat and shirt and stand stripped to the waist in dead silence for a moment, then, with great deliberation, he'd take a sharp pointed dagger from a table, test it and bend it slightly with his long thin fingers, and then proceed, amid a breathless hush from the audience, to carve out his left nipple. It was very realistically done even to a dark stream of blood which ran down over his ribs. Then suddenly, with a quick jerk, he'd throw the dagger away, whip out a handkerchief, and staunch the blood and cry "Voilà" and the curtain fell. He had, I think, a small rubber squeezer filled with red solution concealed in his hand, and then having made up his own nipple with flesh colour, he stuck a false red one over the top of it. It always brought forth thunders of applause.

After Algiers we went on to Tunis which was very much the same except that the weather was warmer. Then we had a week's engagement in Genoa which was a great failure—all the young Italian men made such a noise that we couldn't make ourselves heard, so we worked our way back to Paris by slow degrees, playing in Geneva and Montreux on the way.

We tried to get the same rooms we'd had before but they were occupied so we went to a small hotel behind the Invalides and stayed for a few weeks until Aunt Tittie fixed up an autumn contract. Then to fill in the time we went and stayed at a farm near Bordeaux with an old friend of Aunt Tittie's, Madame Brinault. She had been a dancer and had married and retired; she was fat and kind and had three grown-up stepdaughters and a stepson, who looked after the vines. They were all very vivacious and talked at the top of their voices all through meals. They had a monkey which bit every now and then but could be very affectionate when it liked. We used to fish in the pond for eels and small mud fish, and walk all along through the vines and pinch the grapes to see if they were coming along all right.

We stayed there for six weeks, and it did us a lot of good. Aunt Tittie got quite fat from drinking so much milk and cream and she let her hair go for the whole time without dyeing it so that it looked very odd, yellow at the ends and brownish-grey at the roots.

We spent most of the next year in Germany playing in Frankfurt, Hambourg, Dresden, Nurembourg, Munich,

Hanover, Heidelberg and Berlin, where Aunt Tittie met Arthur Wheeler, an acrobat, and fell violently in love with him. We stayed on there for several months, playing sometimes in suburban halls and sometimes in cafés in Potsdam and Berlin itself. Arthur Wheeler was a thick-set bad-tempered little man and he used to beat Aunt Tittie often, but I don't think she minded. He came with us in the summer to a place called Achenzee in the Tyrol and we stayed in a pension hotel and used to go out for picnics on the lake. He taught me to swim and dive. The lake water was ice cold even with the hot sun on it, but I got used to it and often swam seven or eight times a day. Wheeler used to lie on the grass by the side of the water with a towel tied round his middle, and do acrobatics, frequently with such violence that the towel would fall off and Aunt Tittie would laugh until she cried and say: "That's it, Arthur, give the poor Germans a treat!"

Every evening we used to sit outside the pension and have dinner. The tables were set almost in the road and processions of German families would march by, very hot and tired from their climbing. Even the young men had fat stomachs and they all wore shorts, and embroidered braces and small hats.

Every evening at about six o'clock we had beer at an open-air restaurant just by the water. We liked watching the steamer come puffing across the lake and then stop at the pier and land the passengers.

One evening when Wheeler had paid for the beer and we were about to walk back to the pension, he suddenly stood stock still, clutched Aunt Tittie's arm and said: "Jumping Jesus, that's my wife!"

I looked up and saw a thin woman in a brown dress walking down the pier and staring fixedly at us. We all stood where we were until she came up to us. She looked very angry and was biting her lips nervously.

"Arthur," she said, "I want to talk to you." Her voice was grating and hard, and completely determined.

Arthur Wheeler started to bluster a bit: "Now look

here, Amy—" he began, but she cut him short by taking his arm and leading him to the other end of the garden where they sat down at a table. I looked at Aunt Tittie who was very white, she hadn't said a word.

"Shall we go back to the pension?" I said. She shook her head. "No, we'll stay here," so we sat down again at the table we'd just got up from, and waited. The steamer gave a sudden hoot of its siren which made me jump, then it went churning away up the lake. It was twilight and the mountains looked jagged against the sky as though they had been cut out of black paper. On the other side of the lake, lights were already twinkling in the villages. The steamer hooted again a good way off and a flock of birds flew chattering out of the big trees behind the restaurant. I looked at Aunt Tittie. She was staring straight in front of her and her face was set and still except for two little pulses twitching at her temples.

Presently Mrs. Wheeler came over to us. Aunt Tittie stood up.

"Arthur's leaving with me on the first boat to-morrow morning," said Mrs. Wheeler. "He's going back to your hotel now to pack his things. I've engaged a room here for us for to-night."

"Oh," said Aunt Tittie. "That will be nice, won't it?"

"If you haven't any money," went on Mrs. Wheeler, "I'm sure Arthur'll give you enough to get you back to wherever you come from."

Aunt Tittie gave a little gasp. "Thank you for nothing," she said, her voice sounded high and strained. "I don't want Arthur's money and you know it."

"You're a low woman," said Mrs. Wheeler. "I don't wish to exchange words with you."

"I'm not so low as to live on a man's earnings for fifteen years and not give him anything in return."

"Your sort couldn't hold a man fifteen years," said Mrs. Wheeler.

"I wouldn't want to hold anyone who didn't want to stay," said Aunt Tittie. "He loves me more than he does you, otherwise he wouldn't be here, would he? And you can put that in your pipe and smoke it."

Mrs. Wheeler trembled. "You're nothing but a low class prostitute," she said hoarsely, whereupon Aunt Tittie gave her a ringing slap on the face which knocked her hat on the side and left a pink stain on her cheek.

Arthur came running up looking very frightened. "Leave off you two, for Christ's sake," he said. "Everyone's looking at you."

"I'm sorry I hit her," said Aunt Tittie. "I never did know when to control myself. Come on home, Arthur, and pack your bag." She turned and walked away. Arthur followed her rather uncertainly and I came last. I looked back at Mrs. Wheeler who was standing quite still where we'd left her with her hat still on one side. I know she was crying because the lamp by the gate showed wet streaks on her face.

We all walked back to the pension in silence. When we got there I stayed outside and let them go in by themselves. I went and sat on the wall by the lake. The water was completely still and lay along the shore like a glass sheet. Presently Arthur Wheeler came out of the house carrying his suit-case, he waved to me half-heartedly and then walked away quickly.

When I went back into the pension, Aunt Tittie was sitting at the window with her head buried in her arms, sobbing. She didn't take any notice of me so I sat on the bed and said nothing. Presently she pulled herself together and got up and looked in the glass. "I'm a pretty sight and no mistake," she said huskily, and tried to smile, then she put on her hat and went out. I watched her from the window wandering along in the opposite direction from the village. I waited up until she came back at about half-past ten. She seemed glad I was there and made a great effort to be cheerful. She took off her hat and fluffed out her hair and we made tea on the gas-ring and ate biscuits with it.

She talked a lot but didn't mention Arthur once. She

said she'd been thinking things out and had decided to go to Vienna; she said she knew an agent there called Max Steiner and that we'd probably get work right away. She said Vienna was a lovely place and she was longing to see it again, she'd been there once before with Mattie several years ago. When I said good night she suddenly hugged me very tight and said: "Well, dear, we're on our own-some again now, so let's enjoy it!"

After this, poor Aunt Tittie was terribly dispirited and unhappy for weeks. We went to Vienna and found that Max Steiner was away so we trudged around to several other agents until we had no more money left. Then I got a job in the Prater Amusement Park at a Houp-la Booth. I had to jerk the hoops onto a stick after the people had thrown them and then sling them back to the proprietor who was a brass-throated fat little man but quite kind. I made enough money that way to get us food, and Aunt Tittie managed to pay for our rooms in a very dirty little hotel by picking up men every once in a while, it wasn't really too easy for her because there were so many young and attractive professionals who knew the best cafés and resented intrusion on their beats. I used to be dreadfully tired when I got home every night and I got awful blisters on my feet from standing about all day.

In October, Aunt Tittie met a very rich old man who took her to Budapesth. When she'd been gone about a week she telegraphed me some money to come at once so I gave a day's notice to the Houp-la Booth and went. Aunt Tittie met me at the station in a smart motor-car; she was well-dressed and looked much happier. She said she had a small flat overlooking the river and that if only her old man could live for a little longer we'd be on velvet, but that he was very, very old indeed, and she was afraid he wouldn't keep through the winter. We laughed a lot and were delighted to be together again. Her flat really was quite nice and I slept in a little servant's room at the back. There was a Hungarian cook who came in by the day and we did the house-work ourselves. The old man didn't trouble us much, he only came to dinner two or three times a week and then didn't stay very late. I used to go out when he came and walk in the town, which was beautiful, and sit about in cafés drinking coffee and listening to the Tziganes.

After we'd been there a few weeks Aunt Tittie met an old friend of hers from Paris in the Hungaria Hotel. He was a Frenchman, and was running a small café on the other side of the river. He came to tea at the flat two days later and we did our turn for him and he said he would engage us. Aunt Tittie was really looking very well just then and had a lot of nice clothes. We started work the following Monday and stayed there the whole winter, we changed our songs every fortnight, and saved quite a lot of money.

In April, Aunt Tittie's old man had to go and do a cure at Baden Baden. He decided to go quite suddenly and wrote a letter to her saying good-bye and enclosed enough money to pay the last month's rent and a bit over besides. We were both very relieved really and never saw him again. A year later we read in the paper that he had died.

We left Budapesth in May and went back to Vienna where we stayed a few days, then went to Prague where we played in an open-air café for six weeks. Then we came back to Paris with enough money to keep us for the summer at least, if we lived cheaply.

That autumn we started again on our travels, we got return engagements in some of the towns we had played before. I was now fourteen and getting very tall. For the next two years our lives went along pretty evenly. We met Arthur Wheeler once in Nice on the Promenade des Anglais; he looked spruce and well and was wearing a straw hat, which he lifted politely, but Aunt Tittie cut him dead, and as we were leaving the next day we didn't see him again. In the summer of 1911 we were back in Paris. Aunt Tittie wasn't well and complained of pains inside. We didn't work for a few weeks and they went away.

In the January following, I had my seventeenth birthday. It came on a Sunday and we were traveling to Spain where we'd neither of us been before. We got out at Bayonne and bought a bottle of champagne and had a celebration all to ourselves in the compartment. We finished the bottle between us and I got drunk for the first time in my life and went shouting up and down the corridor. Aunt Tittie was too weak with laughter to stop me.

We played in a Café Chantant in San Sebastian; it had only just opened and was new and gaudy and smelt of paint. The proprietor was a fat Belgian Jew who wore an enormous diamond and sapphire ring on his little finger. We had been recommended to him by Demaire, our agent in Paris, as a novelty. He didn't seem to think we were very novel and was rude to Aunt Tittie when she asked for the band to play more quietly, but it mattered little as hardly anybody came to the café anyhow and we were paid our salary and dismissed after the first week. We played in several different places in Spain but without much success. The Spaniards were polite and applauded our turn perfunctorily and that was all; there was no enthusiasm, and when Aunt Tittie went from table to table singing "How would you like a little Rose like Me?" they generally sat quite silently and looked at her, and very seldom even held out their hand for the paper roses, so poor Aunt Tittie had to put them down on the table and go on to the next one. It was very discouraging for her; of course, she was beginning to look rather old, and her smile lacked the gaiety it used to have.

When we got to Barcelona we played in a very dirty music-hall which was a bit better because the floor of the auditorium was uncarpeted wood and the people stamped their feet instead of clapping, which made a tremendous noise and made everything we did seem like a triumphant success. We went to a big bull fight one afternoon which upset us both horribly. Aunt Tittie cried all the way back to the hotel, thinking about the horses, and how they trotted into the ring so amicably with a bandage over one eye to prevent them from seeing the bull coming. Some of them screamed dreadfully when they were gored and the memory of it haunted us for days.

We sat outside a café on the way home and had Ochata which is an iced sweet drink made of nuts, and looks like very thick milk. Aunt Tittie kept on bursting into tears and then laughing at herself hysterically, altogether she was in such a state that she had to have some brandy and lie down before the show. Two nights after that when we had finished our turn and I was waiting outside the dressing-room under the stage, while Aunt Tittie dressed, there was suddenly a terrific crash up above and a loud scream and the orchestra stopped dead. I rushed up on the stage to see what had happened. Everyone was running about and yelling. One of the big limelight lamps had exploded and fallen down and set fire to the curtains, which were blazing.

A conjuror who had been doing his turn when the thing fell came rushing past me and knocked me against the wall; his wife, who was his assistant, was shut up in his magic cabinet in the middle of the stage and was hammering on the inside of it to be let out. The stage manager ran towards it to open it, but before he could reach it a whole length of blazing curtain fell right across it.

I ran quickly downstairs to fetch Aunt Tittie and met her coming up in her dressing-gown with grease all over her face. We heard the conjuror's wife shrieking horribly as the cabinet started to burn, but there was no chance of rescuing her because by this time the whole stage was blazing. We tried to beat our way through the thick smoke to the stage-door. Aunt Tittie was choking, and a stage-hand, mad with fright, knocked her down and stumbled right over her; one of his boots cut her face. I helped her up and we finally got out into the alley. There was a terrific crash behind us as part of the roof fell in. Aunt Tittie gave a little gasp and collapsed, so I grabbed her under the arms and dragged her along the alley with her heels scraping over the cobblestones. There were hundreds of people running about screaming and I was terrified that

we'd be thrown down and trampled to death. When I got
Aunt Tittie out of the alley into the street I suddenly
thought of the conjuror's wife trapped inside that cabinet,
and I laid Aunt Tittie on the ground and was violently
sick in the gutter.

When I'd finished, I sat down on the kerb by her side.
Then I noticed that her face was bleeding, so I dabbed it
with my handkerchief and she opened her eyes. The fire
engines had arrived by this time. I could hear them in
the next street. A man came up and we both helped Aunt
Tittie to her feet; she stood swaying for a moment with
our arms supporting her and then gave a scream and
clutched her side and fainted again. I didn't know what
to do, the man couldn't speak French or English, and I
only knew a few words of Spanish. He helped me carry
her along to the street corner and I signed to him to wait
with her while I got a taxi. I ran very fast but couldn't
see one anywhere. Suddenly I saw a motor ambulance
coming out of a side street, I stopped it and directed it
back to where I'd left Aunt Tittie. The two ambulance
men lifted her into it and I said good-bye to the strange
man and thanked him very much, and he raised his bowler
hat and bowed and we drove away to the hospital leaving
him standing there.

When we arrived at the hospital they took Aunt Tittie
into the emergency ward and I sat by her for ages before
anyone came near us. She came to after a little and started
to cry; she said she had a terrible pain in her stomach at
the side! Her voice sounded very weak and husky. There
were lots of other people lying on beds and groaning. One
man's face was almost black and all the hair on the top
of his head was burnt away leaving mottled red patches.
He kept on giving little squeaks like a rabbit, and clutching at the sheet with his hands which were dreadfully
burned.

Presently two Sisters of Mercy came in and went round
to all the beds and tried to make people a little more comfortable. Finally two doctors came with several nurses;

and they went from bed to bed and talked a lot, in low voices. When they got to us I stood up and explained in French about Aunt Tittie's pain. Fortunately one of them understood all right and felt her stomach with his fingers, then he sent one of the nurses away and she came back in a few minutes with a stretcher on wheels. We all got Aunt Tittie on to it and I walked behind it with the doctor through miles of passages.

Eventually we got to a very quiet ward with only a few beds occupied. A Sister of Mercy was sitting reading at a table with a shaded lamp on it. She got up when we came in. Then the doctor took me downstairs to the waiting-room and said that he was afraid Aunt Tittie had a very bad appendix but that he was going to give her a thorough examination and make sure and that I'd better go home and come back in the morning. I said I'd rather stay in case Aunt Tittie wanted me, so he said "very well" and left me. I lay on a bench all night and slept part of the time. In the early morning two cleaners came in and clattered about with pails. I got up and found my way to the main entrance and finally found a nurse who spoke a little French. She said it was too early to find out anything and that I'd better have some coffee and come back, so I went out into the street and found a café that was just opening and drank some coffee and ate a roll. When I got back I met the doctor coming down the steps, he took me into an office and a Sister of Mercy took down particulars about Aunt Titania which I gave her in French, and the doctor translated into Spanish. When that was done he told me that the only chance of saving Aunt Tittie's life was to operate immediately. I asked if I could see her and he said no, that she was almost unconscious and that if I was agreeable he would operate right away. I said he'd better do what he thought best and that I'd wait, so I went back to the waiting-room. A lot of people had come in, several were relatives of people who had been in the fire, most of them moaned and wailed and made a great noise. About three hours later a nurse came and called out my name. I stood up, and she took me into the office again. After a minute or two the doctor came in looking very serious. He told me that there was scarcely any hope of Aunt Tittie living, as when they operated they discovered that the appendix had burst. He said she hadn't come to yet from the anaesthetic, but that I could see her when she did. I asked when that would be and he said he couldn't tell for certain, but that I'd better wait. They let me stay in the office which was nicer than the waiting-room, and the Sister of Mercy gave me some dry biscuits out of a tin on her desk. She had a round face, and glasses, and peered at me through them sympathetically. Presently a nurse appeared and signed to me to follow her. We went several floors in a lift. There was a wheel stretcher in it with a man lying on it and an orderly standing by the side. The man didn't move at all and his head was covered with bandages.

This time Aunt Tittie was in a private room which was very dim and there was a screen round the head of the bed and another near the door. When I went in I could hardly see for a minute; the nurse drew up a chair and I sat down by the bed. Aunt Tittie was lying quite still with her eyes closed. Her face was dead white and she had a nightdress on of thick flannel which was buttoned up to the chin. She looked terribly, terribly tired and every now and then her mouth gave a little twitch. I felt a longing to put my arms round her and hold her tight and tell her how much I loved her, but when I thought about that I wanted to cry, so I looked away for a moment and tried to control myself. Presently she opened her eyes and moved her head to one side; she saw me and said "Hello, dearie," in a whisper. Then she frowned and closed her eyes again. I took her hand which was outside the coverlet, and held it. It felt dry and hot. After a little while she moved again and tried to speak, her hand clutched mine very hard and then relaxed. I put my head down close to hers and she said: "Take care of yourself." I started crying then, hopelessly, but I was careful not to make any noise and her eyes were still shut so she couldn't see. Suddenly she gave a little moan and the nurse came out from behind the screen and motioned me to go out of the room. I disengaged my hand from Aunt Tittie's very gently; she didn't seem to notice, and I went out into the passage. There was a window at the end and I stood and looked out across the hospital grounds to the town. It was a very windy day and there was a flagstaff upon the hill with the flag standing straight out from it looking as though it were made of wood. Every now and then it fluttered and subsided for a moment and then blew out straight again.

I waited about all day in the hospital, but they wouldn't let me in to see Aunt Tittie again, because they said she was unconscious, and in the evening at about seven o'clock she died. I went back to the hotel and lay on my bed, trying to be sensible and think things out, but I wasn't very successful and finally gave way and cried for a long time until I dropped off to sleep. When I woke up it was about eleven o'clock and I felt better, but I couldn't sleep any more so I went out and wandered about the town. I walked right down to the harbour and watched the ships. There was a big liner, standing a little way out, all the decks were brilliantly lighted and I could hear music faintly. I suddenly realised that I hadn't had anything to eat all day, so I went into a restaurant which was filled with sailors, and had a plate of stew and some coffee, everything was very greasy and I couldn't eat much of it.

The next day I went through all Aunt Tittie's things and discovered that she had twenty sovereigns locked in her jewel-case, also a brooch with diamonds and two rings, one with very small rose diamonds, and the other plain gold. I myself had fourteen pounds saved, mostly in francs. I went back to the hospital and interviewed the doctor about the operation and funeral expenses. He was very kind, and when I told him how much I had, said that he wouldn't charge for the operation. In spite of this, however, I had to pay out a good deal and when the whole business was over I had about seventeen pounds left. Aunt

Tittie was buried two days later. An English clergyman appeared and did it all. He was officious, and kept on asking me questions about her. I bought a bunch of flowers and put them on the grave, and I went back and packed up everything and bought a ticket for Paris.

The Paris train was crowded, and I sat in the corridor all night and thought about Aunt Tittie, until my heart nearly burst with loneliness and I pressed my head against the window and longed to be dead, too.

ASHES OF ROSES

LEONORA GLANCED IDLY through the pile of fan letters on her dressing table. She had got in for the matinee earlier than usual, and Alice had not arrived yet, otherwise the letters would already have been opened and neatly arranged for her.

Suddenly, among the genteelly coloured envelopes she came upon one that was white and quite plain. It looked businesslike, but was not typed. She turned it over in her hands and read an embossed address in an oval on the flap: "Hogarth and Currie—Solicitors."

She looked at the writing again. It seemed vaguely familiar; the envelope was very tightly stuck down, so she slit it open with her nail file.

My dear Leonora,

I expect you will be surprised to hear from me after so many years. Perhaps you will have forgotten my very existence. In case you have, I will remind you of Lorelei in 1924 and Hyde Park on a May afternoon. Those days seem very far away. I have spent most of the intervening years in Malaya, but came home in 1939 just after War broke out. Having been refused for the Army, I have been up here ever since working for the above firm. I have been married twice since the old days when we knew each other. Time does march on, doesn't it? Judging by your photographs in the papers you have hardly changed at all! I am coming to the play to-night and wondered if you would be free to have supper with me afterwards at the Caledonian. It would be so nice to see you again and talk over old times. If by any lucky chance you are free, could you leave

a message for me with the stage-door man? I do hope you
will be able to.

Yours sincerely,

FELIX MESEURIER

Leonora slowly put the letter down and closed her eyes.
She then opened them again, and looked at herself in the
glass with interest to see if the shock had done anything
to her face; it hadn't. There she was, looking exactly the
same as she always looked when she was about to make
up. The butter muslin was tied round her head as usual
to prevent the powder getting into her hair; nothing er-
ratic had happened to her features. She passed her hand
wearily across her forehead—the gesture she always used
in the last act in the "Good-bye" scene with Henry. She
looked lovely as she did it, lovely and hopeless and resigned. Then she shook her head and smiled wanly, and
suddenly, with neither loveliness, wanness, nor resignation, she clapped her hand over her mouth and burst out
laughing. Felix Meseurier!—Felix! After nearly twenty
years! It wasn't possible. She picked up the letter and re-
read it: "Judging by your photographs in the papers you
have hardly changed at all!" Like hell she hadn't!

She leaned forward and scrutinised her face in the mirror. "Hardly" was the operative word. She remembered
herself distinctly, too distinctly, in *Lorelei* in 1924. That
was the year she'd had the Foulsham and Banfield photographs taken at considerable personal expense, and had
finally persuaded the "Guv'nor" to allow a frame containing four of the best poses to be hung in the theatre foyer.
She could see them clearly even now. One was a large
head with the eyes looking upwards with a rather startled
expression, as if someone were going to throw something
at her from a great height. In two of the others she was
posed in an unrelaxed manner on a sort of music stool
with spindly legs, and in the fourth she was looking archly
round a screen with her hair down.

She had been nineteen when those photographs were

taken. Now, looking at herself in the glass in the star dressing room of the King's Theatre, Edinburgh, it was 1944 and she was forty. The face peering with such roguish assurance round that screen in Foulsham and Banfield's studio had been unlined and chubby; the face now looking back at her from the mirror was neither. It was a lovely face, certainly, actually lovelier perhaps than it had been twenty years ago, but youth had vanished from it forever.

Alice came fussing in full of apologies: she had waited in a queue for twenty minutes for the tram and then, just as she reached the step, the conductress had shouted "Full up," and given her a push into the bargain. Leonora began to make up. Helen, the assistant stage manageress, knocked on the door and said, "Half an hour please, Miss Jarvis." Alice bustled about the room getting her first-act dress ready and running the tap into the basin so that the water would be warm and ready to wash in. Felix Meseurier!

Leonora expertly massaged the Max Factor foundation into her skin and sighed; *Lorelei*—Hyde Park on a May afternoon! A little while later, when the first act had been called and she was getting into her dress, she said with a casualness that was only a fraction overdone, "Alice, dear, leave a message at the stage door for a Mr. Meseurier— you'd better spell it out because that old man's awfully stupid, M E S E U R I E R—say that I shall be delighted to have supper with him to-night, and will he come round after the show and pick me up."

2

One of the greatest attractions of *Lorelei* at the Walgrave Theatre was undoubtedly the sextette which came in the middle of the third act. The girls who sang it were Maureen Clayton, Josie Gay, Phyllis Greville, Leonora Jarvis, Etta Malvern, and Violet Primrose. They all dressed together in Number 14 dressing room on the third floor.

They were a carefully picked little bunch of houris, and all their twelve legs were impeccable although their voices were less uniformly perfect. Maureen, Etta, and Phyllis carried the vocal ardours of the number, while Josie, Leonora, and Violet opened and shut their pretty mouths and emitted occasional thin, but not entirely unpleasant, sounds. All six of them, however, had the charm of youth and the assurance of comparative inexperience. Maureen, aged twenty-six, was the eldest and had actually played two leads on tour. Josie Gay, twenty-five, was actually the veteran because she had been on the stage since she was nine. Etta, a pretty creature utterly devoid of ambition, was the same age as Leonora. In fact, they both celebrated their twentieth birthdays in the same week, and there was a write-up about it in the *Daily Mirror* with a photograph of them both cutting a large cake with candles on it and a few of the principals standing around wearing strained, good-humoured smiles. Phyllis and Violet were the babies, being nineteen and eighteen respectively.

In the show the girls had comparatively little to do apart from the sextette. They had a concerted entrance in the first act, when they all came chattering and laughing down a ship's gangway and, for a few minutes, provided a demure background for Martha Dorcas's first number. She was the leading comedienne and they were all supposed to be her daughters. After this they were not on again until the finale of the second act when, together with the entire company, they had to stand about while Judy Clandon, the leading lady, sang a loud and reproachful aria to Clyde Markham, the leading man, at the end of which she flung a glass of champagne into his face and collapsed, sobbing violently, into the arms of Martha Dorcas. In the third act there were the sextette and the finale of the whole show. None of the girls had any lines to speak, except Maureen, who played a brief "feed" scene with Budge Ripley, the comedian, in the opening of Act Three and in addition understudied Judy Clandon.

Number 14, therefore, was the real hub of their theatre

lives. Here they argued, quarrelled, giggled, manicured their nails, tried new ways of doing their hair, made underclothes, gave tea parties on matinee days to other members of the company (nobody outside the theatre was allowed backstage during performances), and discussed sex in general and their own love affairs in particular. The dressing room was presided over and kept in reasonable order by Mrs. Leftwich, "Leffie," their dresser. "Leffie" was overworked, harassed, sharp-tongued, and beloved by them all. She had been in the profession herself years ago and, at one time, had played quite good parts on tour. However, she had sacrificed her career at the age of twenty-nine and married an electrician in Bradford who had taken to the bottle. After some years of acute conjugal incompatibility he had been knocked down by a tram just outside the Kennington Oval tube station, and had died in St. Thomas's Hospital, leaving Leffie with the relief of his departure offset by the burden of having to bring up two children. Both of these were now adult. The son, Bob, had gone to Canada and married and settled down; the daughter, Nora, had also married, but far from settling down had run off with someone else only a month after the wedding. It was the general opinion of Number 14 that Nora had gone thoroughly to the bad because, however pressed, Leffie would seldom speak of her.

Number 14 came to life every evening at about seven-thirty and on Wednesdays and Saturdays at one-thirty. Leffie always arrived on the dot, took the key off the hook in the stage-door box, and trudged up the three flights. She invariably unlocked the door and went in with a faint sinking of the heart just in case everything wasn't all right. There was really no reason why it should not be, as she herself was the last to leave at night having tidied up meticulously and placed neat chintz covers over each of the six dressing places, but this daily apprehensiveness was accounted for by the fact that, years ago when she had been dressing May Garson at the Vaudeville, she had come in one night as usual to find that the room had been ran-

sacked and all May Garson's clothes pinched, including
her fur coat which, like a fool, she'd left hanging up in
the cupboard. That had been a "do" and no mistake—
policemen and cross-questionings and one thing and another. The nightmare of it still lingered in her mind.

One evening towards the end of April 1924, when the
show had been on for three months and had settled into
an established success, Leffie was just about to take the
key off the hook as usual when Frank, the doorman, jerked
his head in the direction of a figure standing in the rather
cramped space between the outer and inner doors. "Someone wants to speak to you." He gave a lewd wink and
wiggled his tongue up and down in his cheek. "I think
he's after one of your young specials!"

Leffie went up to the stranger. He was a good-looking,
well-dressed young man with a soft black hat pulled down
over his eyes, which he raised politely. "Are you Miss
Jarvis's dresser?"

Leffie nodded. "That's right," she said.

The young man smiled, a charming smile exposing very
white teeth. "I wonder if you would be very kind and give
her this note when she comes in?" He handed her an
envelope and two half crowns which she took rather dubi-
ously.

"Do you know Miss Jarvis?"

He smiled again. "Unfortunately not—that is, not personally. I've seen her several times in the show."

"I see." Leffie put her head a little on one side and
looked at him appraisingly.

"I know I could have left it in the rack in the ordinary
way," he went on, "but I thought I'd rather give it to you
and be sure she'd get it all right. My intentions," he added,
"are quite honourable."

Leffie nodded laconically. "All right," she said, "I'll see
she gets it."

The young man raised his hat again. "Thank you so
much—I'm very grateful."

He went out into the alley. Leffie turned the note over

in her hands, put the five shillings into her pocket, and went thoughtfully upstairs. While she was whisking the covers off the dressing places and setting the various wrappers over the backs of the chairs all ready to be slipped on the moment their owners arrived, she hummed breathily a little tune to herself, but, behind the tune, somewhere in the back of her mind, she was aware of a certain perplexity, a faint pang of questioning conscience. It was not taking the note and the five shillings exactly: there was nothing either wrong or unusual in that, but there was something all the same, something that made her feel uneasy. He was a nice-looking young man all right and his clothes were good—she looked at the note which she had propped up against Leonora's powder box—quite gentlemanly writing.

Suddenly she sat down, still staring at the note, and rubbed her chin pensively. Concentrated thought processes were difficult for Leffie; she lived her life almost entirely by instinct. What really was gnawing at her conscience was a sense of responsibility. Not that there was any logical reason for this. It was not part of her duties to guard the moral behaviour of her charges; all she was paid for was to dress them, keep them in order as much as possible, and see to it they went down when they were called and did not miss any entrances; still, she was an elderly woman and they were young, and she wouldn't like any harm to come to a hair of their heads.

A romanticist would, of course, be lyrically moved at the thought of those six young creatures, so full of life and potentialities all starting their careers together with the glamorous possibilities of stardom or wealthy marriages beckoning them on into the future. A cynic would merely have seen Number 14 dressing room as a forcing house for egoism, artificiality, and female predatoriness.

Mrs. Leftwich was neither a romanticist nor a cynic; she was a realist. To her, Maureen, Josie, Phyllis, Leonora, Etta, and Violet were six girls whose job it was to make successes of their lives or their careers, or both if possible.

She had grown fond of them and they of her; each of them tipped her regularly every Saturday night—always the same sum, which had obviously been agreed on among themselves in secret conclave. They sometimes borrowed money from her which was invariably paid back at the end of the week. They always shared whatever they had with her in the way of food or drink, and, above all, they trusted her and frequently asked her advice.

Occasionally the advice was extremely difficult to give. There was, for instance, that dreadful Saturday not long after the show opened when Phyllis had lingered on in the dressing room until all the others had gone and then burst into floods of hysterical tears and confessed that she was over two months gone and that something would have to be done about it or she would kill herself. That was a teaser and no mistake. Leffie had sent her home in a taxi, having promised to meet her next day outside the Piccadilly Hotel at two-thirty, and that same night had gone traipsing round to the Palace Theatre to see old Mrs. Greerson, who knew a woman who knew a doctor somewhere near Olympia.

The next afternoon they had met as arranged, and had gone off to Addison Road. Leffie would never forget that little jaunt to her dying day. The doctor was an oily-looking man with spurts of iron-gray hair growing out of his ears. Leffie had had to wait for two hours in a sort of front parlour with nothing to look at but a back number of *Woman and Home* without a cover and a large picture over the mantelpiece of a dog with a rabbit in its mouth. Fortunately it had all gone off all right, and she had taken Phyllis away in a taxi and deposited her at her cousin's, well briefed with a trumped-up story of having fainted at the pictures.

It must here be noted that the ethics of stage life differ considerably from those of other, more conventional worlds. Leffie, it is true, had been extremely shocked by this incident, but not on account of its moral aspects. Having been born and bred in the theatre she had no

inherent reverence for virginity. In her experience it was
an overrated commodity at the best of times and far too
much fuss was made about it at that. What shocked her
over this particular episode was not that Phyllis had had
an affair with a gentleman unnamed, but that she should
have been silly and inefficient enough to let herself get
into trouble through it and thereby jeopardise her professional career. In Leffie's opinion, a strapping girl of
nineteen ought to have more sense. The silliest part of it
all, of course, was to let it drag on until she was well into
her third month. However, all was well that ended well.

What was worrying her now, about the young man and
the note and the two half crowns, she was unable to explain to herself. Perhaps it was something to do with his
teeth or his voice—a gentle, dangerous voice. At all events,
she shrugged her shoulders, Leonora was a bright, ambitious girl and well capable of looking after herself.

3

Felix Meseurier stood in the foyer of the Walgrave
Theatre casually smoking a cigarette and occasionally
glancing at his wrist watch to give any of the attendants
who might be observing him the impression that he was
waiting for someone. From his particular point of vantage
just to the left of the box office he commanded an excellent
view of a large frame on the opposite wall containing four
portrait studies of Leonora Jarvis. If being in love means
a physical attraction of the first magnitude then Felix
Meseurier was in love. He could hardly look at the photographs without trembling.

There he stood, slim and handsome in his dinner jacket,
listening to the orchestra tuning up for the overture, and
staring across the heads of the people passing by him.
Every now and then he would look away, but his eyes always returned avidly to that pert, lovely little face and
those long, exciting legs. He was rather a saturnine-looking

young man, a fact of which he was perfectly aware and which secretly pleased him. His father had been French and had died years ago. His mother, a determined and thoroughly efficient woman, ran a small chemist's shop in Uxbridge. Her one weakness in life had been, and still was, Felix. He on his side was fond of her and reasonably filial, in that he visited her dutifully once a week.

He was a selfish creature, but not more so than many other young men of his generation. Having been called up in 1916, he had been invalided out of the Army in 1917 with incipient t.b. This had necessitated his spending a year at a sanatorium near Woking, from which he emerged completely cured a few weeks after the Armistice was signed. His sojourn in the Army had been undistinguished to the point of bathos, a dismal little record of influenzas, bad colds, and finally pleurisy, the results of which obtained for him his ultimate discharge. With one part of his mind he regretted this. He liked to visualise himself as romantically valiant, as indeed who does not? His sense of realism, however, caused him to admit to himself in secret that he was relieved beyond words that he had never got nearer to the war than a bleak camp in Derbyshire.

In 1919, through his mother's resolute determination, he got a job as a clerk in a shipping office in the City, and now, after four years, he had laboriously climbed to being a sort of secretary-cum-assistant to the manager of the branch. This dazzling eminence had been achieved less by hard work than by a romantic attachment to the manager's daughter, a plain but fiercely emotional girl two years his senior. It was an understood thing that ultimately when, in the words of the girl's father, he had "proved himself," they were to be married.

This whole situation might have been intolerable were it not for the fact that the manager, Herbert Renshaw, his wife, and Sheila lived at Sevenoaks, just mercifully far enough away to make constant propinquity difficult. Felix lived on his salary, with occasional assistance from his mother, in a bed-sitting-room in Ebury Street. Every now and then he went to Sevenoaks—as dutifully as, but even less enthusiastically than, he went to Uxbridge. Sometimes, fortunately not very often, Sheila Renshaw came to London for the day. This involved much play-acting and nerve strain. First of all, there would be the halting, boyish request to Mr. Renshaw for an afternoon off; then lunch and a matinee, followed by the inevitable embarrassing taxi drive, hand in hand, to Victoria. Sometimes Mrs. Renshaw would come up too and meet them archly for tea; this at least ameliorated the horror of the latter part of the afternoon. It was perfectly apparent that Sheila loved him intensely. She was a stocky girl with nice eyes and no neck to speak of. Felix alternated between tolerating her and actively loathing her. He had not yet really faced up to the ultimate showdown, but knew that sooner or later he would have to. In the meantime life jogged along pleasantly and he had enough leisure to enjoy himself as much as he could.

The fact must be faced that Felix's principal preoccupation was sex. Sex in any reasonable form whatever. This may or may not have been something to do with his t.b. tendencies, but, whatever the cause, it was his pre-eminent interest and it had been for almost as long as he could remember. There was never a day in his life that he had not been ready and willing to respond to physical contact. So engrossed was he with the manifold physical pleasures that his body could provide that he had never given a desultory thought to other safety valves, such as reading, debate, music, or drink. What was most curious of all was the fact that he had never once experienced the emotion of being in love. He was highly predatory, but completely unpossessive; sensual and passionate, but incapable of jealousy. To go to bed with another fellow creature who attracted him seemed to him the most natural thing in the world, and it was astonishing how far this amiable conviction carried him. But to feel himself in any way bound to them or in their debt would never have occurred to

him. With all this it must not be imagined that he lacked
subtlety when in pursuit of what he wanted; far from it,
he was capable of infinite patience and also, alas, of infinite charm.

This, then, was the affable young wolf who was standing
in the foyer of the Walgrave Theatre gazing romantically
at photographs of an attractive young woman of twenty.

4

Leonora Jarvis had been on the stage for four years. Her
father and mother had died when she was a baby, and she
had no memory of them; her earliest recollections were of
Aunt May and Uncle Hubert and the house in Sandgate, a
light, clean, chilly house overlooking the sea. At the age
of eight she had been sent to a small day school near by
and, two years later, to a larger school in Folkestone in
which she was a weekly boarder and could come home for
week ends every Saturday afternoon by catching a bus outside Timothy White's.

Aunt May and Uncle Hubert were kind but undemon-
strative, and, although her early years may have lacked the
warmth of parental affection, they in no way lacked creature comforts. The house, during the summer months,
accommodated boarders of aggressive gentility. Leonora
naturally preferred the off seasons, when there was no one
left but old Mr. Radlett, who was a permanent, because
then she was permitted to move from the poky little room
on the top floor at the back which she inhabited when the
house was full, and to spread herself in the second-floor
front. Here she could kneel on clear winter nights, with
the window wide open and an eiderdown wrapped around
her, and look out over the dark sea. Sometimes, when it
was very clear, she could see the rhythmic flash of the Gris
Nez lighthouse below the horizon but reflected in the sky.
Here, with the smell of the sea, the sound of the waves
pounding the shingle, and the sharp wind blowing the

curtains out into the room, she could make plans for the future.

She was not a particularly romantic child, but she had always been determined, and since the second January of the War, when she had been taken by a school friend and family to a pantomime at the Pleasure Garden Theatre, she had formed one steadfast resolution, and that was to be an actress. It took her three years to achieve even the beginnings of this ambition, but through Uncle Hubert dying, and Aunt May giving up the house and moving into a flat in Maida Vale, and various other helpful circumstances, achieve it she did.

In the year 1919, after a series of impassioned scenes with Aunt May and Miss Bridgeman, the rather fierce companion whom Aunt May had taken to live with her, Leonora was sent to Madame Alvani's Acting and Dancing Academy in Baker Street. In 1920—aged sixteen—she played an animated water lily in a Christmas production at the Villiers Theatre. For this she was paid three pounds a week, from which Madame Alvani deducted ten per cent commission. Her next engagement was on tour with an ancient but select farce. In this she played a small part and understudied the ingenue lead. Her salary was again three pounds a week, but this time she did not have to pay commission, as she had got the job through Kay Larkin, an associate water lily a year older than herself who knew the ropes and had taken her straight to the management. Aunt May's and Miss Bridgeman's fears for her chastity were allayed by the fact that she was sharing rooms with Kay and, what was better still, Kay's mother. Had either of the good ladies ever clapped eyes on Kay's mother they might have been less tranquil. However, no moral harm came to Leonora during the engagement, and even if it had they would certainly have been the last to hear about it.

By the end of November 1923, when Oscar Morley (the Guv'nor) had engaged her for the sextette in the forthcoming production of *Lorelei*, she had achieved quite a lot of experience, if little fame. She had toured, been in the chorus of two West End revues, done a whole season of repertory in Nottingham, and played a bright, gay prostitute with a heart of gold in an ambitious problem play at the Everyman in Hampstead which never came to the West End. Through all these routine vicissitudes she had managed to remain, through circumstance and a certain natural fastidiousness, a virgin.

She had imagined herself to be in love on two occasions, once with the leading man in Nottingham, who was at least fifteen years older than she and heavily and happily married, and then with a young man who had been invalided out of the Navy and had appeared in her life when she was in the chorus of the *1922 Revue* at the Parthenon. This had been quite serious and lasted all through the summer. He had taken her out to supper at Rule's and occasionally the Savoy grill. He had driven her on warm, languorous Sunday evenings in a small, spluttering two-seater to Maidenhead, where they had danced at Murray's and driven home through the dawn, stopping at the side of the road at frequent intervals to exchange ardent, but innocuous, embraces. He was a nice, good-looking boy, shy, and with impeccable manners.

On one of these romantic jaunts he had stammeringly proposed marriage, but Leonora, who by that time had been introduced to his mother and sister at tea at the Carlton, knew with every instinct in her that no good would come of it and that, if she accepted him, she would somehow be betraying him as well as herself. So she refused him firmly but with a sad heart, and a few weeks later he came tragically to say good-bye to her. His mother and sister had decided to go out to visit his other sister, who was married and lived in New Zealand. He was to go with them on account of his health and being able to live an outdoor life and one thing and another. It all sounded rather garbled, but Leonora thought she detected the underlying truth, which was that he really did love her more than was good for him, and his family, reasonably enough, were intent on getting him out of harm's way.

They had a farewell supper at Rule's, sitting in an alcove staring miserably at each other over sausages and bacon and gins and tonics. The two-seater was outside, and they drove down to Richmond and back although it was a raw October night. He dropped her off outside the flat in Fulham Road that she was sharing with Hester Lancaster. They stood sadly on the pavement hand in hand, looking abstractedly at a street lamp swinging on the other side of the road. Then he suddenly kissed her almost violently, and said in a choked voice, "I shall never forget you and some part of me will always love you." With this he had jumped into the car and driven away. Leonora, blinded with tears, had fumbled for her latchkey, let herself in, and flung herself sobbing onto Hester's bed, where finally, soothed by wise, sympathetic advice and hot Ovaltine, she fell into a deep sleep.

For quite a while after that she had been heavy-hearted, but gradually, assisted by Hester and her own natural resilience, she forgot lost love in the everyday excitements of living. Hester was a laconic, drily humorous woman in her late twenties. They had met, shared digs, and become close friends during the tour of *Lady from Spain*. Hester's talent for acting was meagre; as far as a successful theatrical career was concerned, she was doomed to disappointment and she knew it, but she had a swift, cultured mind, and was a wise and restraining influence on Leonora. For over two years since the death of Aunt May they had been sharing the flat in Fulham Road.

Leonora came gaily into the dressing room with Josie. Phyllis, Violet, and Etta were already making up, but Maureen was late as usual. Leffie took her hat, bag, and coat from her and hung them on a peg.

"There's a billy doo for you, dear," she said laconically. "I propped it up against the tin."

Leonora glanced at it casually as she slipped out of her dress. "It's probably from the Prince of Wales," she said. "Badgering me to go to one of those dreary evenings at

Buckingham Palace."

"It might be from Alfie Stein," said Josie, "badgering you for his ten per cent."

"Not me." Leonora sat down and pulled her wrapper round her. "I've never had an agent in my life since Miriam Moss got me a tour that only lasted for three split weeks." She opened the letter and read it through. Leffie, watching her in the glass, saw her frown for a moment, smile, and then pass her hand rather abstractedly across her forehead.

"Well—come on, dear—don't keep us in suspense!" Josie banged on the dressing table with the back of her brush.

Leonora folded the letter carefully and put it back in the envelope and sighed. "Sorry to disappoint you all," she said, slapping some grease on her face. "It's only from my cousin Edward. He's eighteen, lives in Birmingham, and has spots, and he's coming to the Saturday matinee." She turned to Leffie. "Leffie, darling, put that in my bag for me, will you, or I shall forget to answer it." Leffie, unsmiling, took it from her, put it in Leonora's handbag, and snapped it to quite hard. Leonora gave her a swift look in the glass and went on with her make-up.

5

Felix stood in the alley outside the stage door. There was a group of girls near him, clutching autograph books and talking in whispers; occasionally one of them giggled. Felix, with elaborate nonchalance, took out his cigarette case and lit a cigarette. His whole body was taut and tremulous with suppressed excitement. He had watched the show from the front row of the dress circle on the side: it was the seventh time he had seen it, but he had never before been so near. During the second verse of the sextette Leonora had been actually only a few yards away from him. He had never taken his eyes off her for an instant; noting avidly every turn of her head; the little flounce she gave to her dress as she danced upstage; a secret smile she exchanged with one of the other girls when they were standing in a row right on the footlights for the last refrain; the demure, provocative swing of her hips as she went off, last but one, and the lissome grace of her curtsey when they all ran on to take the call. When the encore was over and they had finally gone, he had discovered that his hands, gripping the edge of the circle, were moist with excitement and had left a damp mark on the plush.

One by one and in groups, various members of the company emerged from the stage door. Budge Ripley, the comedian, came out in a hurry and went, almost at a run, up the steps at the end of the alley, where a taxi was waiting for him. The autograph collectors argued among themselves as to whether it really had been he or not. One of the show girls came out in a chinchilla coat, a spray of gardenias fastened to the lapel with a jewelled clip. A uniformed chauffeur was waiting for her. He raised his cap respectfully and helped her carefully up the steps towards the car as though she were infinitely fragile and might break.

Felix waited on. He recognised Maureen Clayton and Etta Malvern walking by him engrossed in animated conversation. He nearly accosted them to ask if Leonora was on her way down, but thought better of it and lit another cigarette. Judy Clandon came out followed by an elderly man in tails and a silk hat. The group of girls closed round her, and she signed their books and said good-bye to them with a great display of unaffected charm. When she had gone they moved off. Felix was left alone, except for a man in a mackintosh standing a little farther down. He was smoking a pipe and reading an evening paper in the light of the hanging lamp over the upper circle exit. At last Leonora came out. His heart seemed to jump into his throat; she was alone. Raising his hat, he stepped forward.

"Miss Jarvis." His voice sounded as though it belonged to someone else.

She stopped and smiled. "Are you Mr. Mes—Meseurier?" She had a little trouble with the name.

"Yes." He put out his hand which she accepted without embarrassment. "I hope you didn't mind me writing that letter. I couldn't help it."

She let her hand lie in his for a moment and then gently withdrew it. "I thought it was a very nice letter."

Suddenly Felix's overstrung, nervous shyness vanished. Everything was going to be all right. He grinned with a mixture of boyish humility and slight roguishness. "Is there any hope of your doing what I asked? Coming to have supper with me?"

Leonora shook her head. "I'm afraid not," she said. "I have to get straight home."

"Oh!" His voice was heavy with disappointment. They moved off together up the alley steps and into the street.

"You see," said Leonora, "I share a flat with a friend of mine, and if I go out without letting her know she gets rather worried."

"Couldn't you telephone her? We needn't be late."

Leonora shook her head. "Not to-night—honestly, I'd rather not to-night."

"Where is your flat? Is it far?"

"It's in the Fulham Road—I get the tube from Leicester Square."

"Would you mind if I came with you?"

Leonora shot him a look out of the corner of her eye as they turned into Garrick Street.

"Wouldn't it be taking you out of your way?"

Felix smiled—rather a nice smile, she thought. "I wish you lived at Hendon!"

He slipped his hand under her elbow to guide her across the road and kept it there when they reached the other side. She gave him another sidelong glance; his face was serious and, she had to admit, extremely attractive, and he wore his soft dark hat with an air. She began to wonder if, after all, she hadn't been a little hasty in refusing to have supper with him; there really wouldn't be any harm in it, and she was perfectly capable of looking after herself. The prospect of going straight home was rather dreary. Of course what she had said about Hester being worried about her wasn't strictly true. Hester probably wouldn't be home herself for an hour or more; she was playing a small part in a straight play at the Shaftesbury, it did not ring down until half-past eleven, and Hester always took her time anyway. She felt his hand tighten under her arm as they crossed St. Martin's Lane. He must have sensed that her obduracy was cracking a little, for he returned to the attack gently and very persuasively.

"I wouldn't like you to think that I made a habit of waiting outside stage doors and badgering girls to have supper with me." There was a tone of urgent sincerity in his voice. "As a matter of fact, this is the first time in my life that I've ever done it, and at that it's taken me weeks to summon up enough courage—as you see." He slowed down perceptibly—the Leicester Square station was distressingly near.

"You see, I really meant what I said in the letter. It would mean so very much to me to get to know you a little. Don't you think you could possibly change your mind—about supper, I mean? I'll drive you straight home in a taxi afterwards, so you really wouldn't be so very much later than if you went in the tube."

They came to a standstill in the entrance of the station. Leonora disengaged her arm from him and looked up at the clock. It was only twenty-five minutes to twelve. There were a lot of people about, and there was a long queue at the ticket window. The hot, familiar smell of the station assailed her nostrils unpleasantly. It would be far nicer to go home in a taxi, and if they weren't more than an hour over supper she could be in bed by one o'clock at the latest.

Felix watched her, and again was aware of an inward trembling: her fawn-coloured coat was tight-fitting and most tantalisingly outlined the curves of her young body; she was wearing a perky red cloche hat from under which a wisp of chestnut hair escaped in a jaunty little curl; her eyes were gray green, heavily lashed, and set wide apart; her nose, which was short and retroussé, while it may have impaired the beauty of her face from the strictly classical point of view, undoubtedly enhanced its vitality and charm; her mouth was enchanting, full-lipped and with a dimple in each corner, and as Felix looked at it with longing it suddenly opened in a radiant smile and she said, "Oh, all right!"

They had supper in a small restaurant in Soho. The atmosphere was oppressively Italian and there was a pervasive smell of garlic and cigar smoke, but the food was good, the chianti passable, and the red-shaded lamp on the table seemed to isolate them from the rest of the room and to enclose them in a glowing, shadowed, intimate world of their own. Felix ordered hors d'oeuvre, ravioli with powdered Parmesan cheese to sprinkle over it, and zabaglione in little shallow cups. He suggested liqueurs with the coffee, but she refused, finally compromising by having a crème de menthe frappé. Felix had brandy and bought himself a cigar.

By this time all restraint and shyness had fled. Felix, with a masterly sensitivity that many an older roué would have envied, refrained from any suggestion of love-making. He talked gaily and naturally without a trace of flirtatiousness. His acute hunting instinct warned him to establish firmly a friendly basis before attempting anything further.

Leonora, although not entirely deceived, thoroughly enjoyed herself. Her instincts also were fairly acute, and she had been about with ardent young men enough to be able to size up the situation without undue confusion. She found him attractive and nice-looking; she liked the way his eyes went up at the corners and the wave in his glossy dark hair. His eyes were brown and perhaps just a little too close together; he had a deep voice and his smile was infectious and charming; his teeth were perfect, even and gleaming white—no toothpaste firm could wish for a better advertisement. His greatest attraction, however, was his hands, muscular and slim with long, tapering fingers; his wrists, she had to admit, were rather hairy, but still you couldn't have everything.

They were almost the last to leave the restaurant. He took her coat from the cloakroom woman and helped her on with it himself. The patron wished them an expansive good night. Leonora noticed with satisfaction that Felix had tipped generously. When they got outside, the street was deserted and shone under the lights as though it had been raining. Their footsteps echoed in the silence as they walked down towards Shaftesbury Avenue. Felix hailed a taxi just outside the Queen's Theatre, and Leonora told the driver the address. When they had driven about halfway down Piccadilly Felix gently took her hand and held it. He said rather huskily, "You don't mind, do you?" She said, "Of course not," and inwardly commenting, "Here we go," she braced herself for the inevitable kiss. This, however, was not forthcoming. He seemed quite content to sit there silently holding her hand; every now and then he gave it a little friendly squeeze, but that was all.

When the cab drew up outside her front door, Felix jumped out immediately and held her arm carefully as she stepped down onto the kerb. They stood there looking at each other for a moment. Leonora was aware of a faint but unmistakable disappointment that he had not kissed her.

"You were a darling," he said, allowing a note of passionate intensity to creep into his voice, "to come to supper after all. You've no idea how much it meant to me!"

Leonora gave a slight giggle. She felt suddenly unaccountably nervous. "Don't be silly," she said, aware that her voice sounded rather breathless. "I had a lovely time."

She began fumbling in her bag for her latchkey; she found it and looked up at him. In the light from the street lamp she observed a little pulse beating in his temple. She held out her hand. "Good night, and thanks a lot."

He shook hands with her silently, and she turned and went up the little path to the front door. When she had, rather agitatedly, fitted the key into the lock, she turned back and waved. He was still standing there staring after her. Her wave seemed to snap him out of his trance, for he waved back, called, "Good night," quite ordinarily, gave an address to the driver, and jumped into the cab. As she closed the door behind her she heard it drive away. She walked upstairs feeling a bit deflated. He hadn't kissed her; he hadn't even asked to see her again.

6

There is much to recommend Hyde Park on a sunny Sunday afternoon, particularly in spring when the grass is newly green and there is a feeling of lightness in the air. Subconsciously affected by this, the most prosaic citizens frequently give way to a certain abandon. Fathers of families take off their coats and waistcoats and lie on their backs chewing bits of grass and gazing up at the sky; their wives sit near them, keeping an eye on the children and allowing the sun to burn semicircular areas of pink onto their necks. Younger people lie unashamedly very close, sometimes asleep, sometimes lazily awake, murmuring laconically to each other, sucking sweets, smoking cigarettes, relaxed and content, soothed into a sensual lassitude by the promise in the air and the gentle weather. As a general rule decorum is observed, although occasionally passion flames suddenly between them and they lie with arms and legs entwined, oblivious of passers-by, lost in brief ecstasy. Police constables regulate these transient excesses with admirable discretion; nothing is allowed to get out of control, the decencies are upheld, the birds sing, and the cries of children, the barking of dogs, and the far-off strains of a military band, together with the gentle, incessant rumble of traffic in the distance, provide a muted orchestration to this unremarkable, but at the same time unique, London pastoral.

On a Sunday afternoon in May 1924 Leonora and Felix,

having lunched at the Rendezvous and strolled down Piccadilly into the Park, lay in the shade of a tree near the Round Pond. At least Leonora was in the shade because she was afraid of getting freckles. Felix, intent on acquiring a tan, had taken off his shirt and was stripped to the waist in the sun. This was their third meeting since the evening two weeks ago when they had had supper at the Italian restaurant and he had driven her home in a taxi. He had called for her unexpectedly one Wednesday after the matinee and taken her to tea at the Thistle tearooms at the top of the Haymarket. The day after that he had sent a large bunch of flowers to her at the theatre with a card on which was written, "The words are old and ever new—forgive my heart for loving you." This was a quotation from Judy Clandon's number in Act Three of *Lorelei*, and under it were the initials F.M. The following Monday night after the show he had called for her in the pouring rain and they had supper together again, this time impressively at the Savoy grill. This time, also, he had kissed her on the way home in the taxi, but not until they were past Brompton Oratory and the drive was nearly over; the kiss, however, well-timed and admirably executed, had lasted with mounting intensity until the taxi drew up before her front door.

Today from the moment they had met outside the Piccadilly Circus tube station until now there had been no indication, either in his voice or in his manner, that he had ever kissed her at all or had the faintest intention of kissing her again. Throughout lunch he had been gay and talkative. Never once had his hand closed over hers; never once had she detected in his cheerful brown eyes that look of sudden longing, of suppressed desire. He had actually made fun of a couple sitting in the far corner of the restaurant because they looked so obviously, so overwhelmingly, in love.

Leonora's first reaction to this technique was one of acute irritation. This was presently superseded by a strange unhappiness, a desolation of the heart, an inexplicable desire to burst into tears. She rallied, however, with commendable poise and chattered and laughed as gaily as he. This successful effort at self-control had not only carried her triumphantly through lunch and down Shaftesbury Avenue and the whole length of Piccadilly, but had strung her nerves high. She had worked herself into a mood of tingling, brittle defiance. She'd show him all right, the next time he started any of his nonsense, that that kiss—the tremulous memory of which she hastily put out of her mind—had meant as little to her as it obviously had to him.

Now, sitting under the tree with the warm spring sunshine all around her, this mood suddenly and unaccountably evaporated, leaving her shivering and vulnerable. Felix was lying a yard or so away from her. His naked chest and arms shone in the strong light. She felt a violent urge to fling herself onto him, to feel his mouth under hers, and the warmth of his body pressed against her. Appalled by this sudden wave of passion which swept over her and receded, leaving her trembling and exhausted, she leant her head back against the tree trunk and closed her eyes.

Felix, whose telepathic instincts seldom failed him, turned his head sharply and looked at her; swiftly and almost in one movement his arms were around her and his lips pressed into the hollow of her neck. She gave a little cry. He kissed her mouth lingeringly, and then, when her whole being seemed to be fused in an agony of surrender, he rolled away from her and lay face downwards on the grass, still as death, with his face turned away from her.

A little while later, his hand, familiar and comforting under her arm, guided her gently across Knightsbridge into the deserted Sabbath peace of Lowndes Square. She walked automatically in step with him; neither of them spoke, but the feeling between them was tense. Somewhere below her surface consciousness a conflict was raging: this was silly, cheap, immodest, dangerous—she would regret it until the end of her life. Walking through

empty, echoing London squares in the clear afternoon sunlight with her lover, a comparative stranger; being led
inexorably to the glamour and squalor and ecstasy and
defeat of a bed-sitting-room in Ebury Street. An empty
taxi hoping for a fare drew up close to them as they
crossed Eaton Square. She longed for the courage to shake
off Felix's arm and jump into it. It ground its gears and
drove off. They walked on in silence along Elizabeth
Street and turned the corner.

Felix's bed-sitting-room was on the third floor at the
back of a tall, narrow house. The window looked out over
a small yard, a grimy brick wall, and the backs of the
houses in Chester Square. The landlady lived in the basement, and they had crept in and up the stairs unheard
and unobserved. Leonora noticed a bottle of bright green
hairwash on the dressing table and a photograph of a squat
dark girl in an embossed leather frame. The bed, pretending to be a divan, had neither head nor foot and was
pushed against the wall. There were some coloured Lib-
erty cushions on it, arranged three-cornerwise and looking
self-conscious; on the mantelpiece there were a few books
leaning against a china dog, a tin of Gold Flake cigarettes, a large photograph of three young men in bathing
trunks, and a pair of dumbbells. Leonora stood quite still
in the middle of the room, staring uncertainly at the
three young men and imagining vaguely that the one in
the middle of the group was Felix himself; a beam of sunlight cut sharply through the net curtains, and in the
distance there was the noise of a train shunting. Felix
turned the key in the door, and then came over to her. He
stood looking at her for a moment with a strange, furtive
little smile, and then, with a sort of gentle violence, he
pulled her to him and as his mouth opened on hers she
felt his left hand slip into the bosom of her dress.

7

On a Saturday evening a few weeks later Leonora came into the theatre with Josie Gay. They were late and breathless, having run all the way from Josie's family flat in Covent Garden, the "half" had already been called, and if Len Baxter, the stage manager, saw them they would be ticked off. The stage-door man handed Leonora a letter from the rack as she and Josie rushed through the folding doors, and she took it without looking at it. Leffie glanced at them disapprovingly as they burst into the dressing room.

Leonora flung the letter face downwards on her dressing table while she tore her clothes off and got into her wrapper. She felt gay and without a care in the world. To-morrow was Sunday and she was meeting Felix as usual; she had had a lovely time having dinner with Josie and the Prout family. Josie's father, Syd Prout, the well-known comedian, had died some years ago, leaving his wife with three daughters to bring up. Dawn (Dawn Lawrence), the eldest, had made quite a name for herself playing Cockney character parts. Josie came next and was doing reasonably well; she was a hard-boiled, thoroughly experienced little "pro" and looked a great deal younger than twenty-five with her chubby face and fluffy blond hair.

The family's pride was Shirley, the youngest—the famous Shirley Dale, who already at twenty-four was an established star. Leonora had met her for the first time this evening and had been duly thrilled and impressed. Shirley had arrived unexpectedly and tempestuously just as they were sitting down to dinner. Her clothes were perfect and her manner entirely natural and unaffected, the aura of stardom, although unmistakable, seemed in no way to have interfered with her alert, utterly theatrical sense of humour, a quality which most emphatically distinguished the whole family.

Mrs. Prout (at one time Rosie Claire) was obviously adored by the three girls. They laughed at her and teased her and told hilarious stories of her absent-mindedness, her occasional predilection for having a "couple over the odds," her swiftness of repartee, and her frequent, but always unsuccessful, attempts to become what they described as "county." None of them ever called her "Mother" or even "Mum." She was always "Rosie" or sometimes "Our Rosie." There was certainly a warmth, a cosiness, an intrinsic, down-to-earth reality about the Prout family.

Leonora had been taken to their ramshackle, untidy house in Covent Garden several times, and each time she had come away happy and stimulated and with a little envy in her heart, a regret that she had not had the luck to be born of a comedienne and a principal boy and to be brought up with the fun and jokes and glamour of the theatre as her natural background.

It was not until she had put on the foundation of her make-up and was about to start on her eyelashes that she remembered the letter. She wiped her fingers on her face towel, picked up the letter and turned it over in her hands. With a slight sinking of the heart she recognised Felix's handwriting; perhaps he was putting her off for to-morrow, perhaps he was ill, or had to go and see his mother at Uxbridge or something.

She opened it quickly and read it. Then she sat quite still feeling sick, as though someone had hit her hard in the solar plexus. The chattering voices of the other girls seemed to recede into the remote distance. Like a sound from another world she dimly heard the call-boy's voice in the passage shouting, "Quarter of an hour, please." With an immense effort she read the letter through again.

Dearest Lee,

I hate writing you this letter, but I've got to do it—there is no other way out. I know you'll think me an awful cad for never having told you that I was engaged to be mar-

*ried, but somehow I couldn't screw up the courage—I felt
that it would spoil everything if you knew. I am utterly
heartbroken and miserable—my fiancée's father has found
out about you and me. I don't know how, but he tackled
me with it and there's been the most awful row. He has
forced me to promise never to see you again and he is send-
ing me away to Holland for three months on the firm's
business. By the time you receive this I shall already have
left. Please try to forgive me. I daren't break my word to
him because he is my boss and my whole job depends on
it. I feel so dreadfully unhappy—I can't write any more.
Good-bye.*

Felix

Leonora folded the letter and put it carefully back into
the envelope and automatically began to do her eyelashes.
Nobody must see that she was upset; nobody must notice
anything wrong. She caught Leffie's eye in the mirror, and
forced herself to smile at her. Her hand was shaking, and
it caused her to smudge some eye black on her cheek. She
said, "Blast!" loudly, and heard, to her surprise and relief,
that her voice sounded quite ordinary. She managed to
get through the performance without betraying herself.
Only once, during the sextette, she nearly broke down. It
was in the second chorus when she had her little solo bit
to sing, and just as she stepped forward out of the line a
burning, agonising memory of Felix sprang at her from
the darkness of the auditorium. Last Sunday afternoon—
could it really only be last Sunday?—they had been lying
together on the divan and he had suddenly jumped up
and, wrapping a towel round his middle, minced across
the room in an imitation of her singing these very words.
She had laughed immoderately and he had silenced her by
sliding on top of her and kissing her repeatedly. . . .

Now, with the other five girls humming *bouches fermées*
behind her, she suddenly felt her throat contract. She gave
a painful little gulp, and forced the rhymed couplet out
the wrong way round. As they were dancing off at the end

of the number Josie hissed out of the corner of her mouth, "Drunk again, dear!" Leonora giggled as naturally as she could, "I suddenly got the chokes!"

When the show was over, she took longer than usual to get her make-up off. She was feeling exhausted and wretched, and the strain of keeping up the pretence that nothing out of the way had happened to her was beginning to wear her down. When she had finally got her outdoor clothes on, all the others had gone, and she was fumbling in her bag to find Leffie's Saturday night tip when her fingers encountered the shameful, heartbreaking letter. She had put it carefully in her bag before going down for the first act. Again a wave of sickness engulfed her. She caught Leffie's eye looking at her curiously, her legs seemed to give way under her, and she sank down abruptly on a chair. In a moment Leffie's arms were round her.

"What's the matter, dear? You've been looking peaky all the evening."

Leonora tried gallantly to mutter that she was all right, but the sympathy in Leffie's voice and the hopelessness and misery in her heart were too much for her. She buried her face against Leffie's shoulder and broke into violent, shaking sobs. Leffie, with the tact born of long experience, said nothing at all for quite a long while, merely holding her close and occasionally giving her a gentle, affectionate little pat. Presently, when the violence of her weeping had spent itself, Leffie went over to the cupboard over the washing basin and, taking out a medicine bottle with brandy in it, poured some into a glass and held it to Leonora's lips.

"Here, love," she said, "take a sip of this, and I'll light you a nice cigarette."

Leonora obeyed weakly. The brandy made her gasp a little. Leffie lit a cigarette and handed it to her, then sat down purposefully opposite her with her gnarled hands on her knees and said firmly, "Now then—what's wrong? You'd better tell me and be quick about it, for if it's what

I think it is, there's no sense in fiddling about and wasting time!"

Leonora made a great effort. "I don't think," she gulped, "I don't think it *is* what you think it is, Leffie—it's just that—that——" Her eyes filled with tears again, and she broke off.

"Is it that young man with the smarmy voice and the funny name?"

Leonora nodded.

"I knew it." Leffie clicked her tongue against her teeth. "Has he got you into trouble?"

Leonora shook her head wearily. "No, not exactly—that is—not that sort of trouble." Somewhere at the back of her misery she was aware of a flicker of amusement at Leffie's insistence on the obstetrical aspect of the situation.

"What *has* 'e done then?" went on Leffie inexorably, "led you up the garden path and then buggered off and left you?"

"That's right, Leffie." This time Leonora really did manage a wan smile. "That's exactly what he's done." She reached for her bag, opened it, took out the letter, and handed it to Leffie.

"Here—you'd better read it."

Leffie took it, fixed her glasses on her nose, and read it slowly through. Leonora watched her without emotion. She felt drained of all feeling and immeasurably tired. Leffie finished the letter and put it back in its envelope. "Well," she said. "That's a nice thing, I *must* say! I knew that young gentleman was no good the first time 'e come here with that note for you and give me five bob." She looked at Leonora sharply over her glasses.

"Have you been the 'ole 'og with him?"

Leonora nodded.

"Was it the first time you ever 'ad with anybody?"

"Yes."

"Well then," said Leffie with finality, "the first thing you've got to do is to forget all about him—he's a bad lot if ever I saw one—and the second thing is to keep a careful

eye on yourself for the next few weeks—let's see now."
Leffie wrinkled her brow with the effort of calculation.
"You're not due again until the first week of July, are
you?"

Leonora frowned slightly, Leffie's aggressive realism was
a trifle distasteful. "It's nothing to do with that, Leffie,"
she said with a slight edge on her voice. "That's not what's
worrying me, really it isn't——"

Leffie's face softened suddenly. "I know, dear," she said.
"You mustn't take any notice of me—I always look at the
practical side of things first—I always 'ave done all my life,
that is ever since I was old enough to learn a bit of horse
sense and that's going back a bit, I give you my word."
She leant forward and patted Leonora's hand. "Now, look
'ere, dear——"

Leonora looked at her pale, kindly eyes and was surprised to see that there were tears in them.

"I know what's upsetting you all right—don't you make
any mistake about that—you've let yourself fall in love with
him, and you thought that he was in love with you, and
now you suddenly find that all he was after was just one
thing and that one thing you were fathead enough to let
'im have! Well—that's that, isn't it? What's done's done
and you can't get away from it, but it isn't right to work
yourself into a state and cry your 'eart out for a slimy young
rotter who takes advantage of you and leaves you flat without as much as a by-your-leave, is it, now? He's not worth
one minute of your time if you only knew it. Mind you,
I'm not saying he isn't good-looking and nicely spoken
and all that sort of thing. They always are, that type, but
look at you now. You're young and pretty and getting on
fine, with your whole life before you. Why should you
worry just because some la-di-da young bastard 'asn't got
the decency to treat you right! Why, if he had any sense
he'd be jumping for joy at having the luck to take you
out to tea, let alone have an affair with you. Let him go,
dear, and a bloody good riddance to him at that. Don't
cry any more, and don't get upstage with me for speaking

what's in my mind. You're the lucky one if you only knew
it, and a day will come—and not so far off either—when
you'll laugh your 'ead off to think what a state you got
yourself into over someone who wasn't fit to black your
boots!" Leffie, exhausted by this peroration, rose to her
feet. "If you'll wait two shakes of a duck's arse, I'll tidy
up and walk with you to the tube."

Leonora got up too and straightened her hat in front of
the glass; then she turned, her underlip trembling a little,
and flung her arms round Leffie's angular, undernourished
little body. "Thank you, Leffie," she said with a catch in
her voice; "thank you a lot."

8

Leonora Jarvis was certainly a big draw in Edinburgh.
As a matter of fact, she was a big draw all over the country.
Since 1940 she had, in common with most of the other
West End stars, played in the provinces more consistently
than ever before in her life. Mr. Gilmour, the house manager, stood by the box office at the end of the performance
and watched the crowds passing through the foyer and on
through the exit doors into the blackout. They all looked
cheerful and animated, as though they had had a good
time.

Leonora had made, as usual, a charming little curtain
speech. Gilmour had stopped on the way down from his
office to listen to it. Despite all his years of managerial experience, it always amused and pleased him to observe
the technical grace and courtesy with which established
stars handled their applause. Leonora Jarvis was actually
one of his favourites. She had played the theatre countless
times and never been any trouble, always polite and charming to the staff, always controlled and assured and untem-
peramental even when things went wrong. He remembered the first time she had appeared there a long while
ago, 1927 or 1928. She had played the second part in a

Clarence Wellman comedy supporting Charles Lucas and poor old Jane Lorrimer. It had been the first week of the play's provincial tryout before going to the West End, and on the opening night, after a disastrous dress rehearsal on the Sunday, Leonora had unquestionably walked away with the show. He remembered going round to her dressing room to congratulate her—she had dressed upstairs in those days, not in the star room on the stage level where she was now—he remembered how flushed and happy and excited she had been, and how proudly she had introduced him to her husband, a good-looking young naval lieutenant. Mr. Gilmour sighed sentimentally; that completely happy marriage had been broken by Fate in 1933, when the husband had been killed in an air crash while on his way to rejoin his ship at Malta. The papers had been full of praise of Leonora's behaviour, all the usual journalistic tripe about her playing with a broken heart and never missing a performance. Lot of bloody nonsense. Of course she hadn't missed a performance; being an old ex-actor himself, he realised only too well how fortunate she had been in a crisis like that to have a performance to give. There's nothing like having responsibility and a job to do to get you through trouble.

To-night, watching her make her curtain speech, he had suddenly felt a surge of emotion. Nothing particularly personal, just professional emotion; the theatre was the thing all right, a good artiste in a good play, gracefully acknowledging the enthusiasm of a packed house—you could never achieve a thrill like that in all the ornate super-cinemas in the world! He nodded cheerfully to the doorman, and, stubbing his cigar out in a brass ash tray affixed to the wall outside one of the entrances to the stalls, he pushed the door open, walked down along the side of the empty auditorium, and went through the pass door onto the stage.

A little while later, when he was seated in Leonora's dressing room having his usual chat with her while she put the finishing touches to her street make-up, there was a knock on the door. Alice, Leonora's maid, disappeared discreetly into the passage for a moment and then came back. "It's that Mr.—that gentleman who you was expecting," she said. Mr. Gilmour saw a quick smile flit across Leonora's face. "Tell him to give me just two minutes," she said. Gilmour immediately rose to his feet. "I must be pushing off," he said. "Everything all right—no complaints?"

"A million complaints." Leonora patted his mottled red face affectionately. "Those damned girls with their coffee trays rattling all through the beginning of the second act—one of these nights I shall jump over the orchestra pit and bash their heads in!"

"All right, all right." He held up his hand pacifically. "It won't happen to-morrow night, I promise."

"Does that go for tea as well? To-morrow's a matinee day!"

"Tea trays out before the curtain—cross my heart," said Mr. Gilmour. "Good night, my dear."

"Good night, Gillie." Leonora kissed her hand to him as he went out of the door. She stood still for a moment in the middle of the room, surveying herself in the long glass. Her tailor-made was good, new silk stockings wonderful! God bless darling Bobbie Craig for coming back from Bermuda via Lisbon. Her mink coat, of course, was the crowning glory. Yes, she certainly looked well enough. "It's all right, Alice," she said with the faintest suspicion of a tremor in her voice. "You can ask Mr. Meseurier to come in now."

Alice disappeared into the passage again and, after a moment or two, flung open the door. Leonora heard her say, "This way, sir."

Into the room walked briskly, if a trifle nervously, the first lover of her life, and at the sight of him her heart stopped dead in her breast and the charming welcoming smile was frozen onto her face.

"Leonora!" He took her hand. "This is wonderful—wonderful—I can hardly believe it's really you!"

She felt her hand warmly enveloped in his and watched with awful fascination as with forced, self-conscious gallantry he bent down to kiss it. His head was practically bald except for a few strands of hair which were plastered across his scalp with infinite care like strips of damp patent leather. He straightened himself and gazed into her eyes with a whimsical expression tinged with stale amorousness, a macabre travesty of the way she remembered him looking at her in the past. His figure, the once lithe and graceful body, had assumed with the years the shape of a pear-drop, sloping from the shoulders and swelling into a paunch; his sagging skin was a yellowish-gray and his eyes, the whites of which were slightly bleared, seemed to have crept closer to the bridge of his nose as though they were scared and anxious to get as near to one another as possible. He was wearing a debonair pin-striped brown suit which was a little tight for him, and on the third finger of his left hand was a large ruby ring. He had laid his bowler hat and mackintosh on the couch when he came in.

With a supreme effort Leonora pulled herself together. "Why, Felix!" The words seemed to stick in her throat. "What a lovely surprise! After all these years!" She was horribly aware of the falseness in her voice, but he was blandly unconscious of it.

"You were splendid in the play to-night." He gave a little nod as though to emphasise his approval of her performance. "What I said in my letter proved to be quite true. You've hardly changed at all."

"Neither have you—I should have known you anywhere." Mortified, she noted his serene acceptance of the glib, conventional lie. Suddenly feeling that she could not bear to look at him for another moment, she hurriedly turned and snatched up a cigarette box from the dressing table. "Let's sit down quietly and have a cigarette," she said, "before we go to supper. Alice, ask the taximan to be a dear and wait for five minutes, will you? Then you can go."

"All right, Miss Jarvis." Alice took her hat and coat from the peg behind the door. "Good night, miss—good night, sir." She went out and closed the door behind her. Leonora and Felix were alone. With a quick, almost subservient gesture, he whipped a lighter from his pocket and lit her cigarette and then his own. She murmured, "Thank you," motioned him into the armchair, and inhaled the smoke deeply into her lungs. "If only," she thought wildly, "this one particular Player's Mild might by magic contain some strong anaesthetic that would send me off into complete unconsciousness!" She sat down at the dressing table and, giving a nervous little dab at her hair, tried frantically to think of something to say, but the leaden silence crushed her down and numbed her brain. After an eternity he broke it by leaning forward and saying, with pregnant meaning, "Well?"

She forced herself to turn and look at him. "Well, what?" She gave a gay little laugh.

"Have you forgiven me?"

This was insufferable. How dare he, how could he be so awful as to say that! She felt herself blushing with rage and embarrassment. Still with a smile on her face she replied mechanically, "There's nothing to forgive."

Aware of the strain in the atmosphere but happily misunderstanding the cause, he allowed a distinctly roguish look to come into his eyes and grinned, a slow, knowing, resolutely seductive grin. That grin was the final horror, for, in place of the gleaming white teeth that in the past had so tremendously enhanced his charm, he was now exhibiting, with the utmost complacency, a double set of shining dentures surmounted by gums of gutta percha.

Leonora stared at them hypnotised. Then the dreadful thing happened: her control snapped, and she started to laugh. His grin persisted for a little, but gradually faded. She saw his expression change from arch coquetry to bitter, tight-lipped rage. He stood up. She tried incoherently to cover her mounting hysteria by murmuring something about the sudden shock and the excitement of seeing him

again, but it was no use. She was gone, sunk, lost irretriev-
ably. The tears rolled down her cheeks; she felt her face
becoming suffused and scarlet; some mascara ran into her
eyes, and the sharp, stinging pain of it, far from pulling
her together, merely sent her off into further agonising
paroxysms. She scrabbled wildly in her bag for her handkerchief and, having found it, dabbed ineffectually at her
streaming eyes. She was aware also that she was making
awful explosive noises, groans and gasps and grunts, her
whole body was shaking uncontrollably, and finally, beyond shame and far beyond all hope of restraint, she
stretched her arms out on the dressing table and, burying
her face in them, lay there in utter abandon, sobbing help-
lessly, with her shoulders heaving.

When, after a considerable time, spent and exhausted,
she raised her head, the room was empty.

★

NATURE STUDY

THE HEARTINESS of Major Cartwright had grown beyond being an acquired attribute of mind and became organic. He exuded it chemically as a horse exudes horsiness; as a matter of fact he exuded a certain amount of horsiness as well. He was large and blond and his skin was brickish in colour, the end of his fleshy nose shaded imperceptibly to mauve but not offensively, it blended in with the small purple veins round his eyes which were pale blue and amiable. His best point really was the even gleaming whiteness of his teeth, these he showed a good deal when he laughed, a loud, non-infectious, but frequent laugh.

The barman treated him with deference and he was popular on board owing to his genial efficiency at deck games. In the early morning and later afternoon he played Deck Tennis in saggy khaki shorts, below which he wore neatly rolled stockings and gym shoes and above a rather old blue silk polo shirt opened generously at the neck exposing a few curling fronds of dust-coloured hair.

He was at his best in the smoking-room after dinner, expanding into "outpost of Empire" reminiscence and calling for "stengahs," a bore really but somehow touching in his fidelity to type. It wasn't until after Marseilles, where most of the cronies had disembarked to go home overland, that he turned his attention to me. We sat together in the little winter garden place aft of the promenade deck and had a drink before dinner. The lights at Marseilles were shimmering on the horizon and there was a feeling of emptiness in the ship as though the party were over and there were only a few stragglers left. The stragglers consisted of about a dozen planters and their families and three or four yellowish young men from the Shell company in Iraq, who had joined the ship at Port Said and were going home on leave.

He talked a lot but slowly and with great emphasis, principally, of course, about himself and his regiment. On the few occasions when he forsook the personal for the general it was merely to let fly a cliché such as "That's women all over," or "A man who has a light hand with a horse has a light hand with anything." I gently interposed "Except with pastry," but he didn't hear. He suggested that he should move over from his now deserted table in the saloon and join me at mine for the rest of the voyage. I was about to spring to my usual defence in such circumstances, which is that I always have to eat alone as I am concentrated on making mental notes for a book or play, but something in his eyes prevented me, they were almost pleading, so I said with as much sincerity as I could muster that nothing would please me more, and that was that.

Our tête-à-têtes for the next few days were, on the whole not as bad as I feared—he was perfectly content to talk away without demanding too many answers. By the time we reached Gibraltar I knew a great deal about him. He had a wife, but the tropics didn't agree with her so she was at home living with her married sister just outside Newbury, a nice little place they had although the married sister's husband was a bit of a fool, a lawyer of some sort with apparently no initiative.

The Major had no doubt that his wife would be damned glad to see him again. He was proposing to take a furnished flat in Town for part of his leave and do a few shows, after that Scotland and some shooting. A friend of his called, for some unexplained reason, "Old Bags," had quite a decent little shoot near a place the name of which the Major had as much difficulty in pronouncing as I had in understanding.

I listened to this conversation attentively because I was anxious to discover what, if anything, he had learned from the strange places he had been to, the strange people he had met, the various and varied differences in climate,

circumstances, motives and human life that he had encountered. There he sat, slouched back in a big arm-chair in
the smoking-room, his large legs stretched out in front of
him and a brandy glass in his hand—talking—wandering
here and there among his yesterdays without any particular aim and without, alas, the gift of expressing in the
least what he really wanted to say and, worse still, without
even the consciousness that he wasn't doing so. His limited
vocabulary was shamefully over-worked—most of his words
did the duty of six, like a small orchestra of provincial
musicians thinly attempting to play a complicated score
by doubling and trebling up on their instruments. I wondered what he knew, actually knew of the facts of life, not
complex psychological adjustments and abstractions, they
were obviously beyond his ken and also unnecessary to
his existence. But any truths, basic truths within his own
circumscribed experience. Had he fathomed them or not?
Was there any fundamental certainty of anything whatever in that untidy, meagre, amiable mind? Were the
badly-dressed phrases that he paraded so grandiloquently
aware of their shabbiness, their pretentious gentility? Did
they know themselves to be ill-groomed and obscure, or
were they upheld by their own conceit like dowdy British
Matrons sniffing contemptuously at a Mannequin Parade?

I tried to visualise him in certain specified situations,
crises, earthquakes or shipwrecks, or sudden native upris-
ings. He would behave well undoubtedly, but why? Could
he ever possibly know why? The reason he stood aside to
allow the women and children to go first; the exact motive
that prompted him to rush out into the compound amid a
hail of arrows, brandishing a Service revolver? The im-
pulses that caused his actions, the instincts that pulled
him hither and thither, had he any awareness of them,
any curiosity about them at all? Was it possible that an
adult man in the late forties with a pattern of strange
journeys behind him, twenty years at least of potentially
rich experience, could have lived through those hours and
days and nights, through all those satisfactions, distastes,

despondencies and exhilarations without even a trace of
introspection or scepticism? Just a bland unthinking acceptance without one query? I looked at him wondering-
ly, he was describing a duck shoot in Albania at the moment, and decided that not only was it possible but very
probable indeed.

After dinner on the night before we arrived at Plymouth
he asked me into his cabin to see some of his snapshot
albums. "They might interest you," he said in a deprecatory tone which was quite false, as I knew perfectly well
that the thought that they might bore me to extinction
would never cross his mind. "There's a damn good one of
that sail-fish I told you about," he went on. "And that
little Siamese girl I ran across in K.L. after that Guest
Night."

I sat on his bunk and was handed album after album in
chronological order, fortunately I was also handed a
whisky-and-soda. They were all much the same; groups,
picnic parties, bathing parties, shoots, fishing parties, all
neatly pasted in with names and initials written underneath. "Hong-Kong, March 1927. Mrs. H. Cufly, Captain
H., Miss Friedlands, Stella, Morgan, W.C." He always
indicated his own presence in the group by his initials. I
need hardly say that W.C. figured largely in all the albums.
He had the traditional passion of his kind for the destruction of life, there was hardly a page that was not adorned
with the grinning, morose head of some dismembered
animal or fish.

Suddenly, amid all those groups of people I didn't know
and was never likely to know, my eye lighted on a face
that I recognised. A thin, rather sheep-like face with
sparse hair brushed straight back and small eyes that
looked as if it were only the narrow high-bridged nose that
prevented them from rushing together and merging for
ever.

"That," I said, "is Ellsworth Ponsonby."

The Major's face lit up. "Do you know old Ponsonby?"
I replied that I had known him on and off for several

years. The Major seemed, quite agreeably, stricken by the coincidence.

"Fancy that now!" he said. "Fancy you knowing old Ponsonby." He sat down next to me on the bed and stared over my shoulder at the photograph as though by looking at it from the same angle he could find some explanation of the extraordinary coincidence of my knowing old Ponsonby. Old Ponsonby in the snapshot was sitting in the stern sheets of a small motor-boat. Behind him was the rich, mountainous coastline of the Island of Java, on either side of him were two good-looking young men, one fair and one dark and both obviously bronzed by the sun. Ellsworth Ponsonby himself, even in those tropical surroundings, contrived to look as pale as usual. The word "Old" as applied to him was merely affectionate. He was, I reflected, about forty-three. He was narrow-chested and wearing, in addition to his pince-nez, a striped fisherman's jersey which was several sizes too big for him. The young men were wearing, apparently, nothing at all. I asked who they were, to which the Major replied that they were just a couple of pals of old Ponsonby's, quite decent chaps on the whole. They were making a tour of the Islands in Ponsonby's yacht, the noble proportions of which could just be discerned in the right-hand corner of the photograph.

"Never seen such a thing in my life," said the Major. "Talk about every modern convenience, that yacht was a floating palace; marble bathrooms to every cabin, a grand piano, a cocktail bar, a French chef—those rich Americans certainly know how to do themselves well. I ran across him first in Batavia—I was taking a couple of months' sick leave—had a touch of Dengue, you know, and thought I'd pay a call on an old pal of mine, Topper Watson—wonder if you know him?—used to be in the Sixth—anyway, he'd been invalided out of the army and had this place in Java, plantation of some sort, quite good shooting and some decent horses, unfortunately married a Javanese girl—quite a nice little woman, but that sort of thing gives one the shudders a bit—not that it was any of my affair, after all a man's life's his own to do what he likes with, still it seemed a pity to see a chap like old Topper on the way to going native."

"Ellsworth," I said wearily. "Ellsworth Ponsonby."

"Oh yes, old Ponsonby." The Major gave one of his strong laughs—"Ran up against him in the bar of the Hôtel des Indes—got to yarning—you know how one does, and finally he asked me on board this damned yacht of his. By God, I hadn't eaten such a dinner for years, and the brandy he gave us afterwards!" Here the Major smacked his lips and blew a lumbering kiss into the air. "We sat on deck into the small hours talking."

I wondered if the Major had really permitted Ponsonby to do any of the talking. Apparently he had for he heaved a sigh and said, "Damned sad life old Ponsonby's, he had a raw deal."

As that did not entirely fit in with what I knew of Ellsworth I asked in what way he had had such a sad life and such a raw deal.

"Wife left him," replied the Major laconically, pursing up his large lips and ejecting a smoke-ring with considerable force. "God, but women can be bitches sometimes! Did you ever know her?"

"Yes," I said. "I knew her."

"Ran off with his own chauffeur—can you imagine a decently bred woman doing such a thing? Old Ponsonby didn't say much but you could see it had broken him up completely—women like that ought to be bloody well horsewhipped. He showed me a photograph of her, pretty in rather a flash sort of way, you know, the modern type, flat-chested, no figure at all, not my idea of beauty, but each man to his own taste. After we'd looked at the photograph we went up on deck again—you could see old Ponsonby was in a state, he was trembling and hardly said a word for about ten minutes and then damn it if he didn't start blubbing! I must say I felt sorry for the poor devil, but there was nothing I could say so I poured him out

some more brandy and after a bit he pulled himself together. That was when he told me about her running off
with the chauffeur—after all he'd given her everything, you
know—she was a nobody before she married him. He met
her first in Italy, I believe, just after the War, and they
were married in Rome—then he took her over to America
to meet his people—Boston, I think it was. Then they had
a house in London for a couple of seasons and another one
in Paris, I believe. Then this awful thing happened." The
Major wiped his forehead with his handkerchief, it was
getting rather stuffy in the cabin. "My God," he said pensively, "I don't know what I'd do if a woman did a thing
like that to me—Poor old Ponsonby—" He broke off and
was silent for a moment or two, then he turned to me.
"But you knew her, didn't you?"

   "Yes," I said. "I knew her."

2

   Jennifer Hyde was nineteen when she first met Ellsworth Ponsonby in Alassio just after the War. She was
staying at the Pension Floriana with her Aunt and a couple of girl cousins. Ellsworth was at the Grand Hotel with
his mother. Old Mrs. Ponsonby was remarkable more as a
monument than a human being. Her white hair was so
permanently waved and arranged that it looked like con-
crete. Her face was a mask of white powder and her eyes
were cold and hard. Beneath her chin, which was beginning to sag, she wore a tight black velvet ribbon by day,
and at night a dog-collar of seed pearls and diamonds. She
sat on the terrace of the hotel every morning from eleven
until one, lunched, rather resentfully, at a window table
in the dining-room, retired to her bed regularly from two
until four and then took a short drive through the sur-
rounding country. She over-dressed for dinner and played
bridge afterwards, wearing an expression of thinly dis-
guised exasperation whether she won or lost. Ellsworth

sometimes ate with her, drove with her, and played bridge with her. Whenever he did, the look in her eyes softened a trifle and her face relaxed. She watched him greedily, every gesture that he made, when he was shuffling the cards, when he was taking a cigarette from his elaborate Cartier cigarette-case and lighting it, whatever he did her eyes were on him sharp and terribly loving. When he was not with her he was usually with Father Robert. They would walk up and down the beach sometimes in the moonlight after dinner, their dark shadows bumping along behind them over the dry sand. Father Robert was plump with fine eyes, a thick, sensual mouth and wide soft hands which moved gently when he talked, not in any way to illustrate what he was saying, but as though they were living a different, detached life of their own. Jennifer and her girl cousins used to allude to him as "The Black Beetle."

Ellsworth had been converted to the Catholic Faith when he was nineteen. Oddly enough his mother had put forward no objections, in some strange intuitive way she probably felt that it would keep Ellsworth close to her, and in this she was right. He had always been emotional as a boy and this Catholic business seemed somehow to calm him, also it was an outlet that he could discuss with her without outraging any proprieties. She had hoped, in her secret heart, that once away from the strong guiding influence of Father Ryan in Boston, he might, amid the interests and excitements of travel, become a little less ardent; this hope, however, was doomed to disappointment, for on arrival in London they had been met by Father Hill; in Paris by Father Jules; in Lausanne by Father MacMichael; in Rome by Father Philipo; and here, in Alassio, by Father Robert. She had not really minded the other Fathers, in fact Father MacMichael had been quite amusing, but she quite unequivocally detested Father Robert. This was in no way apparent, as her Bostonian upbringing had taught her to control any but her more superficial feelings; however, the hate was there, lying in her heart, vital, alert, and waiting.

Ellsworth, even if he suspected it, showed no sign and continued to enjoy Father Robert's company as much as he could, which was a great deal.

Mrs. Ponsonby first noticed Jennifer in the lounge of the Hotel, sitting with a young man in flannels and two nondescript girls. Jennifer looked far from nondescript. She radiated a clear, gay, animal vitality. She was wearing a neat white tennis dress and the ends of her dark hair were damp and curly from bathing. Mrs. Ponsonby watched her for a little, covertly, from behind a novel; quick movements, good teeth and skin, obviously a lady, she smiled a lot and talked eagerly in a pleasant, rather husky voice. When she got up to go on to the terrace with the two girls and the young man, still talking animatedly, Mrs. Ponsonby rose too and went up to her room.

From that moment onwards Mrs. Ponsonby proceeded upon a course of stately espionage. Her sources of information were various. Mrs. Wortley, who was a friend of Jennifer's Aunt; the English padre Mr. Selton; Giulio, the barman in the hotel, even the floor waiter was questioned discreetly as his wife was a laundress in the town and dealt with the washing from the Pension Floriana.

In a few days she had found out quite a lot. Jennifer was nineteen, the daughter of a doctor in Cornwall, her name was Hyde. She was evidently not well-off as she had travelled out from England second-class, but she apparently had some wealthy relatives in London, had been out for a season and had been presented. Mrs. Wortley was quite enthusiastic about her. "A thoroughly nice girl," she said. "Modern in one way and yet old-fashioned at the same time, if you know what I mean. I do think, of course, that it's a pity she puts quite so much red on her lips, but after all I suppose that's the thing nowadays, and one is only young once. I remember myself when I was a girl my one idea was to be smart. I remember getting into the most dreadful hot water for turning one of my afternoon dresses into an evening frock by snipping off the sleeves and altering the front of the bodice—" Here Mrs. Wortley laughed indulgently, but Mrs. Ponsonby had lost interest.

A couple of evenings later on the terrace Mrs. Ponsonby dropped her book just as Jennifer was passing. Jennifer picked it up and returned it to her with a polite smile and, upon being pressed, agreed to sit down and have a glass of lemonade. She talked without shyness but also, Mrs. Ponsonby was pleased to observe, without too much self-possession. Before she left to join her friends who were standing about giggling slightly in the doorway, Mrs. Ponsonby had extracted a promise from her to come to lunch on the following day.

The lunch party was quite a success. At first Mrs. Ponsonby had been rather disconcerted to discover that Ellsworth had invited Father Robert, but it was not very long before she decided in her mind that it had been a good thing. To begin with, the presence of Jennifer made Father Robert ill-at-ease. Mrs. Ponsonby watched with immense satisfaction the corners of his mouth nervously twitching. She also noted that he didn't talk as much as usual. Ellsworth, on the other hand, talked nineteen to the dozen; he was obviously, she observed happily, showing off. The general narrowness of Ellsworth was not so apparent in those days, he was only twenty-six and had a certain soft personal charm when he liked to exert it. On this occasion he was only too keen to exert it. He discussed books and plays wittily with Jennifer, and whenever she laughed at anything he said, he shot rather a smug look at Father Robert. Altogether everything was going very well and Mrs. Ponsonby's spirit purred with pleasure as she watched, with cold eyes, Father Robert's left hand irritably crumbling his bread.

About a week later, during which time Jennifer and Ellsworth had struck up a platonic, pleasant friendship, Mrs. Ponsonby made her supreme gesture by dying suddenly in the lounge after dinner.

Jennifer Ponsonby was, to put it mildly, a reckless gambler, but her gaiety at the tables whether winning or losing was remarkable. She had a series of little superstitions, such as placing one card symmetrically on top of the other and giving the shoe two sharp peremptory little whacks before drawing—if she drew a nine she chuckled delightedly, if she made herself Baccarat she chuckled equally delightedly. Her luck, on the whole, was good, but she won gracefully, shrugging her shoulders and giving a little deprecatory smile when anyone failed to win a Banco against her.

It was the summer of 1933, and I had stopped off in Monte Carlo on my way home from Tunis. Everybody was there, of course, it was the height of the summer season. The Beach Hotel was full and I was staying at the Hôtel de Paris which, actually, I preferred. Jennifer was staying with old Lily Graziani on Cap Ferrat, but she escaped whenever she could and came over to Monte Carlo to dine and gamble. I played at the same table with her for an hour or two, and then when I had lost all that I intended to lose, I asked her to come and have a drink in the bar while the shoe was being made up.

We perched ourselves on high stools and ordered "Fine a l'eaus" and talked casually enough. She asked me where I'd been and whether or not I'd seen so-and-so lately, and I asked her what she'd been up to and what had become of so-and-so. Presently a chasseur appeared and said that her table was starting again. She slipped down from her stool and said, almost defiantly, "You haven't asked after Ellsworth, but you'll be delighted to hear that he's very well indeed," then she gave a sharp little laugh, more high-pitched than usual, and disappeared into the Baccarat room.

I felt a trifle embarrassed and also vaguely irritated.

I hadn't mentioned Ellsworth on purpose. (A), because it might have been tactless as I hadn't the remotest idea whether they were still together or not; and (b), because I didn't care for him much anyhow, and never had. I ordered another drink and, when I had drunk it, strolled upstairs to watch the cabaret. There was an inferno of noise going on as I came in, the band was playing full out while two American negroes were dancing a complicated routine in white evening suits and apparently enjoying it. I sat down at a corner table and watched the rest of the show. It was reasonably good. The usual paraphernalia of elaborately undressed beauties parading in and out. The usual low comedy acrobatic act. The usual mournful young woman crooning through the microphone. I glanced round the room occasionally. All the same faces were there. They had been here last year and the year before, and would be here next year and the year after. They changed round a bit, of course. Baby Leyland was with Georgie this year, and Bobbie had a new blonde. The Gruman-Lewis party looked tired and disgruntled, but then they always did. I felt oppressed and bored and far too hot. I watched Jennifer come in with Tiny Matlock. They were hailed by Freda and Gordon Blake and sat down at their table. It was one of the noisier tables. I think Alaistair, who was sitting at the end, must have been doing some of his dirtier imitations, because they were all laughing extravagantly, rather too loudly, I thought, considering the hundreds of times they must have heard them before.

Jennifer laughed with the rest, meanwhile refurbishing her make-up, holding the mirror from her vanity-case at one angle in order to catch the light. Her movements were swift and nervous, she stabbed at her mouth with the lipstick and then, holding the glass at arm's length, looked at it through narrowed eyes and made a slight grimace. Suddenly, in that moment, I can't think why, I knew quite definitely that she was wretched. My memory ran back over the years that I had known her, never in-

timately, never beyond the easy casualness of Christian
names, but always, I reflected, with pleasure. She had always been gay company, charming to dance with, fun to
discover unexpectedly in a house-party. I remembered the
first time I had met her in London, it must have been
1920 or 1921, the pretty young wife of a rich American.
That was a long time ago, nearly thirteen years, and those
years had certainly changed her. I watched her across the
room. She was talking now, obviously describing something, gesticulating a little with her right hand. There
was a moment's lull in the general noise, and I caught for
a second the sound of her husky laugh, quite a different
timbre from that which she had given as she left the bar.
"You haven't asked after Ellsworth, but you'll be delighted
to hear that he's very well indeed."

I decided to walk back to my hotel, rather than take a
taxi, the night was cool and quiet after the cigarette smoke
and noise of the Casino. I had nearly reached the top of
the first hill when I heard a car coming up behind me.
It seemed to be coming a great deal too fast, so I stepped
warily against the parapet to let it go by. It came whirling
round the corner with a screech of brakes, a small open
Fiat two-seater. It stopped noisily about a yard away from
me and I saw that Jennifer was driving it. "I saw you
leaving the Casino and chased you," she said rather breathlessly, "because I wanted to say I was sorry."

I stepped forward. "What on earth for?"

"If you didn't notice so much the better, but I've had a
horrid feeling about it ever since I left you in the bar.
I tossed my curls at you and spoke harshly, it's no use
pretending I didn't because I did, I know I did."

"What nonsense!" I said.

"Get in, there's a darling, and I'll drive you wherever
you want to go—where do you want to go? I've got to get
to Cap Ferrat."

"Not as far as that anyhow, just the Hôtel de Paris."

I got in and sat down beside her. She let in the clutch
and we drove on up into the town. The streets were de-

serted as it was getting on for three in the morning. Suddenly she stopped the car by the kerb in front of a sports shop, the window was filled with tennis racquets, golf clubs and sweaters.

"I'm now going to do something unforgivable," she said in a strained voice. "I've been trying not to for hours, but it's no use." She sat back in the driving seat and looked at me. "I'm going to cry. I hate women who cry, but I can't help it, everything's absolutely bloody, and I know it's none of your business and that this is an imposition, but we've been friends on and off for years and—" Here she broke off and buried her face in her hands. I put my arm round her. "I don't think you'd better be too sympathetic," she muttered into my shoulder. "It'll probably make me worse." Then she started to sob, not hysterically, not even very noisily, but they were painful sobs as though she were fighting them too strongly—

"For God's sake let go!" I said sharply. "If you don't you'll probably burst!"

She gave me a little pat and relaxed a bit. Two or three cars passed, but she kept her head buried against my shoulder. I sat quite still and looked gloomily at the tennis racquets. I felt rather bewildered and quite definitely uncomfortable. Not that I wasn't touched, that out of all the people she knew she should surprisingly have selected me to break down with. My discomfort was caused by a strange feeling of oppression, a similar sensation to that which one experiences sometimes on entering a sad house, a house wherein unhappy, cruel things have taken place. I almost shuddered, but controlled it. Some intuition must have made her feel this, for she sat up and reached her hand behind her for her vanity-case. "I am so dreadfully sorry," she said. I smiled as reassuringly as I could and lit a cigarette for her. She wiped her eyes, powdered her nose, took it and sat silently for a little—I noticed her lip tremble occasionally, but she didn't cry any more. Suddenly she seemed to come to some sort of decision and leant forward and re-started the engine. "I'll drop you home now," she said in a stifled voice which struck me as infinitely pathetic, there was an almost childish gallantry in the way she said it, like a very small boy who has fallen down and broken his knee and is determined to be brave over it.

"You'll do nothing of the sort," I said quickly. "You'll drive me up on to the Middle Corniche and there we'll sit and smoke ourselves silly and watch the sun come up."

She protested: "Honestly, I'm all right now—I swear I am."

"Do what you're told," I said.

She gave the ghost of a smile and off we went.

We stopped just the other side of Eze, left the car parked close in to the side of the wood, having taken the cushions out of it, and arranged ourselves facing the view, with our backs against a low stone wall. Jennifer hardly spoke, and we sat there for quite a long while in silence. Far below us on the right, Cap Ferrat stretched out into the sea like a quiet sleeping animal. Occasionally a train, looking like an elaborate mechanical toy, emerged from a tunnel, ran along by the edge of the sea for a little way and then disappeared again, the lights from its carriage windows striping the trees and rocks and houses as it passed. The rumbling sound of it came to us late when it was no longer in sight. Every now and then, but not very often, a car whirred along the road behind us and we could see its headlights diminishing in the distance, carving the darkness into fantastic shapes and shadows as it went. The path of the moon glittered across the sea to the horizon and there were no ships passing.

"I suppose it would be too obvious if I said: 'Now then'?"

Jennifer sighed. " 'Now then,' is a bit discouraging," she said. "Too arbitrary—couldn't we lead into it a little less abruptly?"

"How is Ellsworth?" I said airily. "Or rather, where is Ellsworth?"

"Very well indeed, and in Taormina."

"Why Taormina?"

She fidgeted a little. "He likes Taormina."

There was a long silence while we both looked at Ellsworth in Taormina. I can't vouch for Jennifer's view, but mine was clear. I saw him going down to bathe, wearing sandals, a discreetly coloured jumper and flannel trousers with a faint stripe. I saw him at lunch in the cool monastic hotel dining-room, talking earnestly with a couple of Catholic Fathers. I saw him in the evening, after dinner, sitting in a café with a few of the young locals around him, standing them drinks and speaking in precise, rather sibilant Italian with a strong Bostonian accent.

"He can't get sunburnt, you know," said Jennifer irrelevantly. "And he does try so hard. Isn't it sad?"

"Not even pink?"

"Only very occasionally, and that fades almost immediately."

"Freckles?"

"A few, but in the wrong places."

"How much does he mind?"

"Desperately, I think." Jennifer sighed again, deeply. "It's become a sort of complex with him. He has quite a lot of complexes really. The Catholic Church, Italian Gothic, Walt Whitman and not overtipping. He's a beauty lover, I'm afraid."

"You should never have married a beauty lover."

She nodded. "Beauty lovers certainly are Hell."

"Why did you?"

"Why did I what?"

"Marry him."

"Hold on to your hats, boys, here we go!" She laughed faintly and said, "I think I'd better have another cigarette, I'm told it gives one social poise. I'm afraid my social poise has been rather over-strained during these last few years."

I gave her a cigarette. "Why not begin at the beginning?" I suggested. "You know it's all coming out eventually, you might just as well go the whole hog."

"I wonder where that expression originated?" she said. "It doesn't really make sense—you can't go a hog, whole or otherwise."

"Never mind about that."

"I don't really."

"Why did you marry him?"

"I was an innocent girl," she replied. "When I say innocent girl, I naturally mean a bloody fool. I was ignorant of even the most superficial facts of life. Circumstances conspired against me—doesn't that sound lovely?—but it's honestly true, they did. I was in Italy, staying with Aunt Dora in a pension, and Ellsworth and his mother were at the Grand Hotel. They had a suite, of course, and as far as the hotel was concerned they were the star turn on account of being American and very rich. The old girl took a fancy to me, why I shall never know, and asked me to lunch, and there was Ellsworth. He really was quite sweet in those days and funny; he said funny things and knew a lot and was nice to be with. There was a priest there, too, Father Robert, who I suspect had his eye on the Ponsonby fortune—some priests on behalf of their church have a strong commercial sense—anyhow, he took a hatred to me on sight which I rather enjoyed. Then came the moment when circumstances conspired against me. Old Mrs. Ponsonby upped and died of a heart attack in the lounge of the hotel just as we were all having our after-dinner coffee. It really was very horrid, and I was desperately sorry for poor Ellsworth. That was where the trouble started. Pity may be a Christian virtue, but it's dangerous to muck about with, and can play the devil with common-sense. Well, to continue, as they say, from that moment onwards, Ellsworth clung to me; you see, I had unwittingly and most unfortunately ousted Father Robert from his affections. He cried a good deal, which was natural enough, as he'd never been away from his mother all his life. I went with him to the funeral, which was pretty grim, and did my best to comfort him as well as I could. Then, the night after the funeral he suddenly appeared at our pension and said he wanted to talk to me. My Aunt Dora was in a fine flutter, being one of those nice-minded British matrons

who can only see any rich young man as a prospective bed-
mate for their younger unattached female relatives. I think
she probably regretted that Ellsworth didn't want to talk
to Grace or Vera, who were her own daughters—and God
knows she couldn't have regretted it half as much as I did
later—but still, I was an unmarried niece, and half a loaf
is better than whatever it is, and so out I went into the
sweet-scented Italian night with Ellsworth and her bless-
ing. We walked for a long way, first of all through the town
and then along the beach. Ellsworth didn't say much until
we sat down with our backs to a wall, rather like we're
sitting here, only without the view, just the sea lapping
away and a lot of stars. Then he started. Oh dear!" Jennifer shifted herself into a more comfortable position.
"He told me all about himself from the word go, not in
any exhibitionistic way, but as though he just had to get it
out of his system in spite of caution and decency and
traditionally bred reticence—again like I'm doing now."
She laughed rather sharply. "I wonder why people do it?
I wonder if it's ever any use?"

"It's all right," I said, "when there are no strings attached. Don't get discouraged, it will do you a power of
good."

"You're very sweet," she said. "I do hope I'm not going
to cry again."

There was silence for a few moments and then she went
on, speaking more quickly.

"I can't possibly tell you all he said, because it wouldn't
be fair. I couldn't ever tell anybody, but the main thing
was that he was frightened, frightened to death of himself. That was why he had become a Roman Catholic, that
fear. He wasn't very articulate about it really, and he
jumped from one thing to another so that on the whole
I was pretty bewildered, but I did feel dreadfully touched
and sad for him, and foolishly, wholeheartedly anxious
to help him. He said, among other things, that he'd always
been terrified of women until he met me and that the
thought of marriage sort of revolted him. Of course, he

hadn't had to worry about it much as long as his mother was alive, but now he was utterly lost, he couldn't face the loneliness of having no one. Father Robert had tried to persuade him to join the Church in some capacity or other, I don't exactly know what, but he fought shy of this, because he didn't feel that he had a genuine vocation or enough faith or something. He went on and on rambling here and there. One minute he'd be talking about Father Robert and how wonderful the Church was, because it knew everything about everyone, and could solve all problems if only one believed enough. Then he'd jump back, a long way back, into his childhood and talk about a friend he had at his prep school called Homer—aren't Americans awful giving their children names like that?— Homer was apparently very important, he kept on cropping up. You've no idea how strange it was sitting there on the sand with all that emotion and fright and unhappiness whirling round my head. I was only nineteen and didn't understand half of what he was talking about, but I do remember feeling pent-up and strained and rather wanting to scream. Presently he calmed down a bit and said something about how terrible it was to live in a world where no one understood you, and that Society was made for the normal, ordinary people, and there wasn't any place for the misfits. Then, then, he asked me to marry him. To do him justice he was as honest as he could be. He said I was the only person he could trust and that we could travel and see the world and entertain and have fun. He didn't talk about the money side of it, but he implied a great deal. I knew perfectly well he was rich, anyhow—" She paused for a moment, and fumbled in her bag for her handkerchief. "But that wasn't why I married him, honestly it wasn't. Of course it had something to do with it, I suppose. You see, I'd been poor all my life, Father's practice wasn't up to much and the idea of having all the clothes and things that I wanted, and being able to travel, which I'd always longed to do, probably helped a bit, but it wasn't the whole reason or anything like it, I swear it wasn't. The real reason was much stranger and more complicated and difficult to explain. On looking back on it, I think I can see it clearly, but even now I'm not altogether sure. I was very emotional and romantic and really very nice inside when I was young, far nicer than I am now. There ought to be a law against bringing children up to have nice instincts and ideals, it makes some of the things that happen afterwards so much more cruelly surprising than they need be. I can see, now, that I quite seriously married Ellsworth from a sense of duty—doing my good deed for the day. Girl Guides for ever. I know perfectly well that I didn't love him, at least my brain knew it and told me so, but I didn't listen and allowed my emotions, my confused, adolescent, sentimental emotions, to drag me in the other direction. I remember forcing myself to imagine what it would be like, the actual sex part, I mean, and thinking, quite blithely, that it would be lovely and thrilling to lie in Ellsworth's arms and be a comfort to him and look after him and stand between him and his loneliness. Of course, my imagination over all this wasn't very clear, as my sex experience to date had consisted of little more than an unavowed and beautiful passion for Miss Hilton-Smith, our games mistress at St. Mary's, Plymouth, and a few daring kisses from a young man at a hunt ball in Bodmin. Obviously, I hadn't the remotest idea what I was letting myself in for, so I said 'Yes,' and two days later, still in a haze of romantic and emotional confusion, we went off to Nice, without letting anyone suspect a thing, and were married in some sort of office by a man with a goitre."

Jennifer held out her hand for another cigarette. I lit one for her and, without saying a word, waited for her to go on.

"Then the trouble started." She gave a slight shudder. "I'm not going to tell you all the details, but it was all very frightening and horrid and humiliating, I think humiliating more than anything else. After a few weeks, during which time Father had appeared and Aunt Dora and a

very pompous uncle of Ellsworth's, and there had been a
series of scenes and discussions and a great deal of strain,
Ellsworth and I went to Rome and stayed there for months.
In due course I was received into the Church. I didn't
have much feeling about that one way or another and
Ellsworth was very insistent, so there it was. We were finally married properly with a great deal of music and re-
joicing and a lot of American-born Italian Marchesas giving parties for us. As a matter of fact, old Lily Graziani
was one of them, the nicest one, I'm staying with her
now." She indicated Cap Ferrat with a vague gesture.
"Then we went away, practically right round the world,
starting with Boston and all Ellsworth's relations. Oh,
dear!" she gave a little laugh. "That was very tricky, but
some of them were all right. After that, we went to Honolulu and Japan and China, then to India and Egypt and
back to England. That was when we first met, wasn't it, at
the house in Great Cumberland Place? By that time, of
course, I'd become a bit hardened. I was no longer romantic and innocent and nice. I'd learned a lot of things,
I'd joined the Navy and seen the world. All those lovely
places, all those chances for happiness, just out of reach,
thrown away. Don't misunderstand me, it wasn't the sex
business that was upsetting me, at least I don't think it
was. I'd faced the failure of that ages before. Oh no, it was
Ellsworth himself. I should have been perfectly happy,
well, if not happy, at least content, if Ellsworth had played
up and been kind and ordinary and a gay companion, but
he didn't and he wasn't. I suppose people can't help being
beastly, can they? It's something to do with glandular
secretions and environment and things that happened to
you when you were a child. I can only think that the most
peculiar things certainly happened to Ellsworth when he
was a child and his glandular secretions must have been
something fierce. At any rate, I hadn't been with him
long before I knew, beyond a shadow of doubt, that he was
a thoroughly unpleasant character. Not in any way bad in
the full sense of the word. Not violent or sadistic, or going

off on dreadful drunks and coming back and beating me up. Nothing like that, nothing nearly so direct. He was far too refined and carefully cultured, you said it just now, a beauty lover, that's what he was, a hundred per cent rip-snorting beauty lover. Oh dear, how can one reconcile being a beauty lover with being mean, prurient, sulky and pettishly tyrannical almost to a point of mania? The answer is that one can, because there are several sorts of beauty lovers. There are those who like kindness and good manners and wide seas and dignity, and others who like Bellini Madonnas and Giottos and mysticism and incense and being able to recognise, as publicly as possible, a genuine old this or old that. I don't believe it's enough—" Jennifer's voice rose a little. "I don't believe it's enough, all that preoccupation with the dead and done with, when there's living life all round you and sudden, lovely unexpected moments to be aware of. Sudden loving gestures from other people, without motives, nothing to do with being rich or poor or talented or cultured, just our old friend human nature at its best! That's the sort of beauty worth searching for; it may sound pompous, but I know what I mean. That's the sort of beauty lover that counts. I am right, aren't I? It's taken me so many miserable hours trying to puzzle things out." She stopped abruptly, almost breathless, and looked at me appealingly.

"Yes," I said, "I think you're right."

"The trouble with Ellsworth," she went on more calmly, "was that he had no love in his heart for any living soul except himself. Even his mother, who I suppose meant more to him than anyone else, faded quickly out of his memory. After the first few weeks he hardly ever referred to her, and if he did it was lightly, remotely, as though she had been someone of little importance whom he had once met and passed a summer with. If he had been honest with me or even honest with himself, it would have been all right, but he was neither. He dealt in lies, small insignificant lies; this was at first, later the lies became bigger and more important. He made a lot of friends as we pursued our rather dreary social existence, some of them appeared to be genuinely fond of him, at any rate in the beginning; others quite blatantly fawned on him for what they could get out of him. I watched, rather anxiously sometimes, and occasionally tried to warn him. I still felt there was a chance, you know, not of reforming him, I wasn't as smug as that, but of reaching a plane of mutual companionship on which we could both live our own lives and discuss things, and have a certain amount of fun together without conflict and irritation and getting on each other's nerves. But it wasn't any use. He distrusted me, principally I think because I was a woman. There wasn't anything to be done. It was hopeless. Then, after we'd been married for several years, a situation occurred. It was in New York, we were staying at the Waldorf, and it was all very unpleasant and nearly developed into a front-page scandal. I'm a bit vague as to what actually happened myself, there were so many conflicting stories, but anyhow, Ellsworth was blackmailed, and I had to interview strange people and tell a lot of lies, and a lot of money was handed out and we sailed, very hurriedly, for Europe. After that, things were beastlier than ever. He was sulky and irritable and took to making sarcastic remarks at me in front of strangers. All the resentment of a weak nature, that had been badly frightened, came to the top. Finally, I could bear it no longer and asked him to divorce me. That was the only time I have ever seen him really furious. He went scarlet in the face with rage. He was a Catholic and I was a Catholic. That was that. There could be no question of such a thing. Then I lost my head, and told him what I really thought of him, and that I was perfectly sure that the Catholic business was not really the reason for his refusal at all. He was really worried about what people would say; terrified of being left without the nice social buttress of a wife who could preside at his table, arrive with him at pompous receptions and fashionable first nights and in fact, visually at least, cover his tracks. We had a blistering row, and I left the house, that

was the house in Paris, you remember it, in the Avenue
d'Iéna, and went to London to stay with Marjorie Bridges.
He followed me in a week, and a series of dreary scenes
took place. He actually cried during one of them, and said
that he was really devoted to me deep down and that he
would never again do anything to humiliate me in any
way. I think he was honestly dreadfully frightened of me
leaving him. Frightened of himself, I mean, that old fear
that he had told me about, sitting on the beach, when he
first asked me to marry him. I gave in in the end. There
wasn't anything else to do really. And that's how we are
now. He goes off on his own every now and then and does
what he likes, but never for very long. He hasn't the courage for real adventure. Then we join up again, and open
the house in Paris, and give parties, and do everything
that everyone else does. Sometimes we go for a yachting
cruise through the Greek Islands, or up the Dalmatian
Islands or round about here. Actually, I'm waiting now
for him to come back, and I suppose we'll collect a dozen
people that we don't care for, and who don't care for us,
and off we shall go to Corsica or Mallorca or Tangier.
It's a lovely life."

She sat silently for a moment, looking out over the sea,
and she rose to her feet and began to kick a stone with the
toe of her evening shoe. "That's about all," she said.

I got up, too, and we clambered over the wall and
walked slowly over to the car.

"Not quite all," I said mildly, putting the cushions into
the car. "You haven't yet told me why you were crying."

"Isn't that enough?"

"Not quite."

She got into the car and started fiddling with the engine.
She spoke without looking at me. "I have never been unfaithful to Ellsworth," she said in a dry, flat voice. "I know
I could have easily, but it always seemed to me that it
might make the situation even more squalid than it is
already. Anyhow, I have never found anyone among the
people we meet whom I could love enough to make it

worth it. Perhaps something will happen some day—I wouldn't like to die an old maid."

She started the car and drove me back to Monte Carlo. It was getting quite light and the whole landscape looked as though it had been newly washed. She dropped me at the Hôtel de Paris then, just as she was about to drive away, she leant over the side of the car and kissed me lightly on the cheek. She said: "Thank you, darling, I'll be grateful always to you for having been so really lovingly kind."

I watched the car until it had turned the corner and was out of sight.

4

"—But a chap's own chauffeur," the Major was saying. "I mean that really is going too far—"

"Where are they now?" I interrupted. "She and the chauffeur—did he tell you?"

"Out in Canada, I believe; the man's a Canadian. They run a garage or a petrol station or something—funnily enough, she wouldn't take any of old Ponsonby's money, he offered it, of course, he's that sort of chap, you know 'quixotic,' is that the word?"

"Yes," I said, "that's the word."

The Major collected the photograph albums and packed them in his suit-case, as he did so he hummed a tune rather breathily. My mind went back to that early, newly washed morning four years ago—driving down through the dawn to Monte Carlo. I remembered the emptiness in Jennifer's voice when she said: "Anyhow, I have never found anyone among the people we meet whom I could love enough to make it worth it—perhaps something will happen some day—I wouldn't like to die an old maid."

The Major straightened himself. "What about a night-cap?" he said.

We went up on deck. The air was clear and cold, and

there was hardly any wind. Far away on the port bow a lighthouse on the French coast flashed intermittently.

In the smoking-room the Major flung himself, with a certain breezy abandon, into a leather armchair which growled under the strain.

"Fancy you knowing old Ponsonby," he said. "The world certainly is a very small place. You know there's a lot of truth in those old chestnuts." I nodded absently and lit a cigarette. He snapped his fingers loudly to attract the steward's attention. "I shall never forget that night as long as I live, seeing that poor chap crying like a kid, absolutely broken up. It's a pretty bad show when a man's whole life is wrecked by some damned woman. What I can't get over—" he leant forward and lowered his voice; there was an expression of genuine, horrified bewilderment in his, by now, slightly bloodshot eyes—"is that she should have gone off with his own chauffeur!"

"I suspect," I said gently, "that was why he was crying."

"Steward! Two stengahs!" said the Major.

WHAT MAD PURSUIT?

EVAN LORRIMER'S CELEBRITY VALUE was unquestionably high. In the course of twenty years he had written no less than eleven novels; a volume of war poems, tinged with whimsical bitterness; one play which had been much praised by the London critics and run nearly two months; a critical survey of the life and times of Madame de Staël entitled *The Life and Times of Madame de Staël;* sundry essays and short stories for the more literary weeklies, and an autobiography. The autobiography had been on the whole the least successful of his works, but he in no way regretted having written it. For years he had been aware that incidents, journeys, and personal experiences had been accumulating in his mind until it had come to a point when he could no longer feel free to pursue his historical researches. He felt himself to be congested, or, to put it more crudely, constipated, and that unless he could get rid of this agglomeration of trivia, his real genius, which was writing graphically of the past in terms of the present, would atrophy. The autobiography, therefore, was a sort of cathartic and as such achieved its object. Hardly had the corrected and revised manuscript been delivered to the publishers before he was at work again, drafting out with renewed energy and clarity of thought his great novel of the Restoration, *A London Lady.* There was no doubt in his mind that if *My Steps Have Faltered,* which was the title of the autobiography, had not been written when it was, *A London Lady* would never have been written at all. The success of *A London Lady* transcended by far everything else he had ever written. It went into several editions within the first few weeks of its publication. It was elected, without one dissentient vote, as the Book Society's choice for the month of February. The most important moving picture company in Hollywood acquired the film rights of it at an even higher price than they had paid for *The Life of Saint Paul,* which had been awarded the Pulitzer Prize for the year before, and in addition to all this, its sales in America surpassed those of England a hundredfold before it had been out six weeks. It was on the suggestion of Evan's New York publisher, Neuman Bloch, that he had agreed to do a short lecture tour in the States. He had been naturally apprehensive of the idea at first, but after a certain amount of coaxing, and tempted by the prospect of visiting America for the first time in such singularly advantageous circumstances— full expenses there and back, a tour of only eight weeks visiting the principal towns, and a guaranteed fee for each lecture that appeared to be little short of fantastic—he gathered his courage together, made exhaustive notes on the subjects on which he intended to speak, and set sail on the *Queen Mary.*

Now it would be foolish to deny that Evan Lorrimer enjoyed publicity. Everyone enjoys publicity to a certain degree. It is always pleasant to feel that your name is of sufficient interest to the world to merit a prominent position in the daily newspapers. For many years past, Evan had been privately gratified to read such phrases as "Of course Evan Lorrimer was there, suave and well-groomed as usual," or "That inveterate first-nighter, Evan Lorrimer, arrived a few minutes before the curtain rose and was seen chatting laughingly to Lady Millicent Cawthorne in the foyer," or "Evan Lorrimer whose new novel, *A London Lady,* has caused such a sensation, was the guest of honour at the Pen and Pencil Club on Sunday evening." Such allusions, guileless and dignified, are immensely agreeable. Unimportant perhaps in their essence, but in their implication very important indeed. Just as millions of little coral animals in so many years construct a barrier reef against the sea, so can these small accolades over a period of time, build, if not quite a barrier reef, at least

a fortification against the waves of oblivion. Evan felt this
very strongly. His reviews he read as a matter of course,
regarding them rightly as part of the business. Naturally
he was pleased when they were good and pained when they
were bad, but the gossip columns were different. They
were both unprejudiced and uncritical; they contented
themselves with the simple statement that he was here or
there with so-and-so, or accompanied by such-and-such,
and by their repetitious banality did more to consolidate
his reputation than all the carefully phrased opinions of
the literati put together. But Evan, well used as he was to
being photographed and interviewed and occasionally
signing a few autograph-books, was certainly unprepared
for the violence of his reception in New York. From the
moment the ship paused at Quarantine turmoil engulfed
him. He was belaboured with questions by over a dozen
reporters at the same time, photographed waving to myth-
ical friends by no less than fifteen cameras simultaneously,
hurried on to the dock where he was met by Neuman
Bloch, Mrs. Bloch, the firm's publicity agent, several more
reporters and, most surprisingly, a man who had been at
school with him and whom he hadn't clapped eyes on for
twenty-six years. In the flurry of Customs examination,
interviews, and the effort to sustain a reasonably intelligent flow of conversation with the Blochs, he was completely unable to recall the man's name; however it didn't
matter, for after wringing his hand warmly, and standing
by his side in silence for a few minutes, he disappeared
into the crowd and Evan never saw him again.

Evan Lorrimer at the age of forty-three was, both in
appearance and behaviour, a model of what an eminent
Englishman of letters should be. He was five-foot-ten, his
figure was spare but well-proportioned, he had slim, ex-
pressive hands, dark hair greying slightly at the temples,
deep-set grey eyes, a small neat moustache and an urbane
smile. Perhaps his greatest asset was his voice which was
rich in tone and, at times, almost caressing, particularly
when, with his slyly humorous gift of phrase, he was de-

scribing somebody a trifle maliciously. Lady Cynthia Caw-thorne who, in Lowndes Square had achieved the nearest approach to a London salon since Lady Blessington, was wont to say, with her loud infectious laugh, that had she only been younger she'd have married Evan Lorrimer out of hand if only to hear him repeat over and over again his famous description of being taken, at the age of fifteen, to the Musée Grevin by Marcel Proust.

Evan, like so many people who have attained fame and fortune by their own unaided efforts, was a firm self-disciplinarian. He apportioned his time with meticulous care: so many hours for writing, so many for reading. He ate and drank in moderation and indulged in only enough exercise to keep himself fit. He contrived, although naturally of a highly strung, nervous temperament, to maintain an agreeable poise both physically and mentally and to derive a great deal of enjoyment from life, admittedly without often scaling the heights of rapture, but also without plumbing the depths of despair. This self-adjustment, this admirable balance, was dependent upon one absolute necessity and that necessity was sleep. Eight solid hours per night minimum, with a possible snooze during the day, was his deadline. Without that he was lost, his whole organism disintegrated. He became jumpy and irascible, unable to concentrate. In fact on one occasion, owing to an emotional upheaval when the pangs of not sufficiently requited love gnawed at his vitals for nearly four months, he became actively ill and had to retire to a nursing home. Realising this one weakness, this Achilles heel, he arranged his life accordingly.

At home, in his small house in Chesham Place, his two servants had been trained to a mouse-like efficiency. Until he was called in the morning the house was wrapped in the silence of death. The knocker had been taken off the front door, and both bells, front and back, muffled down to the merest tinkle; the telephone by his bed was switched off nightly and rang in the basement, and even there, after a series of dogged experiments by Albert his valet, it had been reduced to nothing more than a purr. Naturally, taking all this into consideration, the first few nights in New York were a torture to him. He had, of course, been warned that the sharpness of the climate and the champagne quality of the air would enable him to do with less sleep than he was accustomed to in the older, more stagnant atmosphere of England, and although he discovered this to be true to a certain extent, he was unable to repress a slight feeling of panic. If only, he reflected, he could get away into the country for two or three days, to relax, to give himself time to adjust himself, he might come to view the so much swifter tempo of American life with more equanimity.

It was on the fourth day after his arrival, towards the end of a strenuously literary cocktail party given in his honour by the Neuman Blochs, that he met Louise Steinhauser. He was introduced to her by his hostess and immediately taken out on to the terrace to look at the view. This had already happened to him five times, and although he had been deeply impressed by the view the first two times, it was now beginning to pall a little; however Louise was adamant. "Look at it," she said in a husky, rather intense voice. "Isn't it horrible?"

Evan gave a slight start of surprise. Louise went on: "Every time I look at New York from a height like this, I positively shudder. All those millions of people cooped up in those vast buildings give me such a feeling of claustrophobia that I think I'm going mad. If I didn't live out in the country most of the time I really should go mad. My husband, poor darling, comes in every day of course, and we have an apartment at the Pierre—you can just see it from here behind that tower that looks like a pencil with india-rubber on top—but really I hardly ever use it unless I happen to come in for a late party or an opening night or something, and even then I often drive down home afterwards, however late it is."

"How far away is your home in the country?" enquired Evan.

"About an hour in the automobile; at night of course, it's much quicker and I can't begin to tell you how lovely it is to arrive at about two in the morning and smell the sea—my house is right on the sea—and just go to sleep in that wonderful silence—you'd think you were miles away from anywhere, and yet it's actually only a little way from New York. There are no houses near us, we're completely isolated—You really must come down for a week-end, except that I warn you there isn't a thing to do except lie about and relax. Bonwit, that's my husband, plays golf occasionally or a little tennis, but I don't play anything. I find at my age—I shall be forty-four next month, imagine!"—she laughed disarmingly, "I never try to hide my age, it's so silly, after all what *does* it matter. Anyhow, as I was saying, at my age I find that all I want are my comforts, nice books, a few real friends, not just acquaintances, and good food. I'm afraid that's all I can offer you, peace and good food, but if you would like to slip away from all this," she indicated the remainder of the cocktail party milling about inside with a wave of her hand, "and really lead the simple life for a couple of days, you don't even have to bring dinner clothes if you don't want to. Please come, both Bonwit and I would be absolutely enchanted."

Evan had been looking at her carefully while she was talking, carefully and critically. Being a writer, he was naturally observant, his mind was trained to perceive small indicative details. Being a celebrity he was also cautious. He noted Louise's clothes first; they were obviously expensive, the ruby and diamond clip in her small cloche hat could only have come from Cartier. Her pearls might or might not be real, but the clasp most certainly was. In addition to these external advantages he liked her. She was vivacious, humorous and friendly. She also seemed to have a sensible appreciation of the values of life.

"You're most kind," he said. "There's nothing I should like better."

"Now isn't that lovely," cried Louise. "How long are

you going to be here?"

"Alas, only until next Wednesday, then I have to lecture in Chicago."

"I suppose you're booked up for this next week-end?"

Evan shook his head. He had been tentatively invited to the Neuman Blochs' house at Ossining, but he hadn't definitely accepted. "I was supposed to go to the Blochs'," he said, "but I can get out of it."

"Then that's settled," said Louise gaily. "I'm coming in on Saturday to go to *Starlight,* that's a musical comedy that Lester Gaige is in. He's one of my greatest friends, you'll adore him. Why don't you dine with me and come too, and we'll all three drive down afterwards. He's the only person I've invited for this week-end. I daren't have a lot of people when he comes because he insists on being quiet. He says he gives out so much at every performance during the week that he's damned if he'll give a social performance on Sundays. He really is divine, and he certainly won't bother you because he does nothing but sleep."

As they rejoined the cocktail party, Evan felt that the much-vaunted American hospitality was a very genuine and touching trait.

2

Lester Gaige was certainly amusing. At first, watching him on the stage, Evan had been unsure as to whether or not he was going to like him; he seemed to be too debonair, almost arrogant in the manner in which he moved through the bewildering intricacies of *Starlight.* True, he danced beautifully, sang, with no voice but compelling charm, and dominated by sheer force of personality every scene he was in; but there was something about him, a mocking veneer that made you a trifle uneasy as to what you might discover underneath. However, in the car driving down to the country, he was much more human. His clothes were inclined to be eccentric. He had on suède shoes, thin silk socks, very pale grey flannel trousers of exquisite cut, a bois de rose sweater with a turtle neck, a tweed sports jacket of extravagant heartiness and a fur-lined overcoat with an astrakhan collar. In addition he wore a small beret basque and a pair of the largest horn-rimmed glasses Evan had ever seen. The conversation between him and Louise was stimulating if a little local in allusion. They referred to so many people in such a short space of time that Evan became quite confused; but he sat back in the corner of the luxurious Packard and gave himself up to being agreeably soothed and enter-tained. It was obvious that Louise and Lester had been intimate friends for several years; their talk, generally in a gaily reminiscent vein, jumped from London to Paris, from Antibes back to New York, from New York to Venice and from Venice to California. "That amusing party of Irene's when Broddie got blind and had that awful scene with Carola." "That terrible night in Salzburg when Nada refused to go home and finally disappeared into the moun-tains with Sonny Boy for three days." Occasionally Evan, not wishing to appear out of it, ventured a question as to who So-and-so was, and was immediately rewarded by a vivid, if not always entirely kind, description of So-and-so's life, activities and morals. On the whole he enjoyed himself very much. To begin with, they had all three had a Scotch Highball (ridiculous expression) in Lester's dressing-room before they started and then another one at Twenty One where they had to stop for a moment be-cause Lester had to give some message to Ed Bolingbroke, who had been apparently too drunk to understand it, then, not long after they had crossed the Fifty-ninth Street Bridge, Lester had produced a bottle of Scotch from his overcoat pocket, and they had all had an extra swig to keep them warm for the night was bitterly cold; there had been a blizzard the day before and the snow was several inches thick and freezing over.

When they finally reached the Steinhauser home Evan

got out of the car, stretched his cramped legs and gave an exclamation of pleasure. It really was most attractive. A large low white house built on three sides of a square and looking out over Long Island Sound. It was a clear moonlight night and far away on the Connecticut coast lights twinkled across the water. Behind the house was nothing but snow, and a few bleak winter trees. Above all, there was silence, complete and soul-satisfying silence, broken only by the soft lap of the waves on the shore.

Inside, the house was the acme of comfort, a large fire was blazing away on a wide open fireplace in the main living room; before it was set a table laid for supper. A pleasant coloured butler in a white coat met them at the front door. Evan sighed a deep sigh of relief. This was even better than he had imagined.

They sat up until very late over the fire talking. The supper had been delicious, a simple but tasty dish of spaghetti, tomatoes and eggs, a well-mixed green salad with cream cheese and Bar le Duc and further Scotch Highballs. Evan had had two since his arrival and although he was far from intoxicated, he felt enjoyably mellow. Lester, who was really a great deal more intelligent than one would expect a musical comedy actor to be, displayed a flattering interest in Evan's work. He had read *A London Lady*, and been thrilled with it, he was also one of the few people who had read and enjoyed *My Steps Have Faltered*. Evan dismissed his praise of this with a deprecatory laugh, but he was pleased none the less. Louise was a good hostess and, more than that, Evan decided, an extremely good sort. She talked with vivacity and her sense of humour was true and keen. She appeared to be one of those rare types, a rich woman who is completely unaffected by her wealth. She was downright, honest, and withal very attractive. She alluded to her husband frequently, and it was apparent that although they might not quite see eye to eye over certain things, she was deeply attached to him. They had a son at Harvard to whom they were both obviously devoted. Louise showed Evan a photograph of him dressed in the strange robotish armour of an American footballer. He was a husky, fine-looking lad. Lester was highly enthusiastic about him. "That boy is fantastic," he said, "you'd never believe it to look at him, but he paints the most remarkable water-colours! He gave me one when I was playing Boston in *And So What*. It's a seascape, rather Japanesey in quality, almost like a Foujita." Evan looked again at the photograph, slightly puzzled. Really Americans were most surprising. It was difficult to imagine that six feet of brawn and muscle painting demure seascapes, and even more difficult to understand how Lester Gaige playing in *And So What* in Boston could ever have heard of Foujita. Perhaps there was something to be said after all for that American culture that Europeans referred to with such disdain.

It wasn't until nearly four o'clock that Louise suddenly jumped up from the sofa on which she had been lying and cried: "Really this is terrible—I bring you down here to rest and keep you up to all hours talking. We simply *must* go to bed." She led the way through the hall and along a little passage. "I've given you the quietest room in the house," she said over her shoulder, "it's on the ground floor and you'll have to share a bathroom with Lester. I would have given you a room upstairs with a bath to yourself but it isn't nearly so shut away and you might be disturbed by Bonwit getting up early or the servants or something." She opened the door leading into a charmingly furnished bedroom. "This is Lester's," she said, "you're along here." They passed through a gleaming, well-equipped bathroom, along another little passage and there was Evan's room. It was large, with two beds and decorated in a pale, restful green. In addition to the two beds there was a chaise longue piled with cushions in front of the fire which, although it must have been lit hours ago, was still burning cosily. Evan smiled with pleasure. "What a perfect room," he said gratefully. Louise gave the fire a poke. "I know how English people loathe central heating," she said, "and I've told them to have a fire for you all the

time you're here, but if you'll take my advice you'll have
the heat on a little bit as well, because the weather's really
freezing."

After Louise had said good night and gone up to bed,
and Lester and Evan had smoked one more cigarette and
exchanged the usual politenesses as to which of them
should use the bathroom first, Evan, at last alone, opened
the window, and, cold as it was, stood for a moment looking up at the stars and listening to the silence. He sniffed
the icy air into his lungs, and with a sigh of utter content-
ment climbed into bed and was asleep in five minutes.

3

Evan woke at ten-thirty, which was rather early considering how late he had gone to bed. He counted up in
his mind, four-thirty to ten-thirty, only six hours, but still
it didn't matter, he could easily make up for it that night.
He lay there idly looking at the reflection of the sea on the
ceiling and contemplating, with a slight sinking of the
heart, his lecture on Monday night. It was drawing very
near and he was naturally nervous, but still he had certainly been wise to give himself this breathing space immediately before it. He planned to go over his notes some-
time during the day. He was aware, of course, that he
spoke well and that his subject "History and the Modern
Novel" was pretty certain to interest his American audience. He intended to start with the middle ages, the period
of his first two novels, then jump to French eighteenth
century, bringing in his *Porcelaine Courtesan, Madame Is
Indisposed* and *The Sansculotte,* then to the Directoire
and *Madame de Staël;* leaving the Restoration and *A
London Lady* to the last. He was determined, in spite of
the cautious advice of Neuman Bloch, to deliver a few
well-deserved slaps at some of the more successful American writers who so impertinently twisted European history to their own ends. Evan detested slang and the use of

present-day idiom in describing the past. Not that he was a believer in the "Odds Boddikins" "Pish Tushery" school of historical writing; he himself eschewed that with the greatest contempt, but he did believe in being factually accurate insofar as was possible, and in using pure English. Had not the exquisite literacy of *A London Lady* been one of the principal reasons for its success with the Book Society? And not only the Book Society, with the reviewers of both continents and with the general public. One of Evan's most comforting convictions was that the general public had a good deal more discrimination and taste than it was given credit for, and that all this careless, slipshod, *soi disant* modern style with its vulgarity of phrase and cheap Americanisms would, in a very little while, be consigned to the oblivion it so richly deserved.

At this point in his reflections he broke off to wonder whether or not he should ring for some fruit juice and coffee. He remembered from last night that the only entrance to his room was through Lester's and the bathroom and it would be inconsiderate to wake Lester if he were still sleeping. Evan, with a little sigh not entirely free from irritation, decided to go and see. He tiptoed out into the passage and into the bathroom and opened the door leading to Lester's room very quietly. Lester *was* still sleeping in a pair of pastel blue silk pyjamas with his head buried in the pillow. Evan stood there regarding him uncertainly for a moment. It would, of course, be unkind to wake him, and yet on the other hand he might possibly sleep until lunch-time and Evan would have to wait nearly three hours for his coffee. He retired into the bathroom, closing the door softly after him, and pondered the situation. Presently, renouncing indecision once and for all, he flushed the toilet and then listened carefully with his ear to the door. He was rewarded by hearing a few grunts and then the creaking of the bed. Quick as a flash he darted across to the lavatory basin and turned the tap on full, once embarked he intended taking no chances. After a few moments he opened the door again and peeped in.

Lester was sitting up looking, he was glad to observe, quite amiable. Evan coughed apologetically. "I'm awfully sorry," he said, "I'm afraid I woke you up. I'd no idea the tap would make such a row."

"It wasn't the tap," said Lester without rancour, "it was the Lulu."

"How does one get coffee, do you suppose?"

"Let's ring," said Lester. "We can either have it here or put on our dressing-gowns and go into the sun porch—which do you prefer?"

"I don't mind a bit." Evan, his plan having succeeded so easily, was feeling a little guilty and determined to be amenable at all costs.

"I think the sun porch is nicer." Lester jumped out of bed, rang the bell and went into the bathroom to brush his teeth.

While they were breakfasting on the sun porch, an agreeable glass-enclosed room at the side of the house commanding a wide view of the sea and the drive, Bonwit Steinhauser appeared in elaborate plus-fours. He was a red-faced, rather dull-looking man, with a large body that had once been muscular but now was just fat. He said "good morning" affably, and after a little desultory conversation went away. When he had gone Lester pushed his coffee-cup out of his way and leant across the table almost furtively.

"You know I like Bonwit," he whispered as though by such a confession he was straining credulity to the utmost. "There's something really awfully kind about him. Of course everyone says he's a bore and I suppose he is in a way, but when he's had a few drinks, my dear!" He did one of his characteristic gestures of pawing the air with his right hand. "He can be terribly, terribly funny! I shall never forget when I was up here one week-end with Ida Wesley, she's dead as a door-nail now, poor sweet, and Bonwit, who shall be nameless, got so fried—" Here he broke up abruptly and said: "My God!" Evan turned round to see what had startled him and saw a car coming

slowly up the drive. He jumped to his feet. Lester got up
too, and, after looking out carefully for a moment gave a
laugh. "It's all right," he said, "it's only Irene and Suki
and Dwight and Luella—I thought for a minute it was
strangers."

"Are they coming for lunch?" asked Evan apprehen-
sively.

"I expect so," replied Lester, sitting down again. "But
you'll love Irene, she's divine, but *divine*—you've heard
her sing, haven't you?"

Evan shook his head.

"You've never heard Irene Marlow sing?" Lester was
horrified. "You haven't lived that's all, you just haven't
lived! We'll make her sing after lunch. Suki's with her
fortunately, he always plays for her. It really is the most
lovely voice and there's somebody with an amazing sense
of humour! I mean, she really gets herself, which is more
than you can say for most prima donnas, and if you could
hear her when she's in a real rage with Dwight, that's
Dwight Macadoo who shall be nameless. My God! It's
wonderful—bang goes the Italian accent and out pops
Iowa!"

"We'd better go and dress, hadn't we?" suggested Evan,
feeling unequal to greeting a famous Iowan prima donna
in his pyjamas.

"You go and dress," said Lester. "And you might turn
on a bath for me when you've finished. I'll go and deal
with the visiting firemen."

Evan retired to his room, shattered. It was really ap-
palling luck that these people should have selected to-day
of all days to come to lunch. How cross Louise would be.
But still, he comforted himself, she'd be sure to get rid of
them all as soon as possible.

When he emerged, bathed, shaved and dressed in perfectly cut English country clothes he found everybody in
the large living-room. Apparently, while he had been
dressing, some more people had arrived. Bonwit was mixing cocktails behind a little bar in the far corner of the

room. There was no sign of Louise.

Seeing Evan come in, Lester, who was sitting on the
sofa with a fattish little man and two women, jumped up.
"This is my friend," he cried, "I don't think you know my
friend! who shall be nameless," he added with a light
laugh. Evan smiled sheepishly, he was unused to being
nameless, but Lester came over and took him affectionately by the arm. "I must introduce you to everybody,"
he said. "We'd better begin right here and work round
the whole God-damned circle." He raised his voice. "Listen, everybody—this is Evan Lorrimer, one of the greatest
living English novelists, he's my friend and I'm mad about
him!" He turned enquiringly to Evan. "Aren't I, honey?"

Evan summoned up enough poise to give a little smile
and say, "I hope so," whereupon Lester, holding him
firmly by the arm, walked him round the room. A slight
hush fell while this tour was in progress. Evan shook
hands with everyone and responded pleasantly to their
assurances of how glad they were to know him, but he
was unable to catch more than a few names as he went
along, and finally sat down feeling rather confused, in the
place on the sofa that Lester had vacated. The fattish little
man, he discovered, was Otis Meer, who wrote a famous
gossip column for one of the daily papers, and the two
women were Irene Marlow and Luella Rosen. Irene was
flamboyant, but attractively so, she was dressed in a scarlet
sports suit, with a vivid green scarf, her brown hair was
done in clusters of curls and her hat—it couldn't have
been anyone else's—was on the mantelpiece. Luella Rosen
was sharp and black, like a little Jewish bird; she also
was wearing sports clothes, but of a more sombre hue.

Irene smiled, generously exposing a lot of dazzlingly
white teeth. "Lester had been telling us all about you,"
she said—her voice had a trace of a foreign accent—"and
you've no idea how thrilled we are to meet you. I haven't
read your book yet, but I've got it."

"Mr. Lorrimer has written dozens of books, dear," said
Luella.

Irene sat back and closed her eyes in mock despair. "Isn't Luella horrible?" she said. "I'm never allowed to get away with a thing—anyway, I meant your last one, and I know it couldn't matter to you whether I've read it or not; but I really am longing to, particularly now that I've met you." She winked at Evan, a gay confiding little wink nudged him with her elbow. Luella gave a staccato laugh. "Irene's our pet moron," she said. "She's never read a book in her life except *Stories of the Operas*. She's just an Iowa girl who's made good, aren't you, darling?"

"Listen, lamb pie," said Irene, "you leave Iowa out of this. What's the matter with Iowa, anyway?"

"Nothing apart from Julia de Martineau," said Otis Meer, and went into a gale of laughter. Irene and Luella laughed too. Evan was naturally unaware of the full piquancy of the joke. At this point an exceedingly handsome man came up and handed him an "old-fashioned."

"This is my dream prince," said Irene. "Dwight, you know Mr. Evan Lorrimer, don't you?"

"We've met already," said Evan, nodding to Dwight who nodded back with a grin and sat down on the floor at their feet, balancing his own drink carefully in his right hand as he did so. "Where the hell's Louise?" he asked.

"Louise has never been known to be on time for anything," said Luella.

Irene turned to Evan. "Isn't Louise a darling? You know she's one of the few really genuine people in the world. I can't bear people who aren't genuine, can you?" Evan made a gesture of agreement and she went on. "Being a writer must be just as bad as being a singer in some ways, having to meet people all the time and look pleased when they say nice things about your books."

"Tough," said Luella. "My heart goes out to you both." She got up and went over to the bar.

"You mustn't pay any attention to Luella," said Irene, comfortingly, observing that Evan looked a trifle nonplussed. "She always goes on like that, she's actually got the kindest heart in the world, sometimes I really don't know what I'd do without her, she's one of our few really genuine friends, isn't she, Dwight?" Dwight looked up and nodded and then stared abstractedly into the fire. At this moment, Louise came into the room with a scream.

"I'm so terribly sorry, everybody—" she wailed. "I overslept." While she was being swamped with greetings, Evan looked at her in horror. She seemed to be a totally different person. Could this be the same woman whose friendly tranquillity and wise, philosophical outlook had so charmed him last night? Could she have known all these people were coming or was she merely masking her dismay at their appearance and trying to carry everything off with a high hand? If so, she was certainly doing it very convincingly. She seemed to be wholeheartedly delighted to see them. Her eye lighted on him and she came over with her arms around a red-haired woman in black and a small fair man. "My dear," she said, "you really must forgive me—I do hope you slept all right—" She broke off and turned to the red-haired woman. "He's a sleep maniac just like me," she said. Then to Evan again: "You have met everyone, haven't you, and been given a drink and everything?" Evan held up his glass in silent acknowledgment, he was bereft of words, whereupon she snatched it out of his hand. "You must have another at once," she cried. "That looks disgusting," and led him vivaciously to the bar.

During the next half an hour, which Evan spent leaning against the bar, he managed to sort out people a little in his mind. The red-haired woman in black was the Countess Brancati, she had been a Chicago debutante a few years back and had married into the Italian aristocracy. The thin grey man by the window talking to Luella Rosen was her husband. The little fair man was Oswald Roach, commonly known as Ossie. Ossie was a cabaret artist whose specialty was to sing rather bawdy monologues to his own improvisations on the ukulele. The source of this information was Bonwit who, although sweating copiously from the efforts of mixing different sorts of drinks

for everybody, was willing, almost grateful, for an opportunity to talk. "Who is the thin boy with the pale face?"
Evan asked him. Bonwit shook the cocktail-shaker violently. "That's Suki," he said with obvious distaste. "He's
a Russian fairy who plays the piano for Irene, he's all
right until he gets tight, then he goes cuckoo."

Evan was regarding this phenomenon with interest,
when there was a loud commotion in the hall, and two
enormous Alsatians sprang into the room followed by a
neatly dressed girl in jodhpurs and a fur coat. "I came
just as I was," she said, as Louise advanced to kiss her. "I
was riding this morning and Shirley wouldn't wait, she's
gone into the kitchen to see about food for Chico and
Zeppo." She indicated the Alsatians who were running
round the room wagging their tails and barking. "I do
hope you didn't mind us bringing them, but we couldn't
leave them all alone in the apartment for the whole day."
Louise gaily assured her that she didn't mind a bit and
brought her over to the bar. "Here's someone who's been
dying to meet you," she said to Evan. "Leonie Crane,
she's written three plays herself, she's one of my closest
friends and she's read everything you've ever written."
Leonie Crane blushed charmingly and wrung Evan's hand
with considerable force. "Not quite all," she said in a well-
modulated deep voice. "Louise always exaggerates, but I
did think *A Lady of London* was swell. Shirley and I read
it in Capri in the summer."

"*A London Lady*," Evan corrected her gently and she
blushed again. "That's typical of me," she said. "I'm so
vague that Shirley says she wonders how I've lived as long
as I have without being run over—Hallo, Bonny," she
leant over the bar and patted Bonwit's wet hand. "What
about a little hard liquor—I'm dying!"

Leonie was undeniably attractive, she radiated health
and a sort of jolly schoolboyish vitality; her canary-col-
oured silk shirt was open at the neck and her curly brown
hair was cut close to her head. She was a little shy and
tried to conceal it with a certain lazy gaucherie. Evan

found her most sympathetic, and they talked for several minutes and then Shirley appeared. Leonie presented her to Evan with brusque matter-of-fact despatch.

"This is Evan Lorrimer, Shirley—Shirley Benedict." They shook hands. Shirley was on the same lines as Leonie but older and a little more heavily built. She had jet black hair, clear blue eyes, and was wearing a perfectly plain grey flannel coat and skirt. She wore no jewellery except a pair of pearl button earrings. Both girls were singularly free from trifling adornments.

Presently Lester reappeared dressed in an entirely new colour scheme so far as tie and sweater went, but with the same strong, garish sports coat that he had worn the night before. He kissed Leonie and Shirley affectionately, and told Evan that they were both angels and that when he'd got to know them a little better he'd worship them. They all four had an old-fashioned on the strength of this prophecy and Evan began to feel a little drunk. It was not part of his usual routine to drink three tumblers of practically neat whisky in the middle of the day on an empty stomach, but he had now become sufficiently light-headed not to care. After all, there was no sense in just sitting about in corners looking sulky, just because some rather odd people had happened to come over for lunch. It would be both disagreeable and silly. Everyone seemed disposed to be most gay and friendly, why not relax and enjoy himself. Comforted by this successful disposal of his conscience, he agreed with cheerful resignation when Louise suggested that they should all go over to the Hughes-Hitchcocks for one more tiny drink before lunch. He had not the remotest idea who the Hughes-Hitchcocks were, but it was apparent from the enthusiastic assent of everyone present and from Lester's glowing description of them that they were an entrancing young married couple who lived only just down the road. Evan accepted an offer to go in Leonie's car and together with her and Shirley and Lester—the Alsatians were left behind—he went.

Lester's assurance that the Hughes-Hitchcocks lived only

just down the road proved to be inaccurate. Evan, wedged between Shirley, who was driving, and Leonie in a small Dusenberg roadster, with Lester on his lap, suffered cramp and terror simultaneously for a full half an hour's fast going. Shirley drove well, there was no doubt about that, if she had not they would all have been dead within the first five minutes; but it was the sort of driving that is liable to react unfavourably on the nerves of anyone who happens to drive himself. Evan had driven for years. He owned a sedan Studebaker in far away green England and frequently conveyed himself back and forth through the country in it, but not at a pace like this, not at seventy miles an hour over an ice-covered road that had frozen so hard that it was like glass. The fact that he was also unaccustomed to a right-hand drive added considerably to his agony. His instinct time and time again was to seize the wheel and swerve over to the left side to avoid what seemed to be imminent destruction. Fortunately, however, he restrained himself and sat in frozen misery until at last they turned into a large driveway under tall trees.

On the terrace outside the Hughes-Hitchcocks' house, which was a vast grey structure built on the lines of a French chateau, stood several cars. It was obviously quite a large party. Once inside, his legs felt so shaky after Lester's weight and the rigors of the drive, that he accepted with alacrity the first drink that was offered to him, which was a dry Martini in a glass larger than the cocktail glasses he was used to. After a little he relaxed sufficiently to look about him. There were at least twenty people in the room apart from his own party which was arriving in groups. His host, a good-looking hearty young man, brought up a fair girl whom he introduced as Mrs. Martin. Evan, as he shook hands with her, was unable to avoid noticing that she was in an advanced stage of pregnancy. She seemed quite unembarrassed over the situation and looked at him with vague brown eyes. He observed that her fragile young hand was clasping a highball. "Don't be frightened," she said with a simper, "it's not due until Wednesday, and if

it doesn't come then I'm going to have a Caesarian." Evan
felt at a loss to know how to reply to such compelling can-
dour, so he smiled wanly. She gave a slight hiccough and
said: "Excuse me." Evan fidgeted awkwardly.

"Is that necessary?" he asked, and then flushed to the
roots of his hair at the thought that she might imagine he
was referring to the hiccough, but she either hadn't noticed
or was too drunk to care. "Not necessary," she replied with
a little difficulty, "not exactly necessary, but nice work if
you can get it," then she drifted away. Presently Lester
came up and they went over and sat down together in a
window seat. "It's always like this in this house," he said.
"Thousands of people milling around—I can't think how
they stand it. They're such simple people themselves too,
and grand fun, you know, there's no chichi about them,
that's what I like and Hughsie—" here Lester chuckled—
"Hughsie's a riot, my dear, if you get Hughsie alone sometimes and get him to tell you some of his experiences in
the Navy, he'll slay you; of course he's settled down now,
and mind you he adores Sonia, and they've got two of the
most enchanting children you've ever seen, but still what's
bred in the bones comes out in the what have you. . . ."

At this moment Otis Meer joined them. "Christ," he
whispered to Lester, "Charlie Schofield's still trailing
round with that bitch. I thought they were all washed up
weeks ago."

"You should know," replied Lester, "if anybody
should."

Evan asked for this interesting couple to be pointed out
to him.

"That man over by the fireplace, the tall one with the
blonde. He's Charlie Schofield, one of our richest play-
boys. She's Anita Hay, she used to be in 'The Vanities.'
Otis hates her," he added, Evan thought rather unnecessarily.

"She's one of these high-hatting dames," said Otis.
"She'd high hat her own father if she knew who he was."

"Is she invited everywhere with Mr. Schofield?" enquired Evan, who was puzzled by the social aspects of the situation.

"If she's not he just takes her," replied Lester laconically. "He's been crazy about her for years."

Presently Louise came up with Luella Rosen. "I must apologise for dragging you over here," she said to Evan, "but I absolutely promised we'd come, and they're such darlings really, but I'd no idea there was going to be this crowd—have another drink and we'll go in five minutes."

"Can I drive back with you?" asked Evan wistfully.

"Of course," said Louise. "We'll meet in the hall in five minutes."

During the next hour Evan was forced to the conclusion that the time sense, in the wealthier strata of American society, was lacking. Louise showed no indication of wanting to leave. Almost immediately after she had promised to meet Evan in the hall in five minutes, she sat down with Mr. Hughes-Hitchcock and began to play backgammon; her laugh rang out several times and Evan wondered bleakly if "Hughsie" were retailing some of his experiences in the Navy.

Lester had disappeared. Otis Meer, Ossie and the Russian pianist were sitting in a corner engrossed in an intense conversation. Irene Marlow was entertaining a large group of people with a description of her first meeting with Geraldine Farrar—a few disjointed sentences came to Evan's ear—"That vast empty stage—" "My clothes were dreadful, after all I was completely unknown then, just an ambitious little girl from Iowa—" "She said with that lovely gracious smile of hers 'My child—'" What Miss Farrar had said was lost to Evan for at that moment Charles Schofield came and spoke to him.

"We haven't been formally introduced," he said amiably, but I think you know a great friend of mine, the Prince of Wales?" Evan endeavouring not to betray surprise, nodded casually. "Of course," he said, "although I fear I don't know him very well." Actually he had met the Prince of Wales twice, once at a charity ball at Grosvenor

House and once at a supper party at Lady Cynthia Caw-
thorne's. On both occasions he had been presented and
the Prince had been charming, if a trifle vague; neither
conversation could truthfully be said to have established
any degree of intimacy.

"He's a grand guy," went on Charlie Schofield, "absolutely genuine. I've played polo with him a lot. Do you
play polo?"

"No—I don't ride well enough."

"It's a grand game," said Charlie. "I used to play on
Boots Leavenworth's team—you know Boots Leavenworth,
of course?"

Evan did not know the Earl of Leavenworth except by
repute, but he felt it would sound churlish to go on deny-
ing everything. "Rather," he said, "he's awfully nice."

"I suppose you don't know what's happened about him
and Daphne?"

"I think things are much the same," hazarded Evan.

"You mean Rollo's still holding out?"

"When I left England," said Evan boldly, "Rollo was
still holding out."

"God!" said Charlie with vehemence. "Aren't people
extraordinary! You'd think after all that business at
Cannes last summer he'd have the decency to face facts
and come out into the open. As a matter of fact, I've always
thought he was a bit of a bastard, outwardly amusing
enough, you know, but something shifty about him. As
a matter of fact poor Tiger's the one I'm sorry for, aren't
you?"

"Desperately," said Evan.

"Where is Tiger now?"

"I don't know." Evan wildly racked his brains for an
appropriate place for Tiger to be. "Africa, I think."

"Jesus!" cried Charlie aghast, "you don't mean to say
he's thrown his hand in and left poor Iris to cope with
everything?"

The strain was beginning to tell on Evan. He took ref-
uge in evasion. "Rumours," he said weakly. "One hears

rumours, you know how people gossip!"

Fortunately at this moment Shirley and Leonie came up and asked him if he'd like to play ping-pong. "We can't play at all," said Shirley, "we're terrible, but it's good exercise." Evan smiled affably at Charlie and went with them into an enormous room glassed in on three sides, furnished only with a ping-pong table, a few garden chairs and some large plants in pots. It was hotter than a Turkish bath. On the way he confided to them that he didn't play, but would be enchanted to watch them. He sat down, lit a cigarette and they started. They hadn't been playing a minute before he realised how wise he had been to refuse. They played like lightning, grimly, with an agility and concentration that was nothing short of ferocious. He watched them amazed. These two attractive young women, smashing and banging, occasionally muttering the score breathlessly through clenched teeth. Sometimes Leonie gave a savage grunt when she missed a shot, like a prize-fighter receiving a blow in the solar plexus. Presently, they having finished one game and changed round and started another, Evan began to feel drowsy. The hypnotic effect of following the little white ball back and forth and the montonous click of the wooden bats lulled him into a sort of coma. Vague thoughts drifted through his mind. He wondered who Rollo was and why he was probably holding out, and what Tiger might have left poor Iris to cope with—Poor Iris—Poor Tiger—Evan slept.

4

At ten minutes past four precisely the Steinhauser party rose from the lunch table and Evan went to his bedroom and shut the door. Lunch had not started until after three. There had been a certain amount of delay while Louise and Lester were rounding everybody up at the Hughes-Hitchcocks'. Then several arguments as to who should drive back with whom. Evan, with commendable tenacity,

considering that he had just been awakened from a deep
sleep, had clung to Louise like a leech despite all efforts
of Shirley and Leonie to persuade him to go back with
them, and finally succeeded in being brought home at a
more reasonable speed in Louise's Packard. Lunch had
been rather a scramble and consisted principally of clam
chowder which he detested and veal cutlets which, not
surprisingly, were so overdone as to be almost uneatable.
Evan, whose head was splitting, took two aspirin, divested
himself of his shoes, trousers and coat, put on his dressing-
gown and lay thankfully on the bed pulling the eiderdown
up to his chin. If he could get a real sleep now, he reflected,
not just a doze in a chair, and get up at about seven and
bath and change, everyone would have assuredly gone.
They must all have dinner engagements in New York,
and he would be able to dine peaceably with Louise and
Bonwit and Lester, allow a polite hour or so for conversation, and go to bed firmly at ten-thirty. The warmth of
the eiderdown stole around him, his legs began to con-
geal pleasantly with a prickling sensation, the throbbing
of his head gradually diminished and he fell asleep.

About an hour later he felt himself being dragged to
consciousness by somebody shaking him rhythmically.
With intense reluctance he opened his eyes and beheld
Lester bending over him. He moaned slightly and tried
to evade that inexorable hand.

"You must wake up now, honey," said Lester. "You've
had over an hour and Irene's going to sing." Evan's mind,
still webbed with sleep, tried unsuccessfully to grapple
with this announcement. "Who's Irene?" he muttered.

"Don't be silly," said Lester. "Irene Marlow; she's mad
about you, she says she won't so much as open her trap
unless you're there—we've been trying to persuade her for
twenty minutes—she says she'll sing for you or not at all—
come on." He flicked the eiderdown off the bed and pulled
Evan into a sitting posture. It was no use trying to go to
sleep again now, even if Lester had allowed him to. Once
wakened up like that he was done for. He went drearily

into the bathroom and sponged his face, then came back and put on his trousers, coat and shoes. Lester, while he did so, lay on the chaise-longue and discoursed enthusiastically upon the quality of Irene's voice, her passion for Dwight Macadoo and the fact that leaving all her success and glamour aside she was really completely genuine. "It's amazing about that boy," he said apropos of Dwight. "Really amazing—she's absolutely nuts about him and although he may be the biggest thing since *Ben Hur* I must say I think he's just plain dumb! Of course, you can't expect him to be anything else really, he was only a cowboy in Arizona when she met him, galloping about on a horse all day in 'chaps,' and rounding up all those God-damned steers—who shall be nameless—well, anyway, she met him on Grace Burton's ranch and gave her all if you know what I mean, and since that she's taken him everywhere—mind you, I'm not saying he isn't sweet, he is, but he just doesn't utter."

Lester led the way into the living-room. The party was sitting round expectantly. Irene was standing by the piano while Suki, with a cigarette dangling from his lips, was playing a few introductory chords. When Lester and Evan came in everybody said "Shhh" loudly. They sank down on to the floor by the door, Irene flashed Evan a charming smile and started off on "Vissi d'Arte." She sang beautifully. Evan, whose understanding of music was superficial to say the best of it, recognised at once that the quality of her voice and the charm with which she exploited it was of a very high order indeed. When she had finished "Tosca" everyone gave little groans and cries of pleasure, and someone called for "Bohème." Irene sang "Bohème"; then Ossie implored her to sing the waltz from *The Countess Maritza*. She started this and forgot the words half-way through, so she stopped and sang three songs of Debussy in French, and then some Schumann in German. Evan, being by the door in a draught, wished that she'd stop, the floor was beginning to feel very hard and he was afraid of catching cold. Irene, blissfully unaware that even one of her audience wasn't enjoying her performance to the utmost, went on singing for over an hour. When she finally left the piano and sat down, amid ecstasies of admiration, Evan rose stiffly and went over to the bar. Otis was leaning against it with Shirley and Leonie, Bonwit was still behind it.

"Isn't that the most glorious voice you've ever heard?" cried Ossie. "Frankly I'd rather listen to Irene than Jeritza, Ponselle and Flagstad all together in a lump." Evan, repressing a shudder at the thought of Jeritza, Ponselle and Flagstad all together in a lump, agreed wholeheartedly and asked Bonwit for a drink.

"Martini, old-fashioned, Daiquiri, rye and ginger ale, Scotch highball, pay your dime and take your choice," said Bonwit cheerfully. Evan decided on a highball, not that he wished to drink any more for the pleasure of it, but he was chilled by the draught from the door. Bonwit mixed him a strong one, and after a while he began to feel more cheerful. Louise came over. Evan noticed that she looked very flushed, and dragged Ossie away from the bar. "Darling Ossie, you must," she insisted, "everybody's screaming for you—Lester's gone to get your ukulele, you left it in the hall." Ossie, after some more persuasion, sat down in the middle of the room with his ukulele which Lester had handed to him, and began to tune it. Otis shouted out: "Do 'The Duchess'," and Irene cried, "No, not 'The Duchess'," do 'Mrs. Rabbit.' " Louise cried, "No, not 'Mrs. Rabbit', do 'Ella goes to Court'." Several other people made several other suggestions, and there was pandemonium for a few moments. Shirley whispered to Evan, "I do hope he does 'Ella goes to Court', you'll adore it, it's all about Queen Mary."

Ossie silenced the clamor by striking some loud chords; then he sang "Mrs. Rabbit." "Mrs. Rabbit" was a description, half-sung and half-spoken, of the honeymoon night of an elderly lady from Pittsburgh. It was certainly amusing, while leaving little to the imagination. Ossie's rendering of it was expert. He paused, raised his eyebrows,

lowered and raised his voice, and pointed every line with
brilliantly professional technique. Everyone in the room
shouted and wept with laughter. When he had finished
with a vivid account of the death of Mrs. Rabbit from
sheer excitement, the clamor started again. This time he
sang "The Duchess." It was rather on the same lines as
"Mrs. Rabbit" although the locale was different. It described a widow from Detroit who married an English
Duke and had an affair with a Gondolier during their
honeymoon in Venice. Evan permitted himself to smile
tolerantly at Ossie's somewhat stereotyped version of an
English Duke. Finally when he had sung several other
songs, all of which varied only in the degree of their por-
nography, he consented to do "Ella goes to Court." Evan
having finished his highball and noticing another close
to his elbow, took it hurriedly and braced himself for the
worst. "Ella goes to Court" was, if anything, bawdier than
the others had been. It was a fanciful description of a
middle-aged meat packer's wife from Chicago who owing
to the efforts of an impecunious English Countess, is taken
to a Court at Buckingham Palace and becomes intimately
attached to a Gentleman-in-Waiting on her way to the
Throne Room. The whole song was inexpressibly vulgar,
and to an Englishman shocking beyond words. Fortunately
the references to the Royal Family were comparatively
innocuous; if they had not been Evan would undoubtedly
have left the room, but still, as it was, the whole thing
with its sly implications, its frequent descents to bar-room
crudeness, and above all the ignorance and inaccuracy
with which Ossie endeavoured to create his atmosphere,
irritated Evan profoundly. Aware that several people were
covertly watching him to see how he would take this exhibition, he debated rapidly in his mind whether to look
as disgusted as he really felt or to pretend to enjoy it. He
took another gulp of his highball and forced an appre-
ciative smile on his face. "Do you know," said Leonie
when Ossie had finished and the enthusiasm had died
down, "that's the favourite song of the Prince of Wales.

Ossie had to sing it for him over and over again when he was at the Café de Paris in London." Evan was about to reply with some tartness that that could only possibly be another imaginative flight of Ossie's when a diversion was caused by the noisy entrance of four newcomers. "My God!" cried Lester. "It's Carola!" There was a general surge towards a smartly dressed woman with bright eyes and still brighter hair who walked in a little ahead of the others. Lester kissed her, Louise kissed her, everybody kissed her except Evan, who was formally introduced a little later by Otis Meer.

Her name was Carola Binney and she was, according to Leonie and Shirley, the most famous and gifted comedienne on the New York stage. Evan vaguely remembered having heard of her at some time or other. She certainly possessed abundant vitality and seemed to be on the most intimate terms with everybody present. The people with her, Evan learned, were Bob and Gloria Hockbridge who were scenario writers from Hollywood, and Don Lucas. There was probably no one in the world, even Evan, who had not heard of Don Lucas. Evan looked at him and really experienced quite a thrill. He was even handsomer in real life than he was on the screen. His young finely modelled face healthily tanned by the sun; his wide shoulders and long curling lashes; his lazy, irresistible charm. There it all was. "It was exactly," thought Evan, "as tho' some clear-eyed, vital young God from the wider spaces of Olympus had suddenly walked into a night club." Lester brought him over. "This is Don Lucas," he said exultantly. "He's just a struggling boy who's trying to make a name for himself and got side-tracked by somebody once saying he was good-looking."

"Nuts, Les!" said the clear-eyed Olympian as he shook hands. "Glad to know you, Mr. Lorrimer."

Lester, Don and Evan drifted over to the bar where Bonwit gave them each a highball. Evan tried to refuse but Lester insisted. "Phooey!" he cried, placing his arm around Evan's shoulders. "This is a party and life's just one big glorious adventure—which shall be nameless!"

Don, it appeared, was on a three weeks' vacation from Hollywood; he had just completed one picture, "The Loves of Cardinal Richelieu," and was going back on Thursday to start another which was to be called "Tumult," and was based on Tolstoi's *War and Peace*. The Hockbridges were writing it and had apparently done a swell job. Evan glanced across at the Hockbridges. Mr. Hockbridge was a plump bald man in the early forties, while his wife was much younger, possibly not more than twenty-five, with enormous wide blue eyes and platinum blonde hair done in the style of Joan of Arc. Evan tried to imagine them sitting down together and writing the story of *War and Peace* and gave up. After three strong whiskies and sodas such fantasy was beyond him.

Don, within the first few minutes of their conversation, pressed him warmly to come and stay with him when he lectured in Los Angeles. "It's a very simple house," he said. "None of that Spanish crap—all loggias and whatnot, but I can let you have a car and an English valet." "Simple house!" Lester gave a shriek. "It's about as simple as Chartres Cathedral. It's the most gorgeous place in California." He turned to Evan. "You really must go," he went on. "Seriously, I mean it—it's an experience, if you know what I mean, and when I say experience, well!—" He laughed and dug Don in the ribs.

"It would be grand to have you if you'd come," he said. "You mustn't pay any attention to the way Les goes on—we happened to have a party when he was there and Oh boy!" He shook his handsome head and sighed as though shattered by the memory of it. "But if you came you wouldn't be disturbed. I shall be working all day anyhow—you could do exactly as you liked."

Evan thanked him very much, and said it sounded delightful. Lester went off into further eulogies about the magnificence of Don's house but was interrupted by Louise who came up and placed one arm round Don's waist and the other round Evan's.

"We're all going over to the Grouper Wendelmanns for just ten minutes," she said. "Carola's longing to see their house; I must say it's unbelievable what they've done with it." Evan gently disentangled himself. "I don't think I'll come if you don't mind," he said. "I've got to go over my notes for my lecture to-morrow night."

There was a shocked silence for a moment, then Louise gave a wail of distress. "Oh my dear," she cried, "please come, just for a few minutes. The Grouper Wendelmanns will be so bitterly disappointed, they're pining to meet you and they're such darlings."

Evan shook his head. "I'd really rather not," he said firmly.

"Then I won't go either," said Lester.

"Neither will I," said Louise. "We'll none of us go."

Don Lucas patted Evan's shoulder encouragingly. "Come on," he coaxed. "Be a sport."

"They're divine people," said Lester. "They really are, you'll love them, and old Bernadine's a riot; she's Jane Grouper Wendelmann's mother, you know; you can't go back to Europe without having seen Bernadine Grouper."

"Only for just ten minutes," said Louise. "I shall really feel terribly badly if you don't go—it's quite near, just down the road and the house really is lovely, the most perfect taste, they've spent millions on it—"

"Don't worry him if he'd rather not," said Don. "Let's all have another drink."

Evan, touched by the sympathy in Don's voice and embarrassed by Lester's and Louise's obvious disappointment, gave in. "Very well," he said, "but I really must get back in time to go over my notes before dinner."

Louise's face lit up with pleasure. "Of course you shall," she cried. "You're an angel—the four of us shall go in my car—come on, everybody."

5

It was nearly an hour's drive to the Grouper Wendel-manns' house, and in the car Lester suggested playing a word game to pass the time. Evan didn't care for word games, but as he couldn't very well sit in morose silence he capitulated with as good a grace as possible. They played "Who am I?" and "Twenty Questions" and "Shedding Light." Evan acquitted himself favourably and, owing to his superior knowledge of history, won reverent praise for his erudition in "Twenty Questions."

"Shedding Light" bewildered him, but he was glad to see that it bewildered Don Lucas even more. As a matter of fact everything bewildered Don Lucas; his contributions consisted mainly of the names of obscure baseball players and movie directors, but he persevered with naïf charm in the face of the most waspish comments from Lester. Suddenly the games were interrupted by the chauffeur taking a wrong turning and arriving, after a few minutes of violent bumping, on to the edge of a swamp. Louise, who had been too occupied in trying to think of a Spanish seventeenth century painter beginning with M to notice, leant forward, slid back the glass window and shouted a lot of instructions, most of which Lester contradicted. "We ought to have turned to the left by the bridge, I know we ought," she said.

"If we'd done that we should have arrived at the Witherspoons'," said Lester. "And God forbid that we should do that."

"Nonsense," cried Louise. "The Witherspoons are right over on the other side near the Caldicotts."

"If," said Lester with a trace of irritation, "we had gone up that turning just past the Obermeyers' gate and then on over the hill we should have got into the highway and been able to turn right at the cross roads."

"Left," said Louise. "If you turn right at the cross

roads, you come straight to the golf course, and that's miles away, just next to the Schaeffers'."

"You'd better back," said Lester to the chauffeur. "And when you get into the main road again stop at the first petrol station and ask."

Presently after some more bumping and a frightening moment when the frozen surface of the ground nearly caused the car to skid into a ditch, they emerged again on to the main road. About a quarter of an hour later, having followed the instructions of a Negro at a petrol station, and gone back the way they had come for a few miles, they turned up a small lane and arrived at the Grouper Wendelmanns'. The rest of their party had naturally arrived some time before and everybody was playing skittles in a luxurious skittle alley with a bathing pool on one side of it and a bar on the other. Mr. and Mrs. Grouper Wendelmann came forward to meet them both grasping large wooden balls. They were a good-looking young couple in bathing costume. "This is wonderful," cried Mrs. Grouper Wendelmann. "We thought you were dead, we're just going to finish this game, have one more drink and then go in the pool—go and talk to mother, she's stinking!"

Mr. Grouper Wendelmann led them to the bar where the members of his own house-party were sitting on high stools apparently having relinquished the joys of the alley and the pool to the invaders. Old Mrs. Grouper, elaborately coiffed and wearing a maroon tea-gown and a dog-collar of pearls, greeted Evan warmly. "You may or may not know it," she said in a harsh, bass voice, "but you're my favourite man!"

Evan bowed politely and tried to withdraw his hand, but she tightened her grasp and pulled him towards her. "That book of yours," she said portentously, and cast a furtive look over her shoulder as though she were about to impart some scurrilous secret, "is great literature— No, it's no use saying it isn't because I know—Henry James used to be an intimate friend of mine and I knew poor Edith Wharton too, and believe me," her voice sank to a hoarse whisper, "I *know*." She relaxed Evan's hand so suddenly that he nearly fell over backwards. At that moment his host gave him an "old-fashioned" with one hand and piloted him with the other up to an emaciated dark woman in a flowered dinner dress.

"Alice," he said, "you English ought to get together— this is a countryman of yours—Mr. Lorrimer—Lady Kettering," Lady Kettering shook hands with him wearily and gave an absent smile. "How do you do," she said. The sound of an English voice comforted Evan, he hoisted himself on to a vacant stool next to her. Mr. Grouper Wendelmann, having done his duty as a host, left them. "What a lovely house," said Evan. Lady Kettering looked at him in surprise and then glanced round as though she were seeing it all for the first time. "I suppose it is," she replied, "if you like this sort of thing."

Evan felt a little crushed. "Of course I haven't seen much of it, I've only just arrived."

"I've been here for three months," said Lady Kettering, "and I must say it's beginning to get me down. I'm going to Palm Beach next week. I think Palm Beach is bloody, don't you?"

"I've never been there," said Evan.

"Well, take my advice and don't go. It's filled with the most frightening people."

"I shan't be able to anyhow," said Evan. "I'm over here to do a lecture tour."

"How horrible," said Lady Kettering. "Whatever for?"

"My publishers were very insistent that I should." Evan was slightly nettled. "And after all I think it will be interesting to see something of America. This is my first visit."

"You ought to go to Mexico," said Lady Kettering. "That's where you ought to go."

"I'm afraid I shan't have time."

"That's the one thing you don't need in Mexico— Time doesn't exist—it's heaven."

"Why don't you go to Mexico instead of Palm Beach?"

"I've promised to join the Edelstons' yacht and go on a cruise in the Bahamas," said Lady Kettering. "Do you know the Edelstons?"

"No," replied Evan.

"Well, take my advice," she said, "and give them a wide berth. They're bloody."

At this moment Don Lucas came and pried Evan gently off his stool. "Come and swim," he said.

The idea of swimming on a Sunday evening in mid-February seemed fantastic to Evan. "I don't think I will."

"Come on, be a sport."

"I'd rather watch you."

"Nuts to that," cried Don. "Everybody's going to swim, it'll be swell."

Evan allowed himself to be led over to the pool, inwardly vowing that no power on earth would get him into the water. Leonie and Shirley were giving an exhibition of fancy diving from the highest board, while Louise, Lester, Carola Binney, Irene Marlow and Ossie, who were already in bathing suits, sat round the edge and applauded. "Isn't that amazing?" cried Lester as Leonie did a spectacular Jackknife. "I'd give anything in the world to be able to dive like that, but everything, if you know what I mean!"

Don took Evan firmly into a richly appointed men's dressing-room and handed him a pair of trunks. "Now undress," he ordered.

Once more Evan protested. "Really I'd rather not—"

"What the hell—" said Don. "The water's warm and we'll all have fun—come on, be a pal—"

"Honestly—" began Evan.

"Now listen here," Don sat down on a bench and looked at Evan reproachfully, "this is a party and we're all having a good time and you're just bent on spoiling the whole shooting match."

"Why should you be so anxious for me to swim?" asked Evan almost petulantly.

"Because I like you," said Don with a disarming smile.

"I liked you from the word go and you like me too, don't you? Come on, be frank and admit it."

"Of course I like you," said Evan. "I like you very much."

"Very well then," said Don triumphantly. "Do we swim or don't we?"

"You do and I don't."

"You wouldn't like me to get tough now, would you?" said Don in a wheedling voice, but with an undertone of menace. "I could, you know!"

"I'm sure you could, but I fail to see—"

"Come on now, quit stalling." Don advanced towards him and forcibly removed his coat. For one moment Evan contemplated screaming for help, but visualising the ridiculous scene that would ensue he contented himself with struggling silently in Don's grasp. "Please let me go," he muttered breathlessly, "and don't be so silly."

Don had succeeded in slipping Evan's braces off and was endeavouring to unbutton his shirt when Lester came in. "Boys, boys," he cried admonishingly, "do try to remember that this is Sunday—which shall be nameless," and went into gales of laughter. Don released Evan immediately.

"This guy's a big sissy," he said. "He won't swim."

"I don't blame him," said Lester. "The water's like bouillabaisse. It's got more things in it than Macy's window."

"To hell with that, I'm going to swim if it kills me."

"It probably will on top of all that liquor." Lester went over and took a packet of cigarettes out of the pocket of his coat which was hanging on a peg. Then he came and sat on the bench next to Evan who, with a flushed face, was adjusting his clothes. "Relax, honey," he said, "Don always goes on like this when he's had quite a few drinks. Have a Camel?"

Evan took a cigarette, meanwhile Don was tearing off his clothes with ferocious speed. When he was completely naked he stood over Lester and Evan with arms folded and regarded them with scorn. Lester looked up at him. "It's all right, Puss," he said, "we've seen all that and it's gorgeous, now go jump in the pool and sober up."

"I don't know what's the matter with you guys," he grumbled, and went towards the door.

"You'd better put on some trunks," said Lester, "or have I gone too far?"

Don came slowly back and put on a pair of trunks. "Funny, hey?" he said bitterly and went out. A moment later they heard a loud splash and a shriek of laughter.

"What about another little drinkie?" said Lester.

6

About an hour later Evan found himself in a car sitting between Carola Binney and Luella Rosen whom he hadn't spoken to since before lunch. Don and Lester were squeezed together in the front seat next to Dwight Macadoo who was driving. The car apparently belonged to Irene Marlow. Evan had had two more "old-fashioneds" since his struggle with Don and was drunk, but in a detached sort of way. He had lost all capacity for resistance. From now on, he decided, he would drink when he was told to, eat when he was told to, and go where he was taken. There was no sense in fighting against overwhelming odds. He lay back, quite contentedly, with his head on Luella's shoulder and listened to Carola describing a man called Benny Schultz who had directed a play she had tried out in Boston last September—

"Never again—" she was saying vehemently, "would I let that rat come within three blocks of me—My God— you've no idea what I went through—he comes prancing into my dressing-room on the opening night after the first Act—the first Act! believe it or not, and starts giving me notes—'Listen, Benny,' I said, 'you may have directed *Crazy Guilt* and *Mother's Day* and *The Wings of a Dove*, and you may have made Martha Cadman the actress she is, and Claudia Biltmore the actress she certainly isn't, but you're not coming to my room on an opening night and start telling me that my tempo was too fast and that I struck a wrong note by taking my hat off at my first entrance. To begin with I had to take that God awful hat off which I never wanted to wear anyway because the elastic band at the back was slipping, and if I hadn't it would have shot up into the air and got a laugh in the middle of my scene with Edgar; in the second place if you had engaged a supporting company for me who could act and a leading man who had some idea of playing comedy, and at least knew his lines, I wouldn't have had to rush through like a fire engine in order to carry that bunch of art-theatre hams and put the play over, and in the third place I should like to remind you that I was a star on Broadway when you were selling papers on the East Side, and I knew more about acting than you when I was five, playing the fit-ups with *The Two Orphans*. And what's more, if you think I'm going to tear myself to shreds trying to get laughs in the supper scene in the pitch dark—well, you're crazy—' " She paused for a moment, Luella gave a barely audible grunt.

"You've got to have light to play comedy," she went on, "and all the phony highbrow directors in the world won't convince me otherwise."

"For all that I think Benny's pretty good," said Luella.

"He's all right with Shakespeare. I give you that," said Carola. "His Macbeth was fine, what you could see of it, but comedy never—look at the flop he had with *Some Take it Straight*."

"*Some Take it Straight* was the worst play I ever sat through," Luella admitted.

"It needn't have been," cried Carola. "I read the original script. They wanted me to do it with Will Farrow, it really wasn't bad apart from needing a little fixing here and there—then that rat got hold of it and bitched it entirely." •

Lester let the window down. "What's Carola yelling

about?" he enquired.

"Benny Schultz," said Luella.

"I wouldn't trust him an inch, not an inch," said Lester. "Look what he did to Macbeth."

"Are we nearly home?" asked Evan.

"We're not going home—we're going to Maisie's."

Evan lifted his head from Luella's shoulder. "Who's she?" he asked sleepily.

"She's divine," replied Lester. "You'll worship her— I mean she's a real person, isn't she, Luella?"

"It depends what you call real," said Luella. "Personally she drives me mad."

At this point the car turned into a gateway and drew up before a low, rather rambling white-walled house. Everyone got out and stamped their feet on the frozen snow to keep warm, while they waited for the door to be opened, which it presently was by a large forbidding-looking Swedish woman who regarded them suspiciously. Lester embraced her. "It's all right, Hilda," he said, "it's only us."

She stood aside and they all trooped in, shedding their coats in the hall. Lester led the way into a sort of studio panelled in pitch pine with wide bow windows and an immense log fire. The room was luxuriously furnished in a style that Evan supposed was early American. Anyhow in spite of its being extremely over-heated, its simplicity was a relief after the other houses he had visited. He felt as though he had been going from house to house all his life. A grizzled woman with fine eyes and wearing a riding habit greeted them brusquely and introduced the other people in the room. There were two girls called Peggy and Althea, one fat and the other thin, a very pale young man in green Chinese pyjamas called George Tremlett, and a statuesque Frenchwoman with raven hair who appeared to be dressed as a Bavarian peasant. The only two members of their own party present were Leonie and Shirley who were lying on the floor playing with a Siamese cat. There was a large table of drinks along one of the windows. Don Lucas made a bee-line for it. "Donny wants some fire water," he said. "Donny wants to get stinking."

"You were stinking at the Grouper Wendelmanns'," said Luella.

"Isn't he beautiful?" said the Frenchwoman.

When everyone had helped themselves to drinks Evan found himself sitting on a small upright sofa with George Tremlett.

"You arrived in the middle of a blazing row," whispered George with a giggle. "Suzanne and Shirley haven't spoken for two years and suddenly in she walked with Leonie—"

"Which is Suzanne?"

"The dark woman, Suzanne Closanges. She writes poetry either in French or English, she doesn't care which, and she lives here with Maisie."

"Maisie who?" asked Evan.

"Maisie Todd, of course," said George with slight irritation. "This is Maisie Todd's house—I did it."

"How do you mean 'did it'?"

"Designed it," George almost squealed. "I'm George Tremlett."

"How do you do?" said Evan.

"It was lovely doing this house," went on George, "because I had an absolutely free hand—Maisie's like that— we had the grandest time driving all over New England and finding bits and pieces here and there. I found this very sofa we're sitting on tucked away in a fisherman's bedroom at Cape Cod."

"How extraordinary," said Evan—he felt overpoweringly sleepy.

Leonie came over with the Siamese cat and placed it on Evan's lap. "Isn't he adorable?" she said. "I gave him to Maisie for a Christmas present in 1933 and he's grown out of all knowledge."

The cat arched its back, dug its claws into Evan's leg and with a loud snarl hurled itself to the floor. "They're very fierce," went on Leonie picking it up again by the nape of its neck so that it hung spitting and kicking in the air. "And the older they grow the fiercer they get, but Dante isn't fierce though he's older than hell—are you, my darling?" she added affectionately, kissing it on the side of the head. The cat gave a sharp wriggle and scratched her cheek, from her eye, which it missed by a fraction, to her chin. She screamed with pain and dropped it on to a table where it knocked over and smashed a photograph of a lady in fencing costume framed in glass, jumped down and disappeared behind a writing-desk. Evan started to his feet, everyone came crowding over.

"The son of a bitch," wailed Leonie. "He's maimed me for life." With that she burst into tears. Maisie Todd took charge with fine efficiency. She produced a large white handkerchief to staunch the blood, dispatched George to fetch some iodine from her bathroom. Shirley flung her arms round Leonie and kissed her wildly. "Don't, darling, don't cry," she besought her. "For God's sake, don't cry, you know I can't bear it."

"There's nothing to cry about," said Maisie, "it's only a scratch."

"It may only be a scratch," cried Shirley, "but it's terribly deep and it's bleeding."

"Don't fuss," said Maisie.

"It's all very fine for you to say don't fuss," Shirley said furiously, "but it might very easily have blinded her—you oughtn't to keep an animal like that in the house, it should be destroyed."

"Leonie gave it to Maisie herself before she knew you," put in Suzanne with a little laugh.

"Mind your own business," snapped Shirley.

Leonie dabbed her eyes and her cheeks alternately with the blood-stained handkerchief.

"For God's sake shut up, everybody. I'm all right now, it was only the shock."

"Drink this, darling," said Lester, handing her his glass.

"We should never have come—I knew something awful would happen," said Shirley.

"There is nothing to prevent you going." Suzanne spoke with icy dignity. There was a horrified silence for a moment. Shirley left Leonie and went very close to Suzanne.

"How dare you," she said softly. Evan noticed that she was trembling with passion. "How dare you speak to me like that—"

Maisie intervened. "Now listen, Shirley," she began. Shirley pushed her side. "I've always disliked you, Suzanne, from the first moment I set eyes on you, and I wish to say here and now that you're nothing but a fifth-rate gold-digger sponging on Maisie the way you do and making her pay to publish your lousy French poems, and you're not even French at that—you're Belgian!"

Suzanne gave a gasp of fury, slapped Shirley hard in the face and rushed from the room, cannoning into George Tremlett who was coming in with the iodine and knocking the bottle out of his hand on to the floor. "Oh, dear!" he cried sinking on to his knees. "All over the best Hook rug in the house!"

From then onwards everybody talked at once. Maisie dashed out of the room after Suzanne, Leonie started to cry again. The two girls, Althea and Peggy, who had been watching the whole scene from a corner, decided after a rapid conversation to follow Maisie and Suzanne, which they did, slamming the door after them. George was moaning over the Hook rug and trying to rub out the iodine stains with a silk scarf. Lester joined Luella and Carola by the fireplace. Carola was protesting violently at Suzanne's behaviour, while Luella smiled cynically. Lester, genuinely distressed, was sympathising with Shirley and Leonie, while Don added to the din by strolling over to the piano with Dwight Macadoo and playing "Smoke Gets in Your Eyes" with one hand. Presently he desisted. "The piano stinks," he said. "No tone—where's the radio?" Before he could find it Luella, to Evan's intense relief, suggested that they should all go, and led the way firmly into the hall. While they were struggling into their coats and wraps the large Swedish woman watched them silently

with a baleful expression. The freezing night air struck
Evan like a blow between the eyes; he staggered slightly.
Don quickly lifted him off the ground and deposited him
in the car with infinite tenderness.

"You were wrong about that swim," he said affectionately. "It was swell, made me feel like a million dollars.
Now we'll go home and have a little drinkie."

7

They had no sooner got inside the Steinhausers' front
door when Irene came rushing out of the living-room.
"Where the hell have you been?" she cried angrily to
Dwight. "I looked for you all over and when I came
out you'd gone off in my car."

"Now don't be mad at me, darling—" began Dwight.

"Mad at you! I've never been madder in my life—come
in here." She dragged him into the library and banged
the door.

"Well," said Lester, "isn't she the cutest thing—My
dear!" He waved his hand benevolently after them. "These
Prima Donnas—who shall be nameless—"

Louise appeared with a great cry and flung her arms
round Evan. He was dimly aware that she had changed
into a long flowing tea-gown. "*There* you are," she said.
"I couldn't think what had happened to you—you must
be starving." Still holding him tightly she pulled him into
the living-room which had undergone a startling change.
All the furniture had been pushed out on to the Sun Porch
with the exception of the chairs which were arranged
round the walls. An enormous buffet loaded with hams,
turkeys, salads, bowls of fruit, bowls of cream, two large
cakes and piles of plates, stood along one side of the room.
Another smaller table for drinks was joined on to the bar
behind which Bonwit was still officiating, assisted by a
Japanese in a white coat. There were at least fifty people
in the room and the noise was deafening. Evan, dazed as

he was, distinguished the Grouper Wendelmanns, Lady Kettering, and several of the people he had seen at the Hughes-Hitchcocks', including the young expectant mother who was sitting on the floor with her back against one of the piano legs, and a large plate of variegated food on her lap, apparently in a stupor, while Suki played an unending series of complicated syncopation in her ear.

Louise led Evan to the table and gave him a plate on which she piled, with professional speed, a turkey leg, Virginia ham, baked beans, a fish cake, potato salad, lettuce, a wedge of Camembert cheese and a large slice of strange-looking brown bread. "There," she said, "now sit down quietly, and eat, you poor dear." With that she whisked away from him and rushed across to Carola and Luella. He looked round for a vacant chair but there wasn't one, so he stayed where he was and ate standing against the table. The food was certainly good although there was far too much of it on his plate. He was about to slide the cheese and one of the slices of ham into an empty bowl that had held salad when he was arrested by Charlie Schofield putting his hand on his shoulder. He jumped guiltily as though he'd been caught in the act of doing something nefarious.

"I told Alice Kettering what you said about Tiger being in Africa," said Charlie, "and she's in an awful state—she was crazy about him for years you know."

Before Evan could reply Don came up and forced a glass into his hand. "I promised you a little drinkie," he said genially, "and a little drinkie you're going to have."

A big woman in yellow put her arm through Charlie Schofield's and led him away. Evan saw out of the corner of his eye that Lady Kettering was drifting towards him. He retreated on to the Sun Porch followed by Don looking very puzzled.

"What's the idea?"

"Just somebody I don't want to talk to," said Evan with as much nonchalance as he could muster.

"Listen, Pal," said Don. "If there's anyone you don't

like just you tip me off and I'll sock 'em."

Evan, shuddering inwardly at the thought of Don socking Lady Kettering, muttered that it was of no importance really, and leant against the window. Outside the moon had come up and the sea shone eerily in its light like grey silk; far away in the distance a lighthouse flashed. It all looked so remote and quiet that Evan felt inclined to weep. Don squeezed his arm reassuringly. "You know I like you," he said, "I like you better than any Englishman I've ever met. Most Englishmen are high hat, you know, kind of snooty, but you're not high hat at all, you're a good sport."

"Thank you," said Evan dimly.

"I hope you weren't sore at me for trying to make you go in the pool," Don went on. "I wouldn't like to have you sore at me. It isn't often I get a chance to talk to anyone really intelligent—not that you're only just intelligent, you're brilliant, otherwise you wouldn't be able to write all those God-damned books, would you now?"

"Well," began Evan, feeling that some reply was demanded.

"Now don't argue." Don's voice was fierce. "Of course you're brilliant and you know you are, don't you?"

Evan smiled. "I wouldn't exact say—"

Don patted his hand tolerantly. "Of course you do—everybody knows when they're brilliant, they'd be damned fools if they didn't. Jesus, the way you played that question game in the car—if that wasn't brilliant I should like to know what is. But what I mean to say is this: I'm just a simple sort of guy, really, without any brains at all—I've got looks, I grant you that, otherwise I shouldn't be where I am to-day should I? But no brains, not a one. Why, the idea of sitting down and writing a letter drives me crazy, let alone a book. Sometimes when I look at something beautiful like all that," he indicated the view, "or when I run across someone really brilliant like you are I feel low—honest to God I do—"

"Why?" said Evan.

"Because I'm such a damn fool of course. I couldn't write down what that looks like to me, not if you paid me a million dollars I couldn't. I couldn't paint it either, I couldn't even talk about it. What do I get out of life I ask you? Money, yes—I make a lot of dough and so what—Happiness, no—I'm one of the unhappiest sons of bitches in the whole world," he broke off.

"Cheer up," said Evan as cheerfully as he could. He was feeling depressed himself.

"It gets me down," murmured Don, pressing his forehead against the glass of the window. "It just gets me down."

Evan was pained and embarrassed to observe that he was crying. A concerted scream of laughter came from the living-room. Evan peeped in. Everyone was grouped round Carola who, with a man's Homburg hat perched on her head, was doing an imitation of somebody. Evan glanced back at Don, who was still staring out into the night; his shoulders were heaving. Now was the moment to escape, everyone was far too occupied to notice whether he was there or not; if he could get into the hall without Louise seeing him, the rest was easy; he could get into his room, lock the door and go to bed. He crept along behind the buffet, avoiding Mr. Hockbridge, who was asleep on a chair, and reached the hall in safety. From behind the closed door of the library came sounds of strife, apparently Irene's fury at Dwight had in no way abated. Evan paused long enough to hear her scream angrily—"It was Luella's fault, was it—we'll see about that!"—then he darted down the passage, through Lester's room and the bathroom and reached his own room with a sigh of relief. He switched on the lights by the door and started back in horror. Stretched out on his bed was a woman in a heavy sleep. On closer examination he recognized the Countess Brancati. Her black dress was rumpled and her hair was spread over the pillow like pink hay.

A great rage shook Evan to the core. He seized her by the shoulder and pushed her backwards and forwards violently; she continued to sleep undisturbed. He knelt down on the floor by the bed and shouted "Wake up—please wake up" in her face to which she replied with a low moan. He shook her again and one of her earrings fell off; he picked it up and put it on the bed table and stood there looking at her, his whole body trembling with fury and frustration. He gave her one more despairing shove but she paid no attention. Then, with an expression of set determination, he marched back to the living-room. On his way he met Bonwit emerging from the library. "My God," Bonwit said, "there's all hell breaking loose in there," and then, noticing Evan's face, "what's happened to you?"

"There's a woman on my bed," Evan almost shouted.

"I'll bet it's Mary Lou Brancati," said Bonwit. "She always passes out somewhere—come on—we'll get her out."

They went back together. The countess had turned over on to her face. Bonwit slapped her behind; she wriggled slightly and he did it again harder. Presently, after several more whacks, she turned over and muttered, "G'way and leave me alone—" Bonwit whereupon hoisted her up on to the side of the bed and shook her. She opened her eyes and looked at him malevolently. "Get the hell away from me," she said. "What d'you think you're doing!"

"Come on, baby," said Bonwit, "you're missing everything. There's a party going on."

"To hell with it," she replied. "G'way and leave me alone."

"Take her other arm," ordered Bonwit. Evan obeyed and they hauled her struggling and protesting into the bathroom. There Bonwit dabbed her face with a wet sponge; she gave a scream and tried to hit him. Finally they got her into the hall and deposited her in a chair. Bonwit slapped his hands together as though he had just felled a tree and said, "Now you're Okay, fellar."

At that moment the hall suddenly filled with people. Louise came out of the library with her arms around Irene who was sobbing. Dwight followed them miserably.

Unfortunately Luella and Otis Meer came out of the living-room at the same instant followed by Lester, Lady Kettering and the Grouper Wendelmanns. Irene, catching sight of Luella, wrested herself from Louise's arms. "So you're still here," she said harshly. "I'm surprised you have the nerve!"

Luella looked at her coolly. "You're tight, Irene," she said. "You'd better go home."

"You're a snake!" cried Irene, breathing heavily. "A double-faced, rotten snake!"

Lester tried to calm her. "Look here, honey," he said, "there's no cause in getting yourself all worked up."

Irene pushed him aside. "You shut up—you're as bad as she is—you're all of you jealous of Dwight and me and always have been—Luella's been trying to get him for years, and if you think I'm so dumb that I haven't seen what's been going on you're crazy."

"Really," murmured Lady Kettering. "This is too bloody—we'd better go—"

"Go and be damned to you!" said Irene.

Louise gave a cry of distress. Lady Kettering turned and tried to make a dignified exit into the living-room, but was prevented by Ossie, Suki, the Hughes-Hitchcocks and Mrs. Hockbridge, who had crowded into the doorway to see what was happening.

Luella seized Irene by the arm in a grip of steel. "Behave yourself," she hissed. "What do you mean by making a disgusting scene like this about nothing?"

"Nothing!" Irene screamed and writhed in Luella's grasp. Otis Meer gave a cackle of shrill laughter. Dwight tried to coax Irene back into the library. Louise wept loudly and was comforted by Lester and Ossie. Lady Kettering struggled valiantly through the crowd to try to find her cloak. Carola, who had joined the group with Shirley and Leonie, announced in ringing tones that in her opinion the possession of an adequate singing voice was hardly sufficient excuse for behaving like a Broadway floosie. Lester turned on her and told her to shut up and not make everything worse, and in the indescribable pandemonium that ensued, Evan fled.

8

About an hour later, Evan, sitting up rigidly in his bed, began to relax. He had brushed his teeth, taken three aspirins, undressed, tried to lock the door but discovered there was no key, and read four chapters of *Sense and Sensibility* which he always travelled with as a gentle soporific. He had left no stone unturned in his efforts to drag his aching mind away from the horrors he had endured. He had turned out the light twice and attempted to sleep but to no avail. Incidents of the day, people's names, unrelated scraps of conversation crowded into his brain, making even the possibility of lying still out of the question, let alone sleep. Sleep was aeons away, he felt that it was well within the bounds of probability that he would never sleep again. The thought of the lecture he had to give that very night, it was now three a.m., tortured him. He felt incapable of uttering one coherent phrase and as for talking for an hour, his mind reeled at the very idea of it. The continual noise, the endless arrivals and departures, the impact of so many different atmospheres and personalities, the unleashing of vulgar passion he had witnessed, to say nothing of the incredible amount of alcohol he had drunk, had lacerated his nerves beyond bearing. He was outraged, shamed, exhausted and bitterly angry.

Now at last he was beginning to feel calmer. The three aspirins he had taken had made his heart thump rather, his maximum dose as a rule being two, but it was apparently taking effect. He glanced at his watch, ten minutes past three, if he could manage to sleep until eleven he would have had nearly his eight hours and probably be able to get in an extra hour at his hotel before his lecture if he wasn't too nervous. "I'll give myself another ten minutes," he reflected, "and then turn out the light, by that time it ought to be all right."

He lay there still as a mouse, resolutely emptying his mind and concentrating on gentle, peaceful things, the waves of the sea, a vast fourposter bed in some remote English country house, the cool, soft lavender-scented sheets, the soughing of the wind outside in the elms— At this moment the door opened and Bonwit came in on tip-toe. He was in his pyjamas and carrying a pillow and an eiderdown. He looked relieved when he saw Evan wasn't asleep.

"I'm awfully sorry, fellar," he said, "but I've got to come and use your other bed—there's been all hell going on. Irene drove off in her car with Dwight, leaving Suki and Luella behind, the Brancatis went too, leaving Ossie and Otis, and we've only just found Don Lucas—he's in the living-room on the sofa. Ossie and Otis are in with Lester, Luella's in with Louise and Suki's in my room. I've got to get up at seven to go into town but don't be afraid I'll disturb you—I've left my clothes in the bathroom so I can dress in there."

"Oh," said Evan hopelessly, the blackness of despair made further utterance impossible.

Bonwit clambered into bed and switched off his light. "I'm all in," he said. "Good night, fellar."

Evan switched off his light too, and lay staring into the darkness.

In a remarkably short space of time Bonwit began to snore. Evan groaned and tried to fold the pillow over his ears, but it was no good, the snores grew louder. They rose rhythmically to a certain pitch and then died away. Occasionally the rhythm would be broken by a grunt, then there would be silence for a moment, then they'd start again. Evan, after a half an hour of it, suddenly leapt up on an impulse of pure blinding rage, switched on the light and went over to Bonwit's bed and stood looking at him. Bonwit was lying on his back with his mouth wide open—the noise issuing from it was incredible. Evan, flinging all gentleness and consideration to the winds, seized him violently by the shoulders and turned him over. Bonwit gave a terrific snort, turned back again almost immediately and went on snoring louder than ever. Evan began to cry, tears coursed down his cheeks and fell on to his pyjamas—panic assailed him—if this went on he would definitely go mad. He walked up and down the room fighting to prevent himself from losing control utterly and shrieking the house down. He went over to the window and looked out. The night was crystal clear, there wasn't a cloud in the sky. Suddenly he knew what he was going to do, the idea came to him in a flash. He was going away, that's what he was going to do. He was going to dress, telephone for a taxi and leave that horrible house for ever. It was idiotic not to have thought of it before. He would leave a note for Louise in the hall asking her to bring his suitcase into New York with her. He tore off his pyjamas and began to dress. Bonwit stopped snoring and turned over. Evan switched off the light and stood still hardly daring to breathe. If Bonwit woke up and caught him trying to escape, he'd obviously try to prevent him—there would be arguments and persuasions and protests, probably ending in the whole house being roused.

Bonwit started to snore again and Evan, with a sigh of relief, finished dressing. Holding his shoes in his hand he crept down the passage, through the bathroom and into Lester's room. He could dimly make out two forms in one bed and one in the other. He banged against a chair on his way to the door and immediately lay down flat on the floor. Lester moved in his sleep but didn't wake; finally, on hands and knees, Evan crawled out into the other passage and into the hall. Once there, he put on his shoes and went cautiously in search of the telephone; just as he was about to go into the library he remembered that it was in the bar, he had heard Bonwit using it before lunch. He went into the living-room. The curtains were not drawn and moonlight was flooding through the windows. Don was sleeping soundly on a sofa, he looked rather debauched but extraordinarily handsome. Poor Don. Evan shook his head at him sorrowfully and went over to the bar. There was a shutter down over it which was padlocked. This was a terrible blow. Evan thought for a moment of going back and waking Bonwit; but decided against it. If there was no taxi he'd walk and if he didn't know the way he'd find it, at all events he knew he would rather die in the snow than spend one more hour in that house. He scribbled a note to Louise in the library. "Dear Mrs. Steinhauser—" He debated for a moment whether or not to address her as Louise, she had certainly kissed him several times during the day and called him Darling frequently, also he knew her to be a kindly, well-intentioned woman, although at the moment he could cheerfully have strangled her. On the whole he felt that Mrs. Steinhauser better expressed the manner in which he was leaving her house. "Dear Mrs. Steinhauser—Finding myself unable to sleep I have decided to go back to New York. Please forgive this unconventional departure, but it is essential, if I am to lecture with any degree of success, that I relax for several hours beforehand. Please don't worry about me, I am sure I shall find my way to the station quite easily, but if you would be so kind as to have my suitcase packed and bring it in with you to-morrow, I should be more than grateful. With many thanks for your delightful hospitality I am, yours sincerely, Evan Lorrimer." He signed his name with a flourish. "She can stick that in her damned visitors' book," he said to himself. He left the note in a prominent position on a table in the hall, found his hat and coat in a cupboard and let himself quietly out of the front door. The cold air exhilarated him. It was odd, he reflected, how the excitement of escape had completely banished his nervous hysteria. He felt surprisingly well, all things considered. The snow shone in the moonlight and the country lay around him white and still. He noticed a glow in the sky behind a hill. That must be a village, he thought, and set off jauntily down the drive.

About an hour later, when he had walked several miles
and his adventurous spirit had begun to wilt a trifle, he
was picked up by a milk van. The driver was rugged and
friendly and agreed to take him to the nearest station.
They had some coffee together in an all-night lunch room
when they got there; the next train for New York wasn't
due for three-quarters of an hour, and the driver talked
freely about his home and domestic affairs with an accent
that Evan found, at moments, extremely difficult to understand. Finally he drove away in his van, having allowed Evan to pay for the coffee, but refused to accept
two dollars.

"Nuts to that," he said with a laugh. "I like you—you're
not high hat and kind of snooty like most Englishmen—
So long, buddy."

Buddy, warmed by this tribute, went on to the platform
and waited for the train.

When he arrived in New York it was daylight. The
night-porter at his hotel greeted him in some surprise and
handed him a pile of telephone messages and a letter.
When he got to his room he opened the letter first. "Dear
Mr. Lorrimer," he read, "Although we have never met,
your books have given me so much pleasure that I am
taking this opportunity of welcoming you to Chicago,
where I understand you are going to talk to us next week
on 'History and the Modern Novel.' My husband and I
would be so pleased if you would come out to us for the
week-end after your lecture. Our home is on the edge of
the lake and we flatter ourselves it is the nearest approach
to an English country house that you could find in the
whole of the Middle West. It is peaceful and quiet, and
no one would disturb you, you could just rest. If you have
anyone with you we should, of course be delighted to
receive them, too. My husband joins me in the hope that
you will honour us by accepting. Yours very sincerely,
Irma Weinkopf." Evan undressed thoughtfully and got
into bed.

SHORT PLAYS

from *Tonight at 8:30*

★

WE WERE DANCING
A Comedy in Two Scenes

CHARACTERS

LOUISE CHARTERIS
HUBERT CHARTERIS
KARL SANDYS
CLARA BETHEL
GEORGE DAVIES
EVA BLAKE
MAJOR BLAKE
IPPAGA
TWO OR THREE UNNAMED MEMBERS
OF THE COUNTRY CLUB.

SCENE I. *Verandah of the Country Club at Samolo. Evening.*
SCENE II. *The same. Early morning.*

TIME: *The Present.*

SCENE I

The Scene is the verandah of the Country Club at Sam-olo. On the right is a room in which dances are held every Saturday night. For these occasions a dance-band flies up from Pendarla by the new Imperial Inter-State Airways. The band arrives in the afternoon, plays all night and departs early on Sunday for Abbachi where it repeats the

same procedure for the inhabitants there, returning weari-
ly on Mondays to the Grand Hotel, Pendarla where,
during the week, it plays for the Tourists.

When the curtain rises the verandah is deserted. A full
moon is shining over the sea and, far away, above the
chatter and music of the dance-room, there can occasion-
ally be heard the wailing of native music rising up from
the crowded streets by the harbour.

IPPAGA, *a Samolan boy, crosses the verandah from right*
to left carrying a tray of drinks. He is yellowish brown in
colour and, like most Samolans, comparatively tall. He
wears a scarlet fez, a green, purple and mustard-coloured
sarong, black patent-leather shoes, silver ear-rings and
three wooden bracelets.

As he goes off on the left the dance-music stops and
there is the sound of applause.

GEORGE DAVIES *and* EVA BLAKE *come out of the dance-*
room. GEORGE DAVIES *is a hearty, nondescript young man*
dressed in the usual white mess-jacket, black evening
trousers and cummerbund.

EVA, *equally nondescript, is wearing a pink taffeta*
bunchy little dress, pink ribbon in her hair and pink shoes
and stockings which do not quite match. She carries a
diamanté evening bag and a blue chiffon handkerchief
round her wrist. She also wears a necklace of seed pearls
and a pendant.

The dance music starts again. EVA *looks furtively over*
her shoulder.

GEORGE *enters first and walks up to balcony and calls:*

GEORGE: Eva! Eva!
EVA: It's all right, they're playing an encore.
GEORGE: Come on, then.
EVA: Where's the car?
GEORGE: I parked it at the end of the garden, where the
road turns off. My boy's looking after it.
EVA: He won't say anything, will he?
GEORGE: Of course not. He's been with me for years.

EVA: Oh, George!

GEORGE [*impatiently*]: It's all right—come on——

EVA: Where are we going?

GEORGE: Mahica beach, nobody ever comes near it.

EVA: Oh, George!

GEORGE [*taking her hand*]: Come on——

They go off right.

The band is playing a waltz and the stage is empty for a moment.

LOUISE CHARTERIS *and* KARL SANDYS *come dancing in from the left. They are both in the thirties, soignée and well-dressed, and they dance together as though they had never been apart.*

They waltz three times round the stage finishing in the centre with a prolonged kiss. The music ends, there is the sound of applause. TWO WOMEN *and a* MAN *come in. They stop short on observing* LOUISE *and* KARL, *they whisper together for a moment and then go back into the dance-room.*

LOUISE *and* KARL *remain clasped in each other's arms oblivious of everything. The music starts again.*

HUBERT CHARTERIS *and* CLARA BETHEL *come out of the dance-room.* CLARA *is a nice-looking, grey-haired woman in the forties.* HUBERT *her brother, is about the same age. He has dignity and reserve and looks intelligently British.*

They both stand for a moment looking at KARL *and* LOUISE *who, still entranced with their kiss, have not even noticed them.*

HUBERT [*quietly*]: Louise.

LOUISE [*jumping*]: Oh!

CLARA [*reproachfully*]: Louise, really!

LOUISE *and* KARL *step a little away from each other.*

LOUISE [*with a social manner*]: This is my husband. [*She hesitates and turns to Karl.*] I'm afraid I didn't catch your name?

KARL: Karl. Karl Sandys. [*To* HUBERT *and* CLARA.] How do you do?

HUBERT [*with perfect control*]: The car's here, I think

we'd better go if you're ready.

LOUISE: I'm not ready.

CLARA [*going towards her*]: Come along, Louise.

LOUISE: I can't go, really I can't.

HUBERT: This is most embarrassing, please don't make it worse.

LOUISE: I'm sorry, Hubert. I do see that it's all very difficult.

KARL: I fear I was partly to blame.

HUBERT [*ignoring him*]: Please come home now, Louise.

LOUISE [*gently*]: No, Hubert.

HUBERT: I'm afraid I must insist.

LOUISE: We have fallen in love.

KARL: Deeply in love.

HUBERT: I would prefer not to discuss the matter with you, sir.

LOUISE: That's silly, Hubert.

HUBERT [*sternly*]: Please come away.

LOUISE: I've told you, I can't.

KARL: Have a drink?

HUBERT [*irritably*]: Good God!

LOUISE: That is a good idea, Hubert, let's all have a drink.

KARL: We might also sit down.

CLARA: Listen, Louise, you can't behave like this, it's too idiotic.

LOUISE: It's true, can't you see? It's true.

CLARA: What's true? Don't be so foolish.

KARL: We're in love, that's what's true, really it is, Mrs.— Mrs.——

LOUISE: Bethel. This is my husband's sister, Mrs. Bethel.

KARL: How do you do?

CLARA: I appeal to you, Mr.—Mr.——

KARL: Sandys.

CLARA: Mr. Sandys—please go away. Go away at once.

KARL: That's quite impossible.

HUBERT: I detest scenes and I am finding this very unpleasant. I don't know who you are or where you come from, but if you have any sense of behaviour at all you must see that this situation is intolerable. Will you kindly leave the club immediately and never speak to my wife again in any circumstances whatever?

LOUISE: It's more important than that, Hubert, really it is.

KARL: It's the most important thing that has ever happened to me in my whole life, Mr.—Mr.——

LOUISE: Charteris.

KARL: Mr. Charteris.

HUBERT: Once more, Louise, for the last time, will you come home?

LOUISE: No—I can't.

HUBERT: Very well. Come, Clara.

He turns to go away. LOUISE *catches his arm.*

LOUISE: You can't go, either. I know you hate scenes and that you're trying to be as dignified as possible, and that I'm apparently behaving very badly, but it's true, this thing that's happened, I mean—we have fallen in love——

HUBERT: Please let go of my arm, Louise, and don't be ridiculous.

LOUISE: Look at me—look closely—I've been your wife for thirteen years. You're wise and intelligent and you know me well—look at me!

CLARA [*anxiously*]: Please go, Mr. Sandys.

KARL [*shaking his head*]: No.

HUBERT [*to* LOUISE]: I'm looking at you.

LOUISE [*emotionally*]: Well—don't you see?

HUBERT *looks quickly at* CLARA *then at* KARL *and then back to* LOUISE *again.*

HUBERT: Yes—I see.

CLARA: Hubert.

MAJOR BLAKE *comes in from the dance-room. He is a red-faced, elderly man.*

MAJOR BLAKE: I say, have you seen Eva?

HUBERT: What?

MAJOR BLAKE: I can't find Eva.

CLARA: I think she went home.

MAJOR BLAKE: She can't have, the car's there.

CLARA: She told me she was driving back with the Baileys.

MAJOR BLAKE: Oh, did she, did she really?

CLARA: She told practically everybody in the club that she was driving back with the Baileys, I'm surprised she didn't mention it to you.

MAJOR BLAKE: Oh, she's all right then—thanks—thanks awfully.

CLARA [*after a pause*]: You'll be able to pick her up on the way home.

MAJOR BLAKE: It's hardly on the way, it means going all round by the Woo Ching road.

HUBERT: Why not telephone her?

MAJOR BLAKE: They won't have got there yet, it's an hour's drive.

CLARA: Why not wait until they have got there?

MAJOR BLAKE: Yes, I suppose I'd better. Anybody feel like a Stengah?

HUBERT: No, thanks.

MAJOR BLAKE [*to* KARL]: Do you, sir?

KARL: No, thank you.

MAJOR BLAKE: All right—I shall go back to' the bar——

KARL: Bar.

MAJOR BLAKE: Thanks very much.

He goes out to R.

KARL: Who is Eva?

CLARA: His wife.

KARL: And who are the Baileys?

CLARA [*with irritation*]: Does it matter?

KARL: I don't know.

LOUISE: They live in that large reddish-looking house at the top of the hill.

KARL: I've never been to the top of the hill.

CLARA: Good night, Mr. Sandys.

KARL: Good night.

CLARA [*with almost overdone ordinariness*]: Come along, Louise.

LOUISE: Don't be silly, Clara.

CLARA: I'm not being silly. I'm acutely uncomfortable. You're behaving abominably and putting Hubert in an insufferable position. For heaven's sake pull yourself together and be reasonable. You talk a lot of nonsense about being in love. How could you possibly be in love all in a minute like that——?

KARL: We are.

CLARA: Please be quiet and let me speak.

LOUISE: Hubert, do make Clara shut up.

CLARA: You must be insane.

HUBERT: Shut up, Clara.

CLARA: And you must be insane, too, I'm ashamed of you, Hubert.

LOUISE: It's no use railing and roaring, Clara. Hubert's much wiser than you. He's keeping calm and trying to understand and I'm deeply grateful to him——

CLARA: Grateful indeed!

LOUISE: Yes, if he behaved as you seem to think he ought to behave, it would only make everything far worse. I suppose you want him to knock Mr.—— [*To* KARL.] What is your first name?

KARL: Karl.

LOUISE: —Karl in the jaw?

CLARA: I don't want anything of the sort. I want him to treat the situation as it should be treated, as nothing but a joke, a stupid joke, in extremely bad taste.

LOUISE: It's more than that, Clara, and you know it is, that's why you're scared.

CLARA: I'm not in the least scared.

HUBERT: You'd better allow me to deal with this, Clara, in my own way.

CLARA: There is such a thing as being too wise, too understanding.

LOUISE: You're usually pretty intelligent yourself, Clara. I can't think what's happened to you. This thing is here—now—between Karl and me. It's no use pretending it isn't, or trying to flip it away as a joke, nor is it any use taking up a belligerent attitude over it. God knows I'm confused enough myself—utterly bewildered, but I do know that it's real, too real to be dissipated by conventional gestures——

CLARA: What is real? What are you talking about?

KARL: Love, Mrs. Bethel, we've fallen in love.

CLARA: Rubbish!

LOUISE: It's not rubbish! It's not nonsense. Be quiet!

HUBERT [*to* LOUISE]: What do you want me to do?

LOUISE [*looking at* KARL]: I don't know.

KARL: May I ask you a question?

HUBERT [*stiffly*]: What is it?

KARL: Are you in love with Louise?

CLARA: Well really!

HUBERT: I am devoted to Louise. We have been married for many years.

KARL: I said are you in love with her?

HUBERT: I love her.

LOUISE: Don't go on evading, Hubert, you know perfectly well what he means.

HUBERT: Of course I know what he means. [*To* KARL.] I'll answer you truly. I am not in love with Louise in the way that you imagine yourself to be in love with her——

KARL: I worship her.

HUBERT: You know nothing about her.

KARL: I know that suddenly, when we were dancing, an enchantment swept over me. An enchantment that I have never known before and shall never know again. It's obvious that you should think I'm mad and that she's mad too, our behaviour looks idiotic, cheap, anything you like, but it's true, this magic that happened, it's so true that everything else, all the ordinary ways of behaviour look shabby and unreal beside it—my heart's thumping, I'm trembling like a fool, even now when I'm trying so hard, so desperately hard to be calm and explain to you reasonably, I daren't look at her, if I did, my eyes would brim over with these silly tears and I should cry like a child——

LOUISE [*making a movement towards him*]: Oh, my darling——

KARL: Don't, don't speak—let him speak, let him say what's to be done.

KARL *leaves the three of them and goes up to the verandah rail and looks out at the sea.*

CLARA: You didn't even know his name.

LOUISE: Oh, Clara! What the hell does that matter?

CLARA [*walking about*]: This is really too fantastic—it's beyond belief—it's——

LOUISE [*gently*]: Listen. I know you feel dreadfully upset for Hubert and for me too, but it's no use huffing and puffing and getting yourself into a state. Here it is this thing that's happened—it's terribly real—as large as life—larger than life, and we'd all better look at it clearly and as sensibly as we can.

HUBERT: You go home, Clara, you can send the car back for me.

CLARA: I shall do no such thing.

LOUISE [*hurriedly—to* HUBERT]: We'd better go away—he and I—as soon as possible.

HUBERT: Where to?

LOUISE: I don't know—anywhere——

HUBERT: For God's sake be reasonable. How can you? How can I let you?

LOUISE: How much do you mind—really?

HUBERT: That obviously has nothing to do with it.

LOUISE: I want to know.

HUBERT: I want to know, too. I can't possibly tell. You've made this up, this magic that he talked about, you've conjured it out of the air and now it's smeared over everything—over me, too—none of it seems real but it has to be treated as if it were. You ask me how much I mind—you want that as well, don't you, in addition to your new love?

LOUISE: Want what? What do you mean?

HUBERT [*almost losing control*]: You want me to mind—don't you—don't you?

LOUISE: Oh, Hubert—please don't look like that——

HUBERT: You want everything—everything in the world, you always have.

LOUISE: You're pitying yourself. How beastly of you to be so weak, how contemptible of you!

CLARA: Louise!

LOUISE: I've been faithful to you all these years, we stopped being in love with each other ages ago—we became a habit—a well-ordered, useful, social habit. Have you been as faithful to me as I have to you?

KARL: That's nothing to do with us—what's the use of arguing?

He joins the group again.

LOUISE: Answer me. Have you?

HUBERT: No.

CLARA: Hubert!

LOUISE: Fair's fair.

CLARA: Hubert! Louise!

LOUISE: Do stop saying Hubert and Louise, Clara, it's maddening.

KARL: What is all this? Can't you keep to the point both of you? What does it matter whether he's been faithful to you or not, or you to him either? You're not in love with each other any more, that's clear enough, and even if you were this forked lightning that has struck Louise and me would shatter it—scorch it out of existence——

CLARA: Forked lightning indeed!

KARL: Earthquake then, tidal wave, cataclysm!

HUBERT: I've never not loved you, Louise.

LOUISE [*irritably*]: I know that perfectly well. I'm deeply attached to you, too. I hated it when you had your tiresome little affairs on the side——

HUBERT: With your heart?

LOUISE: Of course not. Don't be so damned sentimental. You haven't come near my heart for years.

CLARA: If Hubert doesn't strike you in a minute, I will.

IPPAGA *comes out of the dance-room with an empty tray.*

KARL: Boy, bring four whisky-and-sodas.

IPPAGA: Yes, sir.

LOUISE: They're called Stengahs here.

KARL: Four Stengahs then.

CLARA: I'd rather have lemonade.

KARL: You seem bent on complicating everything. [*To* IPPAGA.] Four Stengahs.

IPPAGA: Yes, sir.

He goes off.

LOUISE: Karl, where were we?

HUBERT: Nowhere—nowhere at all. [*He turns away.*]

KARL [*to* HUBERT]: Listen, Charteris—I know you won't believe me, or even care, but I really am dreadfully sorry, about all this—not about falling in love, that's beyond being sorry about, but that it should happen to be your wife——

HUBERT: Who are you, where do you come from?

KARL: My name is Karl Sandys. I come from Hampshire. My father is Admiral Sandys——

LOUISE: Dear darling, I wouldn't mind if he were only a bosun's mate.

KARL: I know you wouldn't, sweetheart, but I must explain to your husband——

CLARA: How you can have the impertinence to be flippant, Louise, at a moment like this——

LOUISE: There's never been a moment like this, never before in the history of the world—I'm delirious.

HUBERT [*to* KARL]: Please go on.

KARL: I was in the Navy myself but I was axed in 1924.

LOUISE: What's axed?

KARL: Kicked out.

LOUISE: Oh dear, whatever for?

HUBERT: Never mind that, I understand, go on.

KARL: I'm now in the shipping business. I represent the I.M.C.L.

LOUISE: What in God's name is the I.M.C.L.?

HUBERT: Imperial Malayan China Line.

KARL: Passenger and Freight.

HUBERT: I know.

KARL: I've come from Singapore, I've been interviewing

our agents in Pendarla——

HUBERT: Littlejohn Thurston and Company?

KARL: Littlejohn Thurston and Company.

LOUISE [*to* CLARA]: Littlejohn Thurston and Company.

KARL: I flew up here in the morning 'plane because I wanted to see a little of the country before I sail on Wednesday.

LOUISE: Wednesday!

HUBERT: Are you married?

KARL: I was, but we were divorced in 1927.

LOUISE: Oh, Karl. Did you love her?

KARL: Of course I did.

LOUISE: The moment's changed—I'm not delirious any more—I can't think of you ever having loved anybody else——

HUBERT: Have you any money?

KARL: Not very much—enough.

LOUISE: What was her name?

KARL: Ayleen.

LOUISE: You mean Eileen.

KARL: I do not, I mean Ayleen—A-y-l-e-e-n.

LOUISE: Very affected.

KARL: It's you I love, more than anyone in the world, past or future——

LOUISE: Oh, Karl!

HUBERT [*sharply*]: Please—just a moment—both of you.

KARL: I'm sorry. That was inconsiderate.

HUBERT: I'm trying to be as detached as possible. It isn't easy.

LOUISE: I know it isn't, it's beastly for you, I do see that.

CLARA: You're all being so charming to each other it's positively nauseating.

LOUISE: My dear Clara, just because your late husband was vaguely connected with the Indian Army, there is no reason for you to be so set on blood-letting——

CLARA: I'm not—I should like to say——

LOUISE: You're no better than a Tricoteuse.

KARL: What's a Tricoteuse?

LOUISE: One of those horrid old things in the French Revolution with knitting-needles.

HUBERT: All this is beside the point.

LOUISE: Clara's been beside the point for years.

KARL: Dearest, I want you so.

LOUISE: Oh, Karl!

CLARA: This is disgusting——

HUBERT: You'd much better go home, Clara——

CLARA: I've told you before I shall do no such thing, I'm apparently the only one present with the remotest grip on sanity. I shall stay as long as you do, Hubert.

KARL: Dear Mrs. Bethel.

CLARA: I beg your pardon?

KARL: I said, "Dear Mrs. Bethel," because I admire your integrity enormously and I do hope when all this has blown over that we shall be close friends.

CLARA: I think you're an insufferable cad, Mr. Sandys.

LOUISE: Blown over! Oh, Karl.

KARL: Darling, I didn't mean that part of it.

HUBERT: I have something to say to you, Louise. Will everybody please be quiet for a moment?

CLARA: Hubert, I honestly think——

LOUISE: That's exactly what you don't do.

HUBERT: This man, whom you so abruptly love, is sailing on Wednesday.

KARL: On the *Euripedes*.

LOUISE: But the *Euripedes* goes to Australia, I know because the MacVities are going on it.

KARL: That can't be helped, I have to interview our agents in Sydney——

LOUISE: We'll have to go on another boat, I can't travel in sin with the MacVities.

HUBERT: Do you really mean to go with him?

LOUISE: Yes, Hubert.

CLARA: You're stark staring mad all of you; Hubert, for God's sake——

HUBERT: Excuse me—— [*Gently.*] Louise, how true is this to you?

LOUISE: Oh, Hubert, don't be too kind.

HUBERT: Will it be worth it?

LOUISE: Oh yes, yes, of course it will—it must!

HUBERT: What has happened exactly—how do you know so surely, so soon?

SONG: "WE WERE DANCING"

Verse 1

If you can
Imagine my embarrassment when you politely asked me
    to explain
Man to man
I cannot help but feel conventional apologies are all in
    vain.
You must see
We've stepped into a dream that's set us free
Don't think we planned it
Please understand it.

Refrain

We were dancing
And the gods must have found it entrancing
For they smiled
On a moment undefiled
By the care and woe
That mortals know.
We were dancing
And the music and lights were enhancing
Our desire
When the World caught on fire
He and I were dancing.

Verse 2

Love lay in wait for us
Twisted our fate for us

No one warned us
Reason scorned us
Time stood still
In that first strange thrill.
Destiny knew of us
Guided the two of us
How could we
Refuse to see
That wrong seemed right
On this lyrical enchanted night
Logic supplies no laws for it
Only one cause for it.

Repeat Refrain

We were dancing . . . etc.

LOUISE: We were dancing—somebody introduced us, I can't remember who, we never heard each other's names—it was a waltz—and in the middle of it we looked at each other—he said just now that it was forked lightning, an earthquake, a tidal wave, cataclysm, but it was more than all those things—much more—my heart stopped, and with it the world stopped too—there was no more land or sea or sky, there wasn't even any more music—I saw in his eyes a strange infinity—only just him and me together for ever and ever—and—ever——

She faints. KARL *catches her in his arms.*

IPPAGA *enters with a tray of drinks.*

IPPAGA: Stengahs, sir.

KARL: Bring them here, quick.

KARL *lowers* LOUISE *gently into a chair and kneels beside her with his arm under her head.* HUBERT *kneels on the other side of her.* CLARA *kneels in front of her and endeavours to make her swallow a little whisky. After a moment her eyelids flutter and she moves her head.*

The dance music which has been playing intermittently throughout the scene comes to an end, there is the sound of applause, then it strikes up the National Anthem.

LOUISE [*weakly*]: Good God! God Save the King!

She staggers to her feet supported by KARL. *The others rise also and they all stand to attention as the lights fade on the scene.*

SCENE II

When the lights come up on the scene, CLARA, HUBERT, LOUISE *and* KARL *are all sitting in attitudes of extreme weariness. There is a table near them on which are the remains of bacon and eggs and sandwiches.* IPPAGA *is lying on the floor on the right, fast asleep. Dawn is breaking and the stage gets lighter and lighter as the scene progresses.* LOUISE, *in a state of drooping exhaustion, is arranging her face in the mirror from her handbag which* HUBERT *is holding up for her.*

LOUISE [*petulantly*]: —But surely you could interview your agents in Sydney another time——

KARL: I can't see why I should alter the whole course of my career just because of the MacVities.

LOUISE: It isn't only the MacVities, it's Australia.

KARL: What's the matter with Australia?

LOUISE: I don't know, that's what's worrying me.

HUBERT: Haven't you got any agents anywhere else?

KARL: There's Havermeyer, Turner and Price in Johannesburg but I've seen them.

LOUISE: You could see them again, couldn't you? It's not much to ask.

KARL: If I start giving in to you now, darling, we shall never have a moment's peace together.

CLARA: Well I wish you'd make up your minds where you're going and when, it's very early and I'm tired.

LOUISE: You've been wonderfully patient, both of you— I'm tired too.

HUBERT: Would you like another sandwich, dear? There are three left.

LOUISE [*patting his hand*]: No thank you, Hubert, they're filthy.

KARL: I'd like to say too how grateful I am to you, you've been understanding and direct and absolutely first-rate over the whole business.

HUBERT: I'm terribly fond of Louise, I always have been.

CLARA: Fortunately Hubert's leave is almost due so we shan't have to face too much unpleasantness in the Colony.

HUBERT: What time does your 'plane leave?

KARL [*glancing at his watch*]: Seven-thirty—it's now a quarter to six.

LOUISE: I'll come by the night train and join you in Pendarla in the morning.

HUBERT: I shall miss you dreadfully, Louise.

LOUISE: I shall miss you, too.

KARL: I'm not sure that I shan't miss you, too.

LOUISE: Oh, dear, I do wish it didn't have to be Australia.

KARL: Now then, Louise!

CLARA: Some parts of Australia can be lovely.

LOUISE: Yes, but will they?

CLARA: And there's always New Zealand.

KARL: I haven't any agents in New Zealand.

LOUISE: I shall have to write to mother and explain. I'm afraid it will be dreadfully muddling for her.

HUBERT: Serve her right.

LOUISE: Hubert! It's not like you to be unchivalrous about mother.

HUBERT: Now that you're leaving me the situation has changed.

LOUISE: Yes. You're quite right. I do see that.

HUBERT: Without wishing to wound you, Louise, I should like to take this opportunity of saying that she lacks charm to a remarkable degree.

LOUISE: It's funny, isn't it, when you think how attractive father was.

KARL: This seems an ideal moment for you to give us a

detailed description of where you lived as a girl.

LOUISE: I do hope you're not going to turn out to be testy.

CLARA: Never mind, come along, Hubert, we can't stay here any longer, the Fenwicks will be arriving to play golf in a minute.

HUBERT [*to* LOUISE]: Do you want to come now or stay until his 'plane goes?

LOUISE: I'll stay for just a little while, send the car back.

HUBERT [*to* KARL]: Would you care to come to the house and have a bath?

KARL: No, thanks, I can have one here.

HUBERT: Then I shan't be seeing you again.

KARL: Not unless you come and see us off on the boat.

HUBERT: I shan't be able to on Wednesday, I have to go upcountry.

KARL: Well, good-bye, then.

HUBERT: Good-bye.

They shake hands.

Try to make her happy, won't you?

KARL: I'll do my best.

HUBERT: Clara——

CLARA [*to* KARL]: Good-bye.

KARL: Good-bye.

CLARA: I wish my husband were alive.

KARL: Why?

CLARA: Because he'd horsewhip you and, Tricoteuse or no Tricoteuse, I should enjoy it keenly.

KARL: Thank you very much.

CLARA *and* HUBERT *go off.*

LOUISE *gets up and goes to the verandah rail, she leans on it and looks out at the sea.*

LOUISE: I feel as if I'd been run over.

KARL [*joining her*]: Dearest.

LOUISE: Don't.

KARL: Don't what?

LOUISE: Don't call me dearest, just for a minute.

KARL: I love you so.

LOUISE: We ought to be able to see Sumatra really at this time of the morning.

KARL: I don't want to see Sumatra.

LOUISE: I think I will have another sandwich after all.

KARL: All right.

They come down from the rail and pensively take a sandwich each.

LOUISE: Are you happy?

KARL: Wildly happy. Are you?

LOUISE: Dear Karl!

KARL: What's the matter?

LOUISE: You're doing splendidly.

KARL: Don't talk like that, my sweet, it's unkind.

LOUISE: Ayleen would be proud of you.

KARL: That was worse than unkind.

LOUISE: Where is it, our moment? What's happened to the magic?

KARL [*sadly*]: I see.

LOUISE: I wonder if you do really?

KARL: Dance with me a minute.

LOUISE: Very well.

She hasn't quite finished her sandwich so she holds it in her left hand while they waltz solemnly round the stage.

KARL: Of course the music makes a great difference.

LOUISE: There isn't always music.

KARL: And moonlight.

LOUISE: Moonlight doesn't last.

They go on dancing. The sound of a native pipe is heard a long way off in the distance.

KARL: There's music for us.

LOUISE: It's the wrong sort.

KARL: I wish you'd finish your sandwich.

LOUISE: I have.

KARL: Kiss me.

LOUISE: My dear——

They kiss.

You see!

KARL: The joke is on us.

LOUISE: It was a nice joke, while it lasted.

KARL: We've never even been lovers.

LOUISE: I don't want to now, do you?

KARL: Not much.

LOUISE: We missed our chance——

KARL: Don't talk like that, it sounds so depressing——
[*They turn away from each other.*]

LOUISE: What's the name of your agents in Sydney?

KARL: Eldrich, Lincoln and Barret.

LOUISE: Give them my love.

She pats his face very gently and sweetly and goes quickly away. He makes a movement as if to follow her, then pauses and lights a cigarette. He hums for a moment the tune to which they were dancing and then goes up to the rail where he stands leaning against a post looking out into the morning.

GEORGE DAVIES *and* EVA BLAKE *come quietly, almost furtively on from the right; they talk in whispers.*

EVA: It's awfully light.

GEORGE: There's nobody about.

EVA: Oh, George, you're so wonderful!

GEORGE: Shhh!

They kiss swiftly.

I suppose it's all right about the Baileys?

EVA: Yes, Marion promised—she'll never say a word.

GEORGE: I won't take you right up to the house, I'll just drop you off at the end of the garden——

EVA: Oh, George, you think of everything——

KARL: Excuse me, is your name Eva?

EVA: Yes.

KARL: I congratulate you!

EVA *and* GEORGE *go off.*

KARL *comes down and kicks* IPPAGA *gently.*

Wake up—wake up, it's morning——

IPPAGA *stretches himself as the curtain falls.*

★

STILL LIFE

A Play in Five Scenes

CHARACTERS

(In the order of their appearance)

LAURA JESSON
MYRTLE BAGOT
BERYL WATERS
STANLEY
ALBERT GODBY
ALEC HARVEY
YOUNG MAN
BILL
JOHNNIE
MILDRED
DOLLY MESSITER

The action of the play takes place in the refreshment room of Milford Junction Station.

TIME: *The present.*

SCENE I

The scene is the refreshment room of Milford Junction Station. On the left of the stage is a curved counter piled with glass cases containing sandwiches, rock cakes, etc.

*There are rows of tea-cups and glasses symmetrically ar-
ranged, an expression of the fanciful side of* MYRTLE'S
*imagination. Schweppes' bottles of soda and Tonic water
have been placed in circles and squares. Even the rock
cakes mount each other on the glass stands in a disciplined
pattern. There is a metal machine which gushes hot tea, a
sort of cylindrical samovar.*

*For drinking hours there are the usual appurtenances
for the drawing of draught beer, and the wall behind the
counter, except for a door upstage, is lined with looking-
glass shelves supporting bottles, packets of chocolate, packets of cigarettes, etc.*

*There are two windows in the back wall. Their lower
panes are frosted and their upper ones tastefully plastered
with stained glass paper. There is another similar window
on the right-hand wall which is at a slight angle. In this
there is also a door leading on to the platform. There are
three tables against the back wall, a stove in the corner,
and two more tables against the right-hand wall, then the
door and another table set below it. There are several advertisements and calendars in frames, and artificial flowers.*

MYRTLE BAGOT *herself is a buxom and imposing widow.
Her hair is piled high, and her expression reasonably
jaunty except on those occasions when her strong sense of
refinement gets the better of her.*

BERYL WATERS, *her assistant, is pretty but dimmed, not
only by* MYRTLE'S *personal effulgence, but by her firm
authority.*

*When the curtain rises it is about 5.25 p.m. on an eve-
ning in April. The evening sunlight streams through the
right-hand window illuminating gaily the paraphernalia
on the counter.*

A YOUNG MAN *in a mackintosh is finishing his tea at one
of the upstage tables and reading an evening paper.*

LAURA JESSON *is sitting at the downstage table having
tea. She is an attractive woman in the thirties. Her clothes
are not particularly smart but obviously chosen with taste.
She looks exactly what she is, a pleasant, ordinary married*

woman, rather pale, for she is not very strong, and with a definite charm of personality which comes from natural kindliness, humour and reasonable conscience. She is reading a Boot's library book at which she occasionally smiles. On the chair beside her there are several parcels as she has been shopping.

STANLEY *enters from the platform. He wears a seedy green uniform and carries a tray strapped to his shoulders. He goes to the counter. He addresses* MYRTLE *with becoming respect,* BERYL, *however, he winks at lewdly whenever the opportunity.*

STANLEY: I'm out of "Marie's," Mrs. Bagot, and I could do with some more Nestlé's plain.

MYRTLE [*scrutinising the tray*]: Let me see.

STANLEY: An old girl on the 4.10 asked if I'd got an ice-cream wafer. I didn't 'arf laugh.

MYRTLE: I don't see that there was anything to laugh at—a very natural request on a faine day.

STANLEY: What did she think I was, a 'Stop me and buy one?'

BERYL *sniggers.*

MYRTLE: Be quiet, Beryl—and as for you, Stanley, don't you be saucy—you were saucy when you started to work here, and you've been getting saucier and saucier ever since. Here you are—— [*She gives him some packets of biscuits and Nestlé's chocolate.*] Go on now.

STANLEY [*cheerfully*]: Righto.

He winks at BERYL *and goes out.*

MYRTLE: And see here, Beryl Waters, I'll trouble you to remember you're on duty——

BERYL: I didn't do anything.

MYRTLE: Exactly—you just stand there giggling like a fool—did you make out that list?

BERYL: Yes, Mrs. Bagot.

MYRTLE: Where is it?

BERYL: I put it on your desk.

MYRTLE: Where's your cloth?

BERYL: Here, Mrs. Bagot.

MYRTLE: Well, go and clean off Number 3. I can see the crumbs on it from here.

BERYL: It's them rock cakes.

MYRTLE: Never you mind about the rock cakes, just you do as you're told and don't argue.

BERYL *goes over to clean No. 3 table.*

ALBERT GODBY *enters. He is a ticket inspector, somewhere between thirty and forty. His accent is north country.*

ALBERT: Hullo!

MYRTLE: Quite a stranger, aren't you?

ALBERT: I couldn't get in yesterday.

MYRTLE [*bridling*]: I wondered what had happened to you.

ALBERT: I 'ad a bit of a dust-up.

MYRTLE [*preparing his tea*]: What about?

ALBERT: Saw a chap getting out of a first-class compartment, and when he come to give up 'is ticket it was third-class, and I told 'im he'd 'ave to pay excess, and then he turned a bit nasty and I 'ad to send for Mr. Saunders.

MYRTLE: Fat lot of good he'd be.

ALBERT: He ticked him off proper.

MYRTLE: Seeing's believing——

ALBERT: He's not a bad lot Mr. Saunders, after all you can't expect much spirit from a man who's got only one lung and a wife with diabetes.

MYRTLE: I thought something must be wrong when you didn't come.

ALBERT: I'd have popped in to explain but I had a date and 'ad to run for it the moment I went off.

MYRTLE [*frigidly*]: Oh, indeed!

ALBERT: A chap I know's getting married.

MYRTLE: Very interesting, I'm sure.

ALBERT: What's up with you, anyway?

MYRTLE: I'm sure I don't know to what you're referring.

ALBERT: You're a bit unfriendly all of a sudden.

MYRTLE [*ignoring him*]: Beryl, hurry up—put some coal in the stove while you're at it.

BERYL: Yes, Mrs. Bagot.

MYRTLE: I'm afraid I really can't stand here wasting my time in idle gossip, Mr. Godby.

ALBERT: Aren't you going to offer me another cup?

MYRTLE: You can 'ave another cup and welcome when you've finished that one. Beryl'll give it to you—I've got my accounts to do.

ALBERT: I'd rather you gave it to me.

MYRTLE: Time and Taide wait for no man, Mr. Godby.

ALBERT: I don't know what you're huffy about, but whatever it is I'm very sorry.

MYRTLE: You misunderstand me—I'm not——

ALEC HARVEY *enters. He is about thirty-five. He wears a moustache, a mackintosh and a squash hat, and he carries a small bag. His manner is decisive and unflurried.*

ALEC: A cup of tea, please.

MYRTLE: Certainly. [*She pours it out in silence.*] Cake or pastry?

ALEC: No, thank you.

MYRTLE: Threepence.

ALEC [*paying*]: Thank you.

He takes his cup of tea and goes over to a table. He takes off his hat and sits down. LAURA *glances at the clock, collects her parcels in a leisurely manner and goes out on to the platform.* BERYL *returns to her place behind the counter.*

BERYL: Minnie hasn't touched her milk.

MYRTLE: Did you put it down for her?

BERYL: Yes, but she never came in for it.

MYRTLE: Go out the back and see if she's in the yard.

ALBERT [*conversationally*]: Fond of animals?

MYRTLE: In their place.

ALBERT: My landlady's got a positive mania for animals —she' got two cats, one Manx and one ordinary, three rabbits in a hutch in the kitchen, they belong to her little boy by rights, and one of them foolish-looking dogs with hair over its eyes.

MYRTLE: I don't know to what breed you refer.

ALBERT: I don't think it knows itself——
There is a rumbling noise in the distance, and the sound of a bell.

MYRTLE: There's the boat train.
There is a terrific clatter as the express roars through the station.

ALBERT: What about my other cup? I shall have to be moving—the five-forty-three will be in in a minute.

MYRTLE: Who's on the gate? [*She pours him out another cup.*]

ALBERT: Young William.

MYRTLE: You're neglecting your duty, you know—that's what you're doing.

ALBERT: A bit of relaxation never did anyone any harm——

LAURA *enters hurriedly holding a handkerchief to her eye.*

LAURA: Please could you give me a glass of water—I've got something in my eye and I want to bathe it.

MYRTLE: Would you like me to have a look?

LAURA: Please don't trouble. I think the water will do it.

MYRTLE [*handing her a glass of water*]: Here.

MYRTLE *and* ALBERT *watch her in silence as she bathes her eye.*

ALBERT: Bit of coal dust, I expect.

MYRTLE: A man I knew lost the sight of one eye through getting a bit of grit in it.

ALBERT: Painful thing—very painful.

MYRTLE [*as* LAURA *lifts her head*]: Better?

LAURA [*obviously in pain*]: I'm afraid not—oh!

ALEC *rises from his table and comes over.*

ALEC: Can I help you?

LAURA: Oh, no, please—it's only something in my eye.

MYRTLE: Try pulling down your eyelid as far as it'll go.

ALBERT: And then blowing your nose.

ALEC: Please let me look. I happen to be a doctor.

LAURA: It's very kind of you.

ALEC: Turn round to the light, please—now—look up—

now look down—I can see it. Keep still—— [*He twists up the corner of his handkerchief and rapidly operates with it.*] There——

LAURA [*blinking*]: Oh, dear—what a relief—it was agonising.

ALEC: It looks like a bit of grit.

LAURA: It was when the express went through—thank you very much indeed——

ALEC: Not at all.

There is the sound of a bell on the platform.

ALBERT [*gulping down his tea*]: There we go—I must run.

LAURA: How lucky for me that you happened to be here.

ALEC: Anybody could have done it.

LAURA: Never mind, you did and I'm most grateful. There's my train. Good-bye.

She puts out her hand and he shakes it politely. She goes out followed at a run by ALBERT GODBY.

ALEC *looks after her for a moment and then goes back to his table. There is the noise of the train rumbling into the station as the lights fade.*

SCENE II

The scene is the same and the time about the same.
Nearly three months have passed since the preceding scene, and it is now July.

MYRTLE *is resplendent in a light overall.* BERYL'S *appearance is unaltered. The tables are all unoccupied.*

MYRTLE [*slightly relaxed in manner*]: It's all very faine, I said, expecting me to do this that and the other, but what do *I* get out of it? You can't expect me to be cook-housekeeper and char rolled into one during the day, and a loving wife in the evening just because you feel like it. Oh, dear no. There are just as good fish in the sea, I said, as ever came out of it, and I packed my boxes then and there and left him.

BERYL: Didn't you ever go back?

MYRTLE: Never. I went to my sister's place at Folkestone for a bit, and then I went in with a friend of mine and we opened a tea-shop in Hythe.

BERYL: And what happened to him?

MYRTLE: Dead as a door-nail inside three years!

BERYL: Well, I never!

MYRTLE: So you see, every single thing she told me came true—first them clubs coming together, an unexpected journey, then the Queen of diamonds and the ten—that was my friend and the tea-shop business. Then the Ace of spades three times running——

STANLEY *enters*.

STANLEY: Two rock and an apple.

MYRTLE: What for?

STANLEY: Party on the up platform.

MYRTLE: Why can't they come in here for them?

STANLEY: Ask me another. [*He winks at* BERYL.]

MYRTLE: Got something in your eye?

STANLEY: Nothing beyond a bit of a twinkle every now and again.

BERYL [*giggling*]: Oh, you are awful!

MYRTLE: You learn to behave yourself, my lad. Here are your rock cakes. Beryl, stop sniggering and give me an apple off the stand.

BERYL *complies*.

Not off the front, silly, haven't you got any sense. Here—— [*She takes one from the back of the stand so as to leave the symmetry undisturbed.*]

STANLEY: This one's got a hole in it.

MYRTLE: Tell 'em to come and choose for themselves if they're particular—go on now.

STANLEY: All right—give us a chance.

MYRTLE: What people want to eat on the platform for I really don't know. Tell Mr. Godby not to forget his tea.

STANLEY: Righto!

He goes out as ALEC *and* LAURA *come in.* LAURA *is wearing a summer dress,* ALEC, *a grey flannel suit.*

ALEC: Tea or lemonade?

LAURA: Tea, I think—it's more refreshing, really. [*She sits down at the table by the door.*]

ALEC *goes to the counter.*

ALEC: Two teas, please.

MYRTLE: Cakes or pastry?

ALEC [*to* LAURA]: Cakes or pastry?

LAURA: No, thank you.

ALEC: Are those bath buns fresh?

MYRTLE: Certainly they are—made this morning.

ALEC: Two, please.

MYRTLE *puts two bath buns on a plate, meanwhile* BERYL *has drawn two cups of tea.*

MYRTLE: That'll be eightpence.

ALEC: All right. [*He pays her.*]

MYRTLE: Take the tea to the table, Beryl.

ALEC: I'll carry the buns.

BERYL *brings the tea to the table.* ALEC *follows with the buns.*

ALEC: You must eat one of these—fresh this morning.

LAURA: Very fattening.

ALEC: I don't hold with such foolishness.

BERYL *returns to the counter.*

MYRTLE: I'm going over my accounts. Let me know when Albert comes in.

BERYL: Yes, Mrs. Bagot.

BERYL *settles down behind the counter with "Peg's Paper."*

LAURA: They do look good, I must say.

ALEC: One of my earliest passions—I've never outgrown it.

LAURA: Do you like milk in your tea?

ALEC: Yes, don't you?

LAURA: Yes—fortunately.

ALEC: Station refreshments are generally a wee bit arbitrary, you know.

LAURA: I wasn't grumbling.

ALEC [*smiling*]: Do you ever grumble—are you ever sullen and cross and bad-tempered?

LAURA: Of course I am—at least not sullen exactly—but I sometimes get into rages.

ALEC: I can't visualise you in a rage.

LAURA: I really don't see why you should.

ALEC: Oh, I don't know—there are signs, you know—one can usually tell——

LAURA: Long upper lips and jaw lines and eyes close together?

ALEC: You haven't any of those things.

LAURA: Do you feel guilty at all? I do.

ALEC [*smiling*]: Guilty?

LAURA: You ought to more than me, really—you neglected your work this afternoon.

ALEC: I worked this morning—a little relaxation never did anyone any harm. Why should either of us feel guilty?

LAURA: I don't know—a sort of instinct—as though we were letting something happen that oughtn't to happen.

ALEC: How awfully nice you are!

LAURA: When I was a child in Cornwall—we lived in Cornwall, you know—May, that's my sister, and I used to climb out of our bedroom window on summer nights and go down to the cove and bathe. It was dreadfully cold but we felt very adventurous. I'd never have dared do it by myself, but sharing the danger made it all right—that's how I feel now, really.

ALEC: Have a bun—it's awfully bad for you.

LAURA: You're laughing at me!

ALEC: Yes, a little, but I'm laughing at myself, too.

LAURA: Why?

ALEC: For feeling a small pang when you said about being guilty.

LAURA: There you are, you see!

ALEC: We haven't done anything wrong.

LAURA: Of course we haven't.

ALEC: An accidental meeting—then another accidental

meeting—then a little lunch—then the movies—what could be more ordinary? More natural?

LAURA: We're adults, after all.

ALEC: I never see myself as an adult, do you?

LAURA [*firmly*]: Yes, I do. I'm a respectable married woman with a husband and a home and three children.

ALEC: But there must be a part of you, deep down inside, that doesn't feel like that at all—some little spirit that still wants to climb out of the window—that still longs to splash about a bit in the dangerous sea.

LAURA: Perhaps we none of us ever grow up entirely.

ALEC: How awfully nice you are!

LAURA: You said that before.

ALEC: I thought perhaps you hadn't heard.

LAURA: I heard all right.

ALEC [*gently*]: I'm respectable too, you know. I have a home and a wife and children and responsibilities—I also have a lot of work to do and a lot of ideals all mixed up with it.

LAURA: What's she like?

ALEC: Madeleine?

LAURA: Yes.

ALEC: Small, dark, rather delicate——

LAURA: How funny! I should have thought she'd be fair.

ALEC: And your husband? What's he like?

LAURA: Medium height, brown hair, kindly, unemotional and not delicate at all.

ALEC: You said that proudly.

LAURA: Did I? [*She looks down.*]

ALEC: What's the matter?

LAURA: The matter? What could be the matter?

ALEC: You suddenly went away.

LAURA [*brightly*]: I thought perhaps we were being rather silly.

ALEC: Why?

LAURA: Oh, I don't know—we are such complete strangers, really.

ALEC: It's one thing to close a window, but quite another

to slam it down on my fingers.

LAURA: I'm sorry.

ALEC: Please come back again.

LAURA: Is tea bad for one? Worse than coffee, I mean?

ALEC: If this is a professional interview, my fee is a guinea.

LAURA [laughing]: It's nearly time for your train.

ALEC: I hate to think of it, chugging along, interrupting our tea party.

LAURA: I really am sorry now.

ALEC: What for?

LAURA: For being disagreeable.

ALEC: I don't think you could be disagreeable.

LAURA: You said something just now about your work and ideals being mixed up with it—what ideals?

ALEC: That's a long story.

LAURA: I suppose all doctors ought to have ideals, really —otherwise I should think the work would be unbearable.

ALEC: Surely you're not encouraging me to talk shop?

LAURA: Do you come here every Thursday?

ALEC: Yes. I come in from Churley, and spend a day in the hospital. Stephen Lynn graduated with me—he's the chief physician here. I take over from him once a week, it gives him a chance to go up to London and me a chance to observe and study the hospital patients.

LAURA: Is that a great advantage?

ALEC: Of course. You see I have a special pigeon.

LAURA: What is it?

ALEC: Preventive medicine.

LAURA: Oh, I see.

ALEC [laughing]: I'm afraid you don't.

LAURA: I was trying to be intelligent.

ALEC: Most good doctors, especially when they're young, have private dreams—that's the best part of them, sometimes though, those get over-professionalised and strangulated and—am I boring you?

LAURA: No—I don't quite understand—but you're not boring me.

ALEC: What I mean is this—all good doctors must be primarily enthusiasts. They must have, like writers and painters, and priests, a sense of vocation—a deep-rooted, unsentimental desire to do good.

LAURA: Yes—I see that.

ALEC: Well, obviously one way of preventing disease is worth fifty ways of curing it—that's where my ideal comes in—preventive medicine isn't anything to do with medicine at all, really—it's concerned with conditions, living conditions and common-sense and hygiene. For instance, my specialty is pneumoconiosis.

LAURA: Oh, dear!

ALEC: Don't be alarmed, it's simpler than it sounds—it's nothing but a slow process of fibrosis of the lung due to the inhalation of particles of dust. In the hospital here there are splendid opportunities for observing cures and making notes, because of the coal mines.

LAURA: You suddenly look much younger.

ALEC [*brought up short*]: Do I?

LAURA: Almost like a little boy.

ALEC: What made you say that?

LAURA [*staring at him*]: I don't know—yes, I do.

ALEC [*gently*]: Tell me.

LAURA [*with panic in her voice*]: Oh, no—I couldn't, really. You were saying about the coal mines——

ALEC [*looking into her eyes*]: Yes—the inhalation of coal dust—that's one specific form of the diseases—it's called Anthracosis.

LAURA [*hypnotised*]: What are the others?

ALEC: Chalicosis—that comes from metal dust—steel works, you know——

LAURA: Yes, of course. Steel works.

ALEC: And Silicosis—stone dust—that's gold mines.

LAURA [*almost in a whisper*]: I see.

There is the sound of a bell.

There's your train.

ALEC [*looking down*]: Yes.

LAURA: You mustn't miss it.

ALEC: No.

LAURA [*again the panic in her voice*]: What's the matter?

ALEC [*with an effort*]: Nothing—nothing at all.

LAURA [*socially*]: It's been so very nice—I've enjoyed my afternoon enormously.

ALEC: I'm so glad—so have I. I apologise for boring you with those long medical words——

LAURA: I feel dull and stupid, not to be able to understand more.

ALEC: Shall I see you again?

There is the sound of a train approaching.

LAURA: It's the other platform, isn't it? You'll have to run. Don't worry about me—mine's due in a few minutes.

ALEC: Shall I see you again?

LAURA: Of course—perhaps you could come over to Ketchworth one Sunday. It's rather far, I know, but we should be delighted to see you.

ALEC [*intensely*]: Please—please——

The train is heard drawing to a standstill.

LAURA: What is it?

ALEC: Next Thursday—the same time——

LAURA: No—I can't possibly—I——

ALEC: Please—I ask you most humbly——

LAURA: You'll miss your train!

ALEC: All right. [*He gets up.*]

LAURA: Run——

ALEC [*taking her hand*]: Good-bye.

LAURA [*breathlessly*]: I'll be there.

ALEC: Thank you, my dear.

He goes out at a run, colliding with ALBERT GODBY, *who is on his way in.*

ALBERT: 'Ere—'ere—take it easy now—take it easy—— [*He goes over to the counter.*]

LAURA *sits quite still staring in front of her as the lights fade.*

SCENE III

It is now October. Three months have passed since the preceding scene.

The refreshment room is empty except for MYRTLE, *who is bending down putting coal into the stove.*

ALBERT GODBY *enters. Upon perceiving her slightly vulnerable position, he slaps her lightly on the behind—she springs to her feet.*

MYRTLE: Albert Godby, how dare you!

ALBERT: I couldn't resist it.

MYRTLE: I'll trouble you to keep your hands to yourself.

ALBERT: You're blushing—you look wonderful when you're angry, like an avenging angel.

MYRTLE: I'll give you avenging angel—coming in here taking liberties——

ALBERT: I didn't think after what you said last Monday you'd object to a friendly little slap.

MYRTLE: Never you mind about last Monday—I'm on duty now. A nice thing if Mr. Saunders had happened to be looking through the window.

ALBERT: If Mr. Saunders is in the 'abit of looking through windows, it's time he saw something worth looking at.

MYRTLE: You ought to be ashamed of yourself!

ALBERT: It's just high spirits—don't be mad at me.

MYRTLE [*retiring behind the counter*]: High spirits indeed!

ALBERT [*singing*]:
"I'm twenty-one to-day—I'm twenty-one to-day,
I've got the key of the parlour door—
I've never been twenty-one before——"

MYRTLE [*retiring behind the counter*]: Don't make such a noise—they'll hear you on the platform.

ALBERT [*singing*]:

"Picture you upon my knee and tea for two and two for tea."

MYRTLE: Now look here, Albert Godby, once and for all, will you behave yourself!

ALBERT [*singing*]:

"Sometimes I'm 'appy—sometimes I'm blue-oo——" [*He breaks off.*] This is one of my 'appy moments——

MYRTLE: Here, take your tea and be quiet.

ALBERT: It's all your fault, anyway.

MYRTLE: I don't know to what you're referring, I'm sure.

ALBERT: I was thinking of to-night——

MYRTLE: If you don't learn to behave yourself there won't be a to-night—or any other night, either——

ALBERT [*singing*]:

"I'm in love again, and the spring is coming.

I'm in love again, hear my heart-strings humming——"

MYRTLE: Will you hold your noise?

ALBERT: Give us a kiss.

MYRTLE: I'll do no such thing.

ALBERT: Just a quick one—across the counter. [*He grabs her arm across the counter.*]

MYRTLE: Albert, stop it!

ALBERT: Come on—there's a love.

MYRTLE: Let go of me this minute.

ALBERT: Come on, just one.

They scuffle for a moment, upsetting a neat pile of cakes on to the floor.

MYRTLE: Now look at me Banburys—all over the floor.

ALBERT *bends down to pick them up.* STANLEY *enters.*

STANLEY: Just in time—or born in the vestry.

MYRTLE: You shut your mouth and help Mr. Godby pick up them cakes.

STANLEY: Anything to oblige. [*He helps* ALBERT.]

ALEC *and* LAURA *come in.* LAURA *goes to their usual table.* ALEC *goes to the counter.*

ALEC: Good afternoon.

MYRTLE [*grandly*]: Good afternoon.

ALEC: Two teas, please.

MYRTLE: Cake or pastry?

ALEC: No, thank you—just the tea.

ALBERT [*conversationally*]: Nice weather.

ALEC: Very nice.

ALBERT: Bit of a nip in the air, though.

MYRTLE, *having given* ALEC *two cups of tea, and taken the money for it, turns to* STANLEY.

MYRTLE: What are you standing there gaping at?

STANLEY: Where's Beryl?

MYRTLE: Never you mind about Beryl, you ought to be on Number 4, and well you know it.

ALBERT [*reflectively*]: Love's young dream!

ALEC, *meanwhile, has carried the two cups of tea over to the table and sat down.*

STANLEY: There's been a run on the Cadbury's nut milk this afternoon; I shall need some more.

MYRTLE [*looking at his tray*]: How many have you got left?

STANLEY: Only three.

MYRTLE: Take six more then, and don't forget to mark 'em down.

STANLEY: Righto.

STANLEY *goes behind the counter and collects six packets of chocolate, then he goes out whistling.*

ALEC: I didn't mean to be unkind.

LAURA: It doesn't matter.

A YOUNG MAN *comes in and goes to the counter.*

YOUNG MAN: Cup of coffee, please, and a beef sandwich.

MYRTLE: We're out of beef—will ham do?

YOUNG MAN: Yes—ham'll do.

ALBERT *winks at* MYRTLE *over his tea-cup.* MYRTLE *draws a cup of coffee for the* YOUNG MAN *and takes a sandwich out of one of the glass stands.*

ALEC: We can't part like this.

LAURA: I think it would be better if we did.

ALEC: You don't really mean that?

LAURA: I'm trying to mean it—I'm trying with all my strength.

ALEC: Oh, my dearest dear——

LAURA: Don't—please don't——

MYRTLE [*to* YOUNG MAN]: Fourpence, please.

YOUNG MAN: Thank you. [*He pays, and carries his coffee and sandwich over to the table near the stove.*]

ALBERT: It is all right about to-night, isn't it?

MYRTLE: I'll think about it.

ALBERT: It's Claudette Colbert, you know.

MYRTLE: Fat chance I shall get of enjoying Claudette Colbert with you hissing in me ear all the time.

ALBERT: I'll be as good as gold.

BERYL *enters in a coat and hat—she goes behind the counter.*

ALEC: It's no use running away from the truth, darling—we're lovers, aren't we? If it happens or if it doesn't, we're lovers in our hearts.

LAURA: Can't you see how wrong it is? How dreadfully wrong!

ALEC: I can see what's true—whether it's wrong or right.

BERYL [*taking off her hat and coat*]: Mr. Saunders wants you, Mr. Godby.

ALBERT: What for?

BERYL: I don't know.

MYRTLE: You'd better go, Albert, you know what he is.

ALBERT: I know 'e's a bloody fool, if that's what you mean.

MYRTLE: Be quiet, Albert—in front of Beryl.

BERYL: Don't mind me.

MYRTLE: Go on—finish up your tea.

ALBERT: No peace for the wicked——

MYRTLE: Go on——

ALBERT: I'll be back——

MYRTLE: That'll be nice, I'm sure——

ALBERT *goes.*

MYRTLE *retires to the upper end of the counter.* BERYL *goes off and comes on again laden with various packages of comestibles. She and* MYRTLE *proceed to stack them on the upstage end of the counter.*

ALEC [*urgently*]: There's no chance of Stephen getting back until late—nobody need ever know.

LAURA: It's so furtive to love like that—so cheap—much better not to love at all.

ALEC: It's too late not to love at all—be brave—we're both in the same boat—let's be generous to each other.

LAURA: What is there brave in it—sneaking away to someone else's house, loving in secret with the horror of being found out hanging over us all the time. It would be far braver to say good-bye and never see each other again.

ALEC: Could you be as brave as that? I know I couldn't.

LAURA [*breathlessly*]: Couldn't you?

ALEC: Listen, my dear. This is something that's never happened to either of us before. We've loved before and been happy before, and miserable and contented and reckless, but this is different—something lovely and strange and desperately difficult. We can't measure it along with the values of our ordinary lives.

LAURA: Why should it be so important—why should we let it be so important?

ALEC: We can't help ourselves.

LAURA: We can—we can if only we're strong enough.

ALEC: Why is it so strong to deny something that's urgent and real—something that all our instincts are straining after—mightn't it be weak and not strong at all to run away from such tremendous longing?

LAURA: Is it so real to you? So tremendous?

ALEC: Can't you see that it is?

LAURA: It's so difficult, so strained. I'm lost.

ALEC: Don't say that, darling.

LAURA: Loving you is hard for me—it makes me a stranger in my own house. Familiar things, ordinary things that I've known for years like the dining-room curtains, and the wooden tub with a silver top that holds biscuits and a water-colour of San Remo that my mother painted, look odd to me, as though they belonged to someone else—when I've just left you, when I go home, I'm more lonely than

I've ever been before. I passed the house the other day without noticing and had to turn back, and when I went in it seemed to draw away from me—my whole life seems to be drawing away from me, and—and I don't know what to do.

ALEC: Oh, darling——

LAURA: I love them just the same, Fred I mean and the children, but it's as though it wasn't me at all—as though I were looking on at someone else. Do you know what I mean? Is it the same with you? Or is it easier for men——

ALEC: I don't know.

LAURA: Please, dear, don't look unhappy. I'm not grumbling, really I'm not——

ALEC: I don't suppose being in love has ever been easy for anybody.

LAURA [*reaching for his hand*]: We've only got a few more minutes—I didn't mean to be depressing.

ALEC: It isn't any easier for me, darling, honestly it isn't.

LAURA: I know, I know—I only wanted reassuring.

ALEC: I hold you in my arms all the way back in the train—I'm angry with every moment that I'm not alone—to love you uninterrupted—whenever my surgery door opens and a patient comes in, my heart jumps in case it might be you. One of them I'm grateful to—he's got neuritis, and I give him sun-ray treatment—he lies quite quietly baking, and I can be with you in the shadows behind the lamp.

LAURA: How silly we are—how unbearably silly!

ALEC: Friday — Saturday — Sunday — Monday — Tuesday — Wednesday——

LAURA: Thursday——

ALEC: It's all right, isn't it?

LAURA: Oh, yes—of course it is.

ALEC: Don't pass the house again—don't let it snub you. Go boldly in and stare that damned water-colour out of countenance.

LAURA: All right—don't bake your poor neuritis man too long—you might blister him.

The continuation of their scene is drowned by the noisy entrance of two soldiers, BILL *and* JOHNNIE. *They go to the counter.*

BILL: Afternoon, lady.

MYRTLE [*grandly*]: Good afternoon.

BILL: A couple of splashes, please.

MYRTLE: Very sorry, it's out of hours.

JOHNNIE: Come on, lady—you've got a kind face.

MYRTLE: That's neither here nor there.

BILL: Just sneak us a couple under cover of them poor old sandwiches.

MYRTLE: Them sandwiches were fresh this morning, and I shall do no such thing.

BILL: Come on, be a sport.

JOHNNIE: Nobody'd know.

MYRTLE: I'm very sorry, I'm sure, but it's against the rules.

BILL: You could pop it into a couple of tea-cups.

MYRTLE: You're asking me to break the law, young man.

JOHNNIE: I think I've got a cold coming on—we've been mucking about at the Butts all day—you can't afford to let the army catch cold, you know.

MYRTLE: You can have as much as you want after six o'clock.

BILL: An 'eart of stone—that's what you've got, lady—an 'eart of stone.

MYRTLE: Don't you be cheeky.

JOHNNIE: My throat's like a parrot's cake—listen! [*He makes a crackling noise with his throat.*]

MYRTLE: Take some lemonade then—or ginger-beer.

BILL: Couldn't touch it—against doctor's orders—my inside's been most peculiar ever since I 'ad trench feet—you wouldn't give a child carbolic acid, would you? That's what ginger-beer does to me!

MYRTLE: Get on with you!

JOHNNIE: It's true—it's poison to him, makes 'im make the most 'orrible noises—you wouldn't like anything nasty to 'appen in your posh buffay——

MYRTLE: May licence does not permit me to serve alcohol out of hours—that's final!

JOHNNIE: We're soldiers we are—willing to lay down our lives for you—and you grudge us one splash——

MYRTLE: You wouldn't want to get me into trouble, would you?

BILL: Give us a chance, lady, that's all—just give us a chance.

They both roar with laughter.

MYRTLE: Beryl, ask Mr. Godby to come 'ere for a moment, will you?

BERYL: Yes, Mrs. Bagot.

She comes out from behind the counter and goes on to the platform.

BILL: Who's 'e when 'e's at home?

MYRTLE: You'll soon see—coming in here cheeking me.

JOHNNIE: Now then, now then—naughty naughty——

MYRTLE: Kaindly be quiet!

BILL: Shut up, Johnnie——

JOHNNIE: What about them drinks, lady?

MYRTLE: I've already told you I can't serve alcoholic refreshment out of hours——

JOHNNIE: Come off it, mother, be a pal!

MYRTLE [*losing her temper*]: I'll give you mother, you saucy upstart——

BILL: Who are you calling an upstart!

MYRTLE: You—and I'll trouble you to get out of here double quick—disturbing the customers and making a nuisance of yourselves.

JOHNNIE: 'Ere, where's the fire—where's the fire!

ALBERT GODBY *enters, followed by* BERYL.

ALBERT: What's going on in 'ere!

MYRTLE [*with dignity*]: Mr. Godby, these gentlemen are annoying me.

BILL: We 'aven't done anything.

JOHNNIE: All we did was ask for a couple of drinks——

MYRTLE: They insulted me, Mr. Godby.

JOHNNIE: We never did nothing of the sort—just 'aving

a little joke, that's all.

ALBERT [*laconically*]: 'Op it—both of you.

BILL: We've got a right to stay 'ere as long as we like.

ALBERT: You 'eard what I said—'Op it!

JOHNNIE: What is this, a free country or a bloody Sunday school?

ALBERT [*firmly*]: I checked your passes at the gate—your train's due in a minute—Number 2 platform—'Op it.

JOHNNIE: Look 'ere now——

BILL: Come on, Johnnie—don't argue with the poor little basket.

ALBERT [*dangerously*]: 'Op it!

BILL *and* JOHNNIE *go to the door.* JOHNNIE *turns.*

JOHNNIE: Toodle-oo, mother, and if them sandwiches were made this morning, you're Shirley Temple——

They go out.

MYRTLE: Thank you, Albert.

BERYL: What a nerve talking to you like that!

MYRTLE: Be quiet, Beryl—pour me out a nip of Three Star—I'm feeling quite upset.

ALBERT: I've got to get back to the gate.

MYRTLE [*graciously*]: I'll be seeing you later, Albert.

ALBERT [*with a wink*]: Okay!

He goes out.

A train bell rings. BERYL *brings* MYRTLE *a glass of brandy.*

MYRTLE [*sipping it*]: I'll say one thing for Albert Godby —he may be on the small side, but 'e's a gentleman.

She and BERYL *retire once more to the upper end of the counter and continue their arrangement of bottles, biscuits, etc. There is the sound of a train drawing into the station.*

LAURA: There's your train.

ALEC: I'm going to miss it.

LAURA: Please go.

ALEC: No.

LAURA [*clasping and unclasping her hands*]: I wish I could think clearly. I wish I could know—really know what to do.

ALEC: Do you trust me?

LAURA: Yes—I trust you.

ALEC: I don't mean conventionally—I mean really.

LAURA: Yes.

ALEC: Everything's against us—all the circumstances of our lives—those have got to go unaltered. We're nice people, you and I, and we've got to go on being nice. Let's enclose this love of ours with real strength, and let that strength be that no one is hurt by it except ourselves.

LAURA: Must we be hurt by it?

ALEC: Yes—when the times comes.

LAURA: Very well.

ALEC: All the furtiveness and the secrecy and the hole-in-corner cheapness can be justified if only we're strong enough—strong enough to keep it to ourselves, clean and untouched by anybody else's knowledge or even suspicion —something of our own for ever—to be remembered——

LAURA: Very well.

ALEC: We won't speak of it any more—I'm going now— back to Stephen's flat. I'll wait for you—if you don't come I shall know only that you weren't quite ready—that you needed a little longer to find your own dear heart. This is the address.

He scribbles on a bit of paper as the express thunders through the station. He gets up and goes swiftly without looking at her again. She sits staring at the paper, then she fumbles in her bag and finds a cigarette. She lights it— the platform bell goes.

MYRTLE: There's the 5.43.

BERYL: We ought to have another Huntley and Palmer's to put in the middle, really.

MYRTLE: There are some more on the shelf.

BERYL *fetches another packet of biscuits and takes it to* MYRTLE. *There is the noise of the 5.43—*LAURA'S *train—steaming into the station.* LAURA *sits puffing her cigarette. Suddenly she gets up—gathers up her bag quickly, and moves towards the door. She pauses and comes back to* *the table as the whistle blows. The train starts, she puts the paper in her bag and goes quietly out as the lights fade.*

SCENE IV

The time is about 9.45 on an evening in December.
There are only two lights on in the refreshment room as it is nearly closing time.
When the scene starts the stage is empty. There is the noise of a fast train rattling through the station.
BERYL comes in from the upstage door behind the counter armed with several muslin cloths which she proceeds to drape over the things on the counter. She hums breathily to herself as she does so. STANLEY enters, he has discarded his uniform and is wearing his ordinary clothes.

STANLEY: Hallo!

BERYL: You made me jump.

STANLEY: Are you walking home?

BERYL: Maybe.

STANLEY: Do you want me to wait?

BERYL: I've got to go straight back.

STANLEY: Why?

BERYL: Mother'll be waiting up.

STANLEY: Can't you say you've been kept late?

BERYL: I said that last time.

STANLEY: Say it again—say there's been a rush on.

BERYL: Don't be so silly—Mother's not that much of a fool.

STANLEY: Be a sport, Beryl—shut down five minutes early and say you was kept ten minutes late—that gives us a quarter of an hour.

BERYL: What happens if Mrs. Bagot comes back?

STANLEY: She won't—she's out having a bit of a slap and tickle with our Albert.

BERYL: Stan, you are awful!

STANLEY: I'll wait for you in the yard.

BERYL: Oh, all right.

STANLEY *goes out.*

BERYL *resumes her song and the draping of the cake stands.* LAURA *enters—she looks pale and unhappy.*

LAURA: I'd like a glass of brandy, please.

BERYL: We're just closing.

LAURA: I see you are, but you're not quite closed yet, are you?

BERYL [*sullenly*]: Three Star?

LAURA: Yes, that'll do.

BERYL [*getting it*]: Tenpence, please.

LAURA [*taking money from her bag*]: Here—and—have you a piece of paper and an envelope?

BERYL: I'm afraid you'll have to get that at the bookstall.

LAURA: The bookstall's shut—please—it's very important —I should be so much obliged——

BERYL: Oh, all right—wait a minute.

She goes off.

LAURA *sips the brandy at the counter, she is obviously trying to control her nerves.* BERYL *returns with some notepaper and an envelope.*

LAURA: Thank you so much.

BERYL: We close in a few minutes, you know.

LAURA: Yes, I know.

She takes the notepaper and her brandy over to the table by the door and sits down. She stares at the paper for a moment, takes another sip of brandy and then begins to write. BERYL *looks at her with exasperation and goes off through the upstage door.* LAURA *falters in her writing, then breaks down and buries her face in her hands.* ALEC *comes in—he looks hopelessly round for a moment, and then sees her.*

ALEC: Thank God—oh, darling!

LAURA: Please go away—please don't say anything.

ALEC: I can't let you go like this.

LAURA: You must. It'll be better—really it will.

ALEC [*sitting down beside her*]: You're being dreadfully cruel.

LAURA: I feel so utterly degraded.

ALEC: It was just a beastly accident that he came back early—he doesn't know who you are—he never even saw you.

LAURA: I listened to your voices in the sitting-room—I crept out and down the stairs—feeling like a prostitute.

ALEC: Don't, dearest—don't talk like that, please——

LAURA [*bitterly*]: I suppose he laughed, didn't he—after he got over being annoyed? I suppose you spoke of me together as men of the world.

ALEC: We didn't speak of you—we spoke of a nameless creature who had no reality at all.

LAURA [*wildly*]: Why didn't you tell him the truth? Why didn't you say who I was and that we were lovers—shameful secret lovers—using his flat like a bad house because we had nowhere else to go, and were afraid of being found out! Why didn't you tell him we were cheap and low and without courage—why didn't you——

ALEC: Stop it, Laura—pull yourself together!

LAURA: It's true—don't you see, it's true!

ALEC: It's nothing of the sort. I know you feel horrible, and I'm deeply, desperately sorry. I feel horrible, too, but it doesn't matter really—this—this unfortunate, damnable incident—it was just bad luck. It couldn't affect us really, you and me—we know the truth—we know we really love each other—that's all that matters.

LAURA: It isn't all that matters—other things matter, too, self-respect matters, and decency—I can't go on any longer.

ALEC: Could you really—say good-bye—not see me any more?

LAURA: Yes—if you'd help me.

There is silence for a moment. ALEC *gets up and walks about—he stops and stands staring at a coloured calendar on the wall.*

ALEC [*quietly, with his back to her*]: I love you, Laura—I shall love you always until the end of my life—all the shame that the world might force on us couldn't touch the real truth of it. I can't look at you now because I know something—I know that this is the beginning of the end— not the end of my loving you—but the end of our being together. But not quite yet, darling—please not quite yet.

LAURA: Very well—not quite yet.

ALEC: I know what you feel—about this evening, I mean —about the beastliness of it. I know about the strain of our different lives, our lives apart from each other. The feeling of guilt—of doing wrong is a little too strong, isn't it? Too persistent—perhaps too great a price to pay for the few hours of happiness we get out of it. I know all this because it's the same for me, too.

LAURA: You can look at me now—I'm all right.

ALEC [*turning*]: Let's be careful—let's prepare ourselves —a sudden break now, however brave and admirable, would be too cruel—we can't do such violence to our hearts and minds.

LAURA: Very well.

ALEC: I'm going away.

LAURA: I see.

ALEC: But not quite yet.

LAURA: Please not quite yet.

BERYL *enters in hat and coat.*

BERYL: I'm afraid it's closing time.

ALEC: Oh, is it?

BERYL: I shall have to lock up.

ALEC: This lady is catching the 10.10—she's not feeling very well, and it's very cold on the platform.

BERYL: The waiting-room's open.

ALEC [*going to counter*]: Look here—I'd be very much obliged if you'd let us stay here for another few minutes.

BERYL: I'm sorry—it's against the rules.

ALEC [*giving her a ten-shilling note*]: Please—come back to lock up when the train comes in.

BERYL: I'll have to switch off the lights—someone might see 'em on and think we were open.

ALEC: Just for a few minutes—please!

BERYL: You won't touch anything, will you?

ALEC: Not a thing.

BERYL: Oh, all right.

She switches off the lights. The lamp from the platform shines in through the window so it isn't quite dark.

ALEC: Thank you very much.

BERYL *goes out by the platform door, closing it behind her.*

LAURA: Just a few minutes.

ALEC: Let's have a cigarette, shall we?

LAURA: I have some. [*She takes her bag up from the table.*]

ALEC [*producing his case*]: No, here. [*He lights their cigarettes carefully.*] Now then—I want you to promise me something.

LAURA: What is it?

ALEC: Promise me that however unhappy you are, and however much you think things over that you'll meet me next Thursday as usual.

LAURA: Not at the flat.

ALEC: No—be at the Picture House café at the same time. I'll hire a car—we'll drive out into the country.

LAURA: All right—I promise.

ALEC: We've got to talk—I've got to explain.

LAURA: About going away?

ALEC: Yes.

LAURA: Where are you going? Where can you go? You can't give up your practice!

ALEC: I've had a job offered me—I wasn't going to tell you—I wasn't going to take it—but I must—I know now, it's the only way out.

LAURA: Where?

ALEC: A long way away—Johannesburg.

LAURA [*hopelessly*]: Oh God!

ALEC [*hurriedly*]: My brother's out there—they're opening a new hospital—they want me in it. It's a fine opportunity, really. I'll take Madeleine and the boys, it's been torturing me for three weeks, the necessity of making a decision one way or the other—I haven't told anybody, not even Madeleine. I couldn't bear the idea of leaving you, but now I see—it's got to happen soon, anyway—it's almost happening already.

LAURA [*tonelessly*]: When will you go?

ALEC: In about two months' time.

LAURA: It's quite near, isn't it?

ALEC: Do you want me to stay? Do you want me to turn down the offer?

LAURA: Don't be foolish, Alec.

ALEC: I'll do whatever you say.

LAURA: That's unkind of you, my darling. [*She suddenly buries her head in her arms and bursts into tears.*]

ALEC [*putting his arms around her*]: Oh, Laura, don't, please don't!

LAURA: I'll be all right—leave me alone a minute.

ALEC: I love you—I love you.

LAURA: I know.

ALEC: We knew we'd get hurt.

LAURA [*sitting up*]: I'm being very stupid.

ALEC [*giving her his handkerchief*]: Here.

LAURA [*blowing her nose*]: Thank you.

The platform bell goes.

There's my train.

ALEC: You're not angry with me, are you?

LAURA: No, I'm not angry—I don't think I'm anything, really—I feel just tired.

ALEC: Forgive me.

LAURA: Forgive you for what?

ALEC: For everything—for having met you in the first place—for taking the piece of grit out of your eye—for loving you—for bringing you so much misery.

LAURA [*trying to smile*]: I'll forgive you—if you'll forgive me——

There is the noise of a train pulling into the station. BERYL *enters.* LAURA *and* ALEC *get up.*

ALEC: I'll see you into the train.

LAURA: No—please stay here.

ALEC: All right.

LAURA [*softly*]: Good night, darling.

ALEC: Good night, darling.

She goes hurriedly out on to the platform without looking back.

ALEC: The last train for Churley hasn't gone yet, has it?

BERYL: I couldn't say, I'm sure.

ALEC: I'll wait in the waiting-room—thank you very much.

BERYL: I must lock up now.

ALEC: All right. Good night.

BERYL: Good night.

The train starts as he goes out on to the platform.

BERYL *locks the door carefully after him, and then goes off upstage as the lights fade.*

SCENE V

The time is between 5 and 5.30 on an afternoon in March. MYRTLE *is behind the counter.* BERYL *is crouching over the stove putting coals in it.* ALBERT *enters.*

ALBERT [*gaily*]: One tea, please—two lumps of sugar, and a bath bun, and make it snappy.

MYRTLE: What's the matter with you?

ALBERT: Beryl, 'op it.

MYRTLE: Don't you go ordering Beryl about—you haven't any right to.

ALBERT: You heard me, Beryl—'Op it.

BERYL [*giggling*]: Well, I never!

MYRTLE: Go into the back room a minute, Beryl.

BERYL: Yes, Mrs. Bagot.

She goes.

MYRTLE: Now then, Albert—you behave—we don't want the whole station laughing at us.

ALBERT: What is there to laugh at?

MYRTLE: Here's your tea.

ALBERT: How d'you feel?

MYRTLE: Don't talk so soft—how should I feel?

ALBERT: I only wondered—— [*He leans toward her.*]

MYRTLE: Look out—somebody's coming in.

ALBERT: It's only Romeo and Juliet.

LAURA *and* ALEC *come in.* LAURA *goes to the table,* ALEC *to the counter.*

ALEC: Good afternoon.

MYRTLE: Good afternoon—same as usual?

ALEC: Yes, please.

MYRTLE [*drawing tea*]: Quite Springy out, isn't it?

ALEC: Yes—quite.

He pays her, collects the tea and carries it over to the table—something in his manner causes ALBERT *to make a grimace over his tea-cup at* MYRTLE. ALEC *sits down at the table, and he and* LAURA *sip their tea in silence.*

ALBERT: I spoke to Mr. Saunders.

MYRTLE: What did he say?

ALBERT: 'E was very decent as a matter-of-fact—said it'd be all right——

MILDRED *comes in hurriedly. She is a fair girl wearing a station overall.*

MILDRED: Is Beryl here?

MYRTLE: Why, Mildred, whatever's the matter?

MILDRED: It's her mother—she's bad again—they telephoned through to the Booking Office.

MYRTLE: She's inside—you'd better go in. Don't go yelling in at her now—tell her gently.

MILDRED: They said she'd better come at once.

MYRTLE: I thought this was going to happen—stay here, Mildred. I'll tell her. Wait a minute, Albert.

MYRTLE *vanishes into the inside room.*

ALBERT: Better get back to the bookstall, hadn't you?

MILDRED: Do you think she's going to die?

ALBERT: How do I know?

MILDRED: Mr. Saunders thinks she is—judging by what the doctor said on the telephone.

ALBERT: 'Ow do you know it was the doctor?

MILDRED: Mr. Saunders said it was.

ALBERT: She's always being took bad, that old woman.

MILDRED: Do you think Beryl would like me to go along with her?

ALBERT: You can't, and leave nobody on the papers.

MILDRED: Mr. Saunders said I might if it was necessary.

ALBERT: Well, go and get your 'at then, and don't make such a fuss.

MYRTLE *comes back.*

MYRTLE: She's going at once, poor little thing!

ALBERT: Mildred's going with her.

MYRTLE: All right, Mildred—go on.

MILDRED [*half-way to the door*]: What about me 'at?

MYRTLE: Never mind about your 'at—go this way.

MILDRED *rushes off upstage.*

MYRTLE: Poor child—this has been hanging over her for weeks. [*She puts her head round the door.*] Mildred, tell Beryl she needn't come back to-night, I'll stay on.

ALBERT: 'Ere, you can't do that, we was going to the Broadway Melody of 1936.

MYRTLE: For shame, Albert—thinking of the Broadway Melody of 1936 in a moment of life and death!

ALBERT: But look 'ere, Myrtle——

MYRTLE: I dreamt of a hearse last night, and whenever I dream of a hearse something happens—you mark my words——

ALBERT: I've got reserved tickets——

MYRTLE: Send Stanley to change them on his way home. Come in 'ere when you go off and I'll make you a little supper inside.

ALBERT [*grumpily*]: Everybody getting into a state and fussing about——

MYRTLE: You shock me, Albert, you do really—go on, finish up your tea and get back to the gate. [*She turns and goes to the upper end of the counter.*]

ALBERT *gulps his tea.*

ALBERT [*slamming the cup down on the counter*]: Women!

He stamps out on to the platform.

ALEC: Are you all right, darling?

LAURA: Yes, I'm all right.

ALEC: I wish I could think of something to say.

LAURA: It doesn't matter—not saying anything, I mean.

ALEC: I'll miss my train and wait to see you into yours.

LAURA: No—no—please don't. I'll come over to your platform with you—I'd rather.

ALEC: Very well.

LAURA: Do you think we shall ever see each other again?

ALEC: I don't know. [*His voice breaks.*] Not for years, anyway.

LAURA: The children will all be grown up—I wonder if they'll ever meet and know each other.

ALEC: Couldn't I write to you—just once in a while?

LAURA: No—please not—we promised we wouldn't.

ALEC: Please know this—please know that you'll be with me for ages and ages yet—far away into the future. Time will wear down the agony of not seeing you, bit by bit the pain will go—but the loving you and the memory of you won't ever go—please know that.

LAURA: I know it.

ALEC: It's easier for me than for you. I do realise that, really I do. I at least will have different shapes to look at, and new work to do—you have to go on among familiar things—my heart aches for you so.

LAURA: I'll be all right.

ALEC: I love you with all my heart and soul.

LAURA [*quietly*]: I want to die—if only I could die.

ALEC: If you died you'd forget me—I want to be remembered.

LAURA: Yes, I know—I do, too.

ALEC: Good-bye, my dearest love.

LAURA: Good-bye, my dearest love.

ALEC: We've still got a few minutes.

LAURA: Thank God——!

DOLLY MESSITER *bustles into the refreshment room. She is a nicely dressed woman, with rather a fussy manner. She is laden with parcels. She sees* LAURA.

DOLLY: Laura! What a lovely surprise!

LAURA [*dazed*]: Oh, Dolly!

DOLLY: My dear, I've been shopping till I'm dropping—that sounds like a song, doesn't it? My feet are nearly falling off, and my throat's parched. I thought of having tea in Spindle's, but I was terrified of losing the train. I'm always missing trains, and being late for meals, and Bob gets disagreeable for days at a time. Oh, dear—— [*She flops down at their table.*]

LAURA: This is Doctor Harvey.

ALEC [*rising*]: How do you do!

DOLLY [*shaking hands*]: How do you do! Would you be a perfect dear and get me a cup of tea! I don't think I could drag my poor old bones as far as the counter. I must get some chocolates for Tony, too, but I can do that afterwards—here's sixpence——

ALEC [*waving it away*]: No, please——

He goes drearily over to the counter, gets another cup of tea from MYRTLE, *pays for it and comes back to the table, meanwhile* DOLLY *continues to talk.*

DOLLY: My dear—what a nice-looking man. Who on earth is he? Really, you're quite a dark horse. I shall telephone Fred in the morning and make mischief—that is a bit of luck. I haven't seen you for ages, and I've been meaning to pop in, but Tony's had measles, you know, and I had all that awful fuss about Phyllis—but of course you don't know—she left me! Suddenly upped and went, my dear, without even an hour's warning, let alone a month's notice.

LAURA [*with an effort*]: Oh, how dreadful!

DOLLY: Mind you, I never cared for her much, but still Tony did. Tony adored her, and—but, never mind, I'll tell you all about that in the train.

ALEC *arrives back at the table with her tea—he sits down again.* Thank you so very much. They've certainly put enough milk in it—but still it's wet and that's all one can really ask for in a refreshment room—— [*She sips it.*] Oh, dear—no sugar.

ALEC: It's in the spoon.

DOLLY: Oh, of course—what a fool I am—Laura, you look frightfully well. I do wish I'd known you were coming in to-day, we could have come together and lunched and had a good gossip. I loathe shopping by myself, anyway.

There is the sound of a bell on the platform.

LAURA: There's your train.

ALEC: Yes, I know.

DOLLY: Aren't you coming with us?

ALEC: No, I go in the opposite direction. My practice is in Churley.

DOLLY: How interesting! What sort of a doctor are you? I mean, are you a specialist at anything or just a sort of general family doctor?

ALEC: I'm a general practitioner at the moment.

LAURA [*dully*]: Dr. Harvey is going out to Africa next week.

DOLLY: But, my dear, how thrilling! Are you going to operate on the Zulus or something? I always associate Africa with Zulus, but I may be quite wrong.

There is the sound of ALEC's *train approaching.*

ALEC: I must go.

LAURA: Yes, you must.

ALEC: Good-bye.

DOLLY: Good-bye.

He shakes hands with DOLLY, *looks at* LAURA *swiftly once, then presses her hand under cover of the table and leaves hurriedly as the train is heard rumbling into the station.* LAURA *sits quite still.*

DOLLY: He'll have to run—he's got to get right over to the other platform. How did you meet him?

LAURA: I got something in my eye one day, and he took it out.

DOLLY: My dear—how very romantic! I'm always getting

things in my eye and nobody the least bit attractive has ever paid the faintest attention—which reminds me—you know about Harry and Lucy Jenner, don't you?

LAURA [*listening for the train to start*]: No—what about them?

DOLLY: My dear—they're going to get a divorce—at least I believe they're getting a conjugal separation, or whatever it is to begin with, and the divorce later on.

The train starts, and the sound of it dies gradually away in the distance.

It seems that there's an awful Mrs. Something or other in London that he's been carrying on with for ages—you know how he was always having to go up on business. Well, apparently Lucy's sister saw them, Harry and this woman, in the Tate Gallery of all places, and she wrote to Lucy, and then gradually the whole thing came out.

There is the sound of a bell on the platform.

Is that our train? [*She addresses* MYRTLE.] Can you tell me, is that the Ketchworth train?

MYRTLE: No, that's the express.

LAURA: The boat train.

DOLLY: Oh, yes—that doesn't stop, does it? Express trains are Tony's passion in life—he knows them all by name—where they start from and where they go to, and how long they take to get there. Oh, dear, I mustn't forget his chocolate. [*She jumps up and goes to the counter.*]

LAURA *remains quite still.*

[*At counter.*] I want some chocolate, please.

MYRTLE: Milk or plain?

DOLLY: Plain, I think—or no, perhaps milk would be nicer. Have you any with nuts in it?

The express is heard in the distance.

MYRTLE: Nestlé's nut milk—shilling or sixpence?

DOLLY: Give me one plain and one nut milk.

*The noise of the express sounds louder—*LAURA *suddenly gets up and goes swiftly out on to the platform. The express roars through the station as* DOLLY *finishes buying and paying for her chocolate. She turns.*

DOLLY: Oh! where is she?

MYRTLE [*looking over the counter*]: I never noticed her go.

DOLLY *comes over to the table,* LAURA *comes in again, looking very white and shaky.*

DOLLY: My dear, I couldn't think where you'd disappeared to.

LAURA: I just wanted to see the express go through.

DOLLY: What on earth's the matter—do you feel ill?

LAURA: I feel a little sick.

DOLLY: Have you any brandy?

MYRTLE: I'm afraid it's out of hours.

DOLLY: Surely—if someone's feeling ill——

LAURA: I'm all right, really.

The platform bell goes.

That's our train.

DOLLY: Just a sip of brandy will buck you up. [*To* MYRTLE.] Please——

MYRTLE: Very well. [*She pours out some brandy.*]

DOLLY: How much?

MYRTLE: Tenpence, please.

DOLLY [*paying her*]: There!

She takes the brandy over to LAURA, *who has sat down again at the table.*

Here you are, dear.

LAURA [*taking it*]: Thank you.

As she sips it the train is heard coming into the station. DOLLY *proceeds to gather up her parcels as the curtain falls.*

★

FUMED OAK
A Comedy in Two Scenes

CHARACTERS

HENRY GOW
DORIS, *his wife*
ELSIE, *his daughter*
MRS. ROCKETT, *his mother-in-law*

SCENE I. *Morning.*
SCENE II. *Evening.*

The action of the play passes in the sitting-room of the Gows' house in South London.

The time is the present day.

SCENE I

The Gows' sitting-room is indistinguishable from several thousand other suburban sitting-rooms. The dominant note is refinement. There are French windows at the back opening on to a narrow lane of garden. These are veiled discreetly by lace curtains set off by a pelmet and side pieces of rather faded blue casement cloth. There is a tiled fireplace on the right; an upright piano between it and the window; a fumed oak sideboard on the left and, below it, a door leading to the hall, the stairs of the front

*door. There is a fumed oak dining-room suite consisting
of a table, and six chairs; a sofa; an armchair in front of the
fire; a radio, and a plentiful sprinkling over the entire
room of ornaments and framed photographs.*

*When the curtain rises it is about eight-thirty on a spring
morning. Rain is trickling down the windows and breakfast is laid on the table.*

MRS. ROCKETT *is seated in the armchair by the fire; on a
small table next to her is a cup of tea, and a work-basket.
She is a fattish, grey-looking woman dressed in a blouse
and skirt and a pepper and salt jumper of artificial silk.
Her pince-nez snap in and out of a little clip on her bosom
and her feet are bad which necessitates the wearing of large
quilted slippers in the house.*

DORIS, *aged about thirty-five, is seated at the table reading
a newspaper propped up against the cruet. She is thin and
anaemic and whatever traces of past prettiness she might
have had are obscured by the pursed-up, rather sour gentility of her expression. She wears a nondescript coat-frock,
a slave bangle and a necklace of amber glass beads.* ELSIE,
*her daughter aged about fourteen, is sitting opposite to
her, cutting her toast into strips in order to dip them into
her boiled egg. She is a straight-haired ordinary-looking
girl dressed in a navy blue school dress with a glacé red
leather waist belt.*

*There is a complete silence broken only by the occa-
sional rattle of a spoon in a cup or a sniffle from* ELSIE *who
has a slight head cold.*

HENRY GOW *comes into the room. He is tall and spare,
neatly dressed in a blue serge suit. He wears rimless glasses
and his hair is going grey at the sides and thin on the top.
He sits down at the table without a word.* DORIS *automatically rises and goes out, returning in a moment with a
plate of haddock which she places in front of him and resumes her place.* HENRY *pours himself out some tea.* DORIS,
*without looking at him, being immersed in the paper,
passes him the milk and sugar.*

The silence continues until ELSIE *breaks it.*

ELSIE: Mum?

DORIS: What?

ELSIE: When can I put my hair up?

DORIS [*snappily*]: When you're old enough.

ELSIE: Gladys Pierce is the same age as me and she's got hers up.

DORIS: Never you mind about Gladys Pierce, get on with your breakfast.

ELSIE: I don't see why I can't have it cut. That would be better than nothing.

This remark is ignored.

Maisie Blake had hers cut last week and it looks lovely.

DORIS: Never you mind about Maisie Blake neither. She's common.

ELSIE: Miss Pritchard doesn't think so. Miss Pritchard likes Maisie Blake a lot, she said it looked ever so nice.

DORIS [*irritably*]: What?

ELSIE: Her hair.

DORIS: Get on with your breakfast. You'll be late.

ELSIE [*petulantly*]: Oh, Mum——

DORIS: And stop sniffling. Sniffle sniffle sniffle! Haven't you got a handkerchief?

ELSIE: Yes, but it's a clean one.

DORIS: Never mind, use it.

MRS. ROCKETT: The child can't help having a cold.

DORIS: She can blow her nose, can't she, even if she has got a cold?

ELSIE [*conversationally*]: Dodie Watson's got a terrible cold, she's had it for weeks. It went to her chest and then it went back to her head again.

MRS. ROCKETT: That's the worst of schools, you're always catching something.

ELSIE: Miss Pritchard's awful mean to Dodie Watson, she said she'd had enough of it.

DORIS: Enough of what?

ELSIE: Her cold.

There is silence again which is presently shattered by the wailing of a baby in the house next door.

MRS. ROCKETT: There's that child again. It kept me awake all night.

DORIS: I'm very sorry, I'm sure.

MRS. ROCKETT [*fiddling in her work basket*]: I wasn't blaming you.

DORIS: The night before last it was the hot-water pipes.

MRS. ROCKETT: You ought to have them seen to.

DORIS: You know as well as I do you can't stop them making that noise every now and then.

MRS. ROCKETT [*threading a needle*]: I'm sure I don't know why you don't get a plumber in.

DORIS [*grandly*]: Because I do not consider it necessary.

MRS. ROCKETT: You would if you slept in my room—gurgle gurgle gurgle all night long—it's all very fine for you, you're at the end of the passage.

DORIS [*with meaning*]: You don't have to sleep there.

MRS. ROCKETT: What do you mean by that?

DORIS: You know perfectly well what I mean.

MRS. ROCKETT [*with spirit*]: Listen to me, Doris Gow. I've got a perfect right to complain if I want to and well you know it. It isn't as if I was staying here for nothing.

DORIS: I really don't know what's the matter with you lately, Mother, you do nothing but grumble.

MRS. ROCKETT: Me, grumble! I like that, I'm sure. That's rich, that is.

DORIS: Well, you do. It gives me a headache.

MRS. ROCKETT: You ought to do something about those headaches of yours. They seem to pop on and off at the least thing.

DORIS: And I wish you wouldn't keep passing remarks about not staying here for nothing.

MRS. ROCKETT: Well, it's true, I don't.

DORIS: Anyone would think we was taking advantage of you.

MRS. ROCKETT: Well, they wouldn't be far wrong.

DORIS: Mother, how can you! You're not paying a penny more than you can afford.

MRS. ROCKETT: I never said I was. It isn't the money, it's

the lack of consideration.

DORIS: Pity you don't go and live with Nora for a change.

MRS. ROCKETT: Nora hasn't got a spare room.

DORIS: Phyllis has, a lovely one, looking out over the railway. I'm sure her hot-water pipes wouldn't annoy you, there isn't hot water in them.

MRS. ROCKETT: Of course, if I'm not wanted here, I can always go to a boarding-house or a private hotel.

DORIS: Catch you!

MRS. ROCKETT: I'm not the sort to outstay my welcome anywhere——

DORIS: Oh, for heaven's sake don't start that again——

MRS. ROCKETT [*addressing the air*]: It seems as though some of us had got out of bed the wrong side this morning.

ELSIE: Mum, can I have some more toast?

DORIS: No.

ELSIE: I could make it myself over the kitchen fire.

DORIS: No, I tell you. Can't you understand plain English? You've had quite enough and you'll be late for school.

MRS. ROCKETT: Never mind, Elsie, here's twopence, you can buy yourself a sponge-cake at Barret's.

ELSIE [*taking the twopence*]: Thanks, Grandma.

DORIS: You'll do no such thing, Elsie. I'm not going to have a child of mine stuffing herself with cake in the middle of the High Street.

MRS. ROCKETT [*sweetly*]: Eat it in the shop, dear.

DORIS: Go on, you'll be late.

ELSIE: Oh, Mum, it's only ten to.

DORIS: Do as I tell you.

ELSIE: Oh, all right.

She goes sullenly out of the room and can be heard scampering noisily up the stairs.

MRS. ROCKETT [*irritatingly*]: Poor little soul.

DORIS: I'll trouble you not to spoil Elsie, Mother.

MRS. ROCKETT: Spoil her! I like that. Better than half starving her.

DORIS [*hotly*]: Are you insinuating——

MRS. ROCKETT: I'm not insinuating anything. Elsie's getting a big girl, she only had one bit of toast for her breakfast and she used that for her egg. I saw her.

DORIS: It's none of your business and in future I'd be much obliged if you'd keep your twopences to yourself.

MRS. ROCKETT [*hurt*]: Very well, of course if I'm to be abused every time I try to bring a little happiness into the child's life——

DORIS: Anyone would think I ill-treated her the way you talk.

MRS. ROCKETT: You certainly nag her enough.

DORIS: I don't do any such thing and I wish you'd be quiet.

She flounces up from the table and goes over to the window, where she stands drumming her fingers on the pane. HENRY *quietly appropriates the newspaper she has flung down.*

MRS. ROCKETT [*unctuously*]: There's no need to lose your temper.

DORIS: I am not losing my temper.

MRS. ROCKETT: If I'd known when you were Elsie's age what you were going to turn out like I'd have given you what for, I can tell you.

DORIS: Pity you didn't, I'm sure.

MRS. ROCKETT: One thing, I never stinted any of my children.

DORIS: I wish you'd leave me to bring up my own child in my own way.

MRS. ROCKETT: That cold's been hanging over her for weeks and a fat lot you care——

DORIS: I've dosed her for it, haven't I? The whole house stinks of Vapex. What more can I do?

MRS. ROCKETT: She ought to have had Doctor Bristow last Saturday when it was so bad. He'd have cleared it up in no time.

DORIS: You and your Doctor Bristow.

MRS. ROCKETT: Nice thing if it turned to bronchitis. Mrs. Henderson's Muriel got bronchitis, all through neglecting a cold; the poor child couldn't breathe, they had to have two kettles going night and day——

DORIS: I suppose your precious Doctor Bristow told you that.

MRS. ROCKETT: Yes, he did, and what's more he saved the girl's life, you ask Mrs. Henderson.

DORIS: Catch me ask Mrs. Henderson anything, not likely, stuck up thing——

MRS. ROCKETT: Mrs. Henderson's a very nice lady-like woman, just because she's quiet and a bit reserved you say she's stuck up——

DORIS: Who does she think she is anyway, Lady Mountbatten?

MRS. ROCKETT: Really, Doris, you make me tired sometimes, you do really.

DORIS: If you're so fond of Mrs. Henderson it's a pity you don't see more of her. I notice you don't go there often.

MRS. ROCKETT [with dignity]: I go when I am invited.

DORIS [triumphantly]: Exactly.

MRS. ROCKETT: She's not the kind of woman that likes people dropping in and out all the time. We can't all be Amy Fawcetts.

DORIS: What's the matter with Amy Fawcett?

ELSIE comes into the room wearing a mackintosh and a tam-o'-shanter. She stamps over to the piano and begins to search untidily through the pile of music on it.

MRS. ROCKETT: Well, she's common for one thing, she dyes her hair for another, and she's a bit too free and easy all round for my taste.

DORIS: She doesn't put on airs, anyway.

MRS. ROCKETT: I should think not, after the sort of life she's led.

DORIS: How do you know what sort of a life she's led?

MRS. ROCKETT: Everybody knows, you only have to look at her; I'm a woman of the world, I am, you can't pull the wool over my eyes——

DORIS: Don't untidy everything like that, what are you looking for?

ELSIE: 'The Pixie's Parade,' I had it last night.

DORIS: If it's the one with the blue cover it's at the bottom.

ELSIE: It isn't—oh dear, Miss Pritchard will be mad at me if I can't find it.

MRS. ROCKETT: Perhaps you put it in your satchel, dear, here, let me look—— [*She opens* ELSIE's *satchel, which is hanging over the back of a chair and fumbles in it.*] Is this it?

ELSIE: Oh yes, thanks, Grandma.

DORIS: Go along now, for heaven's sake, you'll be late.

ELSIE: Oh, all right, Mum. Good-bye, Mum, good-bye, Grandma, good-bye, Dad.

HENRY: Good-bye.

MRS. ROCKETT: Good-bye, dear, give Grandma a kiss.

ELSIE *does so.*

DORIS: Don't dawdle on the way home.

ELSIE: Oh, all right, Mum.

She goes out. The slam of the front door shakes the house.

DORIS [*irritably*]: There now.

MRS. ROCKETT [*with studied politeness*]: If you are going down to the shops this morning, would it be troubling you too much to get me a reel of white cotton?

DORIS: I thought you were coming with me.

MRS. ROCKETT: I really don't feel up to it.

DORIS: I'll put it on my list.

She takes a piece of paper out of the sideboard drawer and scribbles on it.

MRS. ROCKETT: If it's out of your way, please don't trouble, it'll do another time.

DORIS: Henry, it's past nine.

HENRY [*without looking up*]: I know.

DORIS: You'll be late.

HENRY: Never mind.

DORIS: That's a nice way to talk, I must say.

MRS. ROCKETT: I'm sure if my Robert had ever lazed about like that in the mornings, I'd have thought the world had come to an end.

DORIS: Henry'll do it once too often, mark my words.

MRS. ROCKETT [*biting off her thread*]: Well, that corner's finished.

DORIS [*to* HENRY]: You'll have to move now, I've got to clear.

HENRY [*rising—absently*]: All right.

MRS. ROCKETT: Where's Ethel?

DORIS: Doing the bedroom.

She takes a tray which is leaning against the wall by the sideboard and proceeds to stack the breakfast things on to it.

HENRY *quietly goes out of the room.*

DORIS: Look at that wicked waste. [*Throws more scraps in fire.*]

MRS. ROCKETT: What's the matter with him?

DORIS: Don't ask me, I'm sure I couldn't tell you.

MRS. ROCKETT: He came in very late last night, I heard him go into the bathroom. [*There is a pause.*] That cistern makes a terrible noise.

DORIS: Does it indeed!

MRS. ROCKETT: Yes, it does.

DORIS [*slamming the teapot on to the tray*]: Very sorry, I'm sure.

MRS. ROCKETT: Where'd he been?

DORIS: How do I know?

MRS. ROCKETT: Didn't you ask him?

DORIS: I wouldn't demean myself.

MRS. ROCKETT: Been drinking?

DORIS: No.

MRS. ROCKETT: Sounded very like it to me, all that banging about.

DORIS: You know Henry never touches a drop.

MRS. ROCKETT: I know he says he doesn't.

DORIS: Oh, do shut up, Mother, we're not all like father.

MRS. ROCKETT: You watch your tongue, Doris Gow, don't let me hear you saying anything against the memory of your poor father.

DORIS: I wasn't.

MRS. ROCKETT [*belligerently*]: Oh yes, you were, you were insinuating again.

DORIS [*hoisting up the tray*]: Father drank and you know it—everybody knew it.

MRS. ROCKETT: You're a wicked woman.

DORIS: It's true.

MRS. ROCKETT: Your father was a gentleman, which is more than your husband will ever be, with all his night-classes and his book reading—night-classes indeed!

DORIS: Who's insinuating now?

MRS. ROCKETT [*angrily*]: I am, and I'm not afraid to say so.

DORIS: What of it?

MRS. ROCKETT [*with heavy sarcasm*]: I suppose he was at a night-class last night?

DORIS [*loudly*]: Mind your own business.

HENRY *comes in wearing his mackintosh and a bowler hat.*

HENRY: What's up?

DORIS: Where were you last night?

HENRY: Why?

DORIS: Mother wants to know and so do I.

HENRY: I was kept late at the shop and I had a bit of dinner in town.

DORIS: Who with?

HENRY: Charlie Henderson.

He picks up the paper off the table and goes out. After a moment the front door slams.

The baby next door bursts into fresh wails.

MRS. ROCKETT: There goes that child again. It's my belief it's hungry.

DORIS: Wonder you don't go and give it twopence to buy sponge-cake.

She pulls the door open with her foot and goes out with the tray as the lights fade on the scene.

SCENE II

It is about seven-thirty in the evening. ELSIE *is sitting at the piano practising with the loud pedal firmly down all the time.*

MRS. ROCKETT *is sitting in her chair by the fire, but she is dressed in her street things and wearing a black hat with a veil.*

DORIS, *also in street clothes, is clearing some paper patterns and pieces of material from the table.*

There is a cloth across the end of the table on which is set a loaf, a plate of cold ham, a saucer with two tomatoes in it, a bottle of A.1 sauce and a teapot, teacup, sugar basin and milk jug.

HENRY *comes in, taking off his mackintosh. He gives one look round the room and goes out into the hall again to hang up his things.* ELSIE *stops playing and comes over to* DORIS.

ELSIE: Can we go now?

DORIS: In a minute.

ELSIE: We'll miss the Mickey.

DORIS: Put on your hat and don't worry.

ELSIE [*grabbing her hat from the sideboard*]: Oh, all right.

HENRY *re-enters.*

DORIS: Your supper's all ready, the kettle's on the gas stove when you want it. We've had ours.

HENRY: Oh!

DORIS: And you needn't look injured either.

HENRY: Very well.

DORIS: If you managed to get home a bit earlier it'd save a lot of trouble all round.

HENRY [*amiably*]: Sorry, dear.

DORIS: It's all very fine to be sorry, you've been getting later and later these last few weeks, they can't keep you overtime every night.

HENRY: All right, dear, I'll tell them.

DORIS: Here, Elsie, put these away in the cupboard.

She hands her a pile of material and pieces of paper.
ELSIE *obediently takes them and puts them in the left-hand cupboard of the sideboard.*

HENRY [*sitting at the table*]: Cold ham, what a surprise!

DORIS [*looking at him sharply*]: What's the matter with it?

HENRY: I don't know, yet.

DORIS: It's perfectly fresh, if that's what you mean?

HENRY: Why are you all so dressed up?

ELSIE: We're going to the pictures.

HENRY: Oh, I see.

DORIS: You can put everything on the tray when you've finished and leave it in the kitchen for Ethel.

HENRY: Good old Ethel.

DORIS [*surprised*]: What?

HENRY: I said good old Ethel.

DORIS: Well, it sounded very silly, I'm sure.

MRS. ROCKETT [*scrutinising him*]: What's the matter with you?

HENRY: Nothing, why?

MRS. ROCKETT: You look funny.

HENRY: I feel funny.

MRS. ROCKETT: Have you been drinking?

HENRY: Yes.

DORIS: Henry!

MRS. ROCKETT: I knew it.

HENRY: I had a whisky and soda in town and another one at the Plough.

DORIS [*astounded*]: What for?

HENRY: Because I felt like it.

DORIS: You ought to be ashamed of yourself.

HENRY: I'm going to have another one too, a bit later on.

DORIS: You'll do no such thing.

HENRY: That hat looks awful.

DORIS [*furiously*]: Don't you speak to me like that.

HENRY: Why not?

DORIS [*slightly nonplussed*]: Because I won't have it, so there.

HENRY: It's a common little hat and it looks awful.

DORIS [*with an admirable effort at control*]: Now listen to me, Henry Gow, the next time I catch you drinking and coming home here and insulting me, I'll——

HENRY [*interrupting her gently*]: What will you do, Dorrie?

DORIS [*hotly*]: I'll give you a piece of my mind, that's what I'll do.

HENRY: It'll have to be a very little piece, Dorrie, you can't afford much! [*He laughs delighted at his own joke.*]

DORIS: I'd be very much obliged if you'd kindly tell me what this means?

HENRY: I'm celebrating.

DORIS: What do you mean, celebrating? What are you talking about?

HENRY: To-night's our anniversary.

DORIS: Don't talk so soft, our anniversary's not until November.

HENRY: I don't mean that one. To-night's the anniversary of the first time I had an affair with you and you got in the family way.

DORIS [*shrieking*]: Henry!

HENTY [*delighted with his carefully calculated effect*]: Hurray!

DORIS [*beside herself*]: How dare you say such a dreadful thing, in front of the child, too.

HENRY [*in romantic tones*]: Three years and a bit after that wonderful night our child was born! [*Lapsing into his normal voice.*] Considering all the time you took forming yourself, Elsie, I'm surprised you're not a nicer little girl than you are.

DORIS: Go upstairs, Elsie.

HENRY: Stay here, Elsie.

DORIS: Do as I tell you.

ELSIE: But, Mum——

DORIS: Mother, take her for God's sake! There's going to be a row.

HENRY [*firmly*]: Leave her alone and sit down.

MRS. ROCKETT *hesitates.*

Sit down, I tell you.

MRS. ROCKETT [*subsiding into a chair*]: Well, I never, I——

HENRY [*happily*]: See? It works like a charm.

DORIS: A fine exhibition you're making of yourself, I must say.

HENRY: Not bad, is it? As a matter of fact I'm rather pleased with it myself.

DORIS: Go to bed!

HENRY: Stop ordering me about. What right have you got to nag at me and boss me? No right at all. I'm the one that pays the rent and works for you and keeps you. What do you give me in return, I'd like to know! Nothing! I sit through breakfast while you and mother wrangle. You're too busy being snappy and bad-tempered even to say good morning. I come home tired after working all day and ten to one there isn't even a hot dinner for me; here, see this ham? This is what I think of it! [*He throws it at her feet.*] And the tomatoes and the A.1 bloody sauce! [*He throws them too.*]

DORIS [*screaming*]: Henry! All over the carpet.

HENRY [*throwing the butter-dish face downwards on the floor*]: And that's what I think of the carpet, now then!

DORIS: That I should live to see this! That I should live to see the man I married make such a beast of himself!

HENRY: Stop working yourself up into a state, you'll need all your control when you've heard what I'm going to say to you.

DORIS: Look here——

HENRY: Sit down. We'll all sit down, I'm afraid you'll have to miss the pictures for once.

DORIS: Elsie, you come with me.

MRS. ROCKETT: Yes, go on, Ducks.

She makes a movement towards the door, but HENRY *is*

too quick for her. He locks the door and slips the key into his pocket.

HENRY: I've been dreaming of this moment for many years, and believe me it's not going to be spoilt for me by you running away.

DORIS [*on the verge of tears*]: Let me out of this room.

HENRY: You'll stay where you are until I've had my say.

DORIS [*bursting into tears and sinking down at the table*]: Oh! Oh! Oh!——

ELSIE [*starting to cry too*]: Mum—oh, Mum——

HENRY: Here you, shut up, go and get the port out of the sideboard and give some to your mother—go on, do as I tell you.

ELSIE, *terrified and hypnotised into submission, goes to the sideboard cupboard and brings out a bottle of invalid port and some glasses, snivelling as she does so.* DORIS *continues to sob.*

That's right.

MRS. ROCKETT [*quietly*]: You drunken brute, you!

HENRY [*cheerfully*]: Worse than that, Mother, far worse. Just you wait and see.

MRS. ROCKETT [*ignoring him*]: Take some port, Dorrie, it'll do you good.

DORIS: I don't want any—it'd choke me——

HENRY [*pouring some out*]: Come on—here——

DORIS: Keep away from me.

HENRY: Drink it and stop snivelling.

DORIS: I'll never forgive you for this, never, never, never as long as I live! [*She gulps down some port.*]

HENRY [*noting her gesture*]: That's better.

MRS. ROCKETT: Pay no attention, Dorrie, he's drunk.

HENRY: I'm not drunk. I've only had two whiskies and sodas, just to give me enough guts to take the first plunge. You'd never believe how scared I was, thinking it over in cold blood. I'm not scared any more though, it's much easier than I thought it was going to be. My only regret is that I didn't come to the boil a long time ago, and tell you to your face, Dorrie, what I think of you, what I've been thinking of you for years, and this horrid little kid, and that old bitch of a mother of yours.

MRS. ROCKETT [*shrilly*]: Henry Gow!

HENRY: You heard me, old bitch was what I said, and old bitch was what I meant.

MRS. ROCKETT: Let me out of this room, I'm not going to stay here and be insulted—I'm not——

HENRY: You're going to stay here just as long as I want you to.

MRS. ROCKETT: Oh, am I? We'll see about that——

With astonishing quickness she darts over to the window and manages to drag one open. HENRY *grabs her by the arm.*

HENRY: No, you don't.

MRS. ROCKETT: Let go of me.

DORIS: Oh, Mother, don't let the neighbours know all your business.

HENRY: Not on your life!

MRS. ROCKETT [*suddenly screaming powerfully*]: Help! Help! Police! Help! Mrs. Harrison—help!——

HENRY *drags her away from the window, turns her round and gives her a light slap on the face, she staggers against the piano, meanwhile he shuts the window again, locks it and pockets the key.*

DORIS [*looking at him in horror*]: Oh, God! Oh, my God!

ELSIE [*bursting into tears again*]: Oh, Mum, Mum, he hit Grandma! Oh, Mum——

She runs to DORIS *who puts her arm round her protectively.*

MRS. ROCKETT [*gasping*]: Oh—my heart! I think I'm going to faint—oh—my heart——

HENRY: Don't worry, I'll bring you round if you faint——

MRS. ROCKETT: Oh—oh—oh, dear——

MRS. ROCKETT *slides on to the floor, perceptibly breaking her fall by clinging on to the piano stool.*

DORIS *jumps up from the table.*

DORIS: Mother!

HENRY: Stay where you are.

HENRY *goes to the sideboard and pours out a glass of water.* DORIS, *disobeying him, runs over to her mother.* ELSIE *wails.*

HENRY: Stand out of the way, Doris, we don't all want to get wet.

He approaches with the glass of water. MRS. ROCKETT *sits up weakly.*

MRS. ROCKETT [*in a far-away voice*]: Where am I?

HENRY: Number Seventeen Cranworth Road, Clapham.

MRS. ROCKETT: Oh—oh, dear!

HENRY: Look here, Mother, I don't want there to be any misunderstanding about this. I liked slapping you just now, see? It was lovely, and if you don't behave yourself and keep quiet I shall slap you again. Go and sit in your chair and remember if you feel faint the water's all ready for you.

He helps her up and escorts her to her chair by the fire. She collapses into it and looks at him balefully.

Now then. Sit down, Dorrie, you look silly standing about.

DORIS [*with a great effort at control*]: Henry——

HENRY [*slowly, but very firmly*]: Sit down! And keep Elsie quiet or I'll fetch her one, too.

DORIS [*with dignity*]: Come here, Elsie. Shut up, will you!

She sits at the table, with ELSIE.

HENRY: That's right.

He walks round the room slowly and in silence, looking at them with an expression of the greatest satisfaction on his face. Finally he goes over to the fireplace; MRS. ROCKETT *jumps slightly as he approaches her, but he smiles at her reassuringly and lights a cigarette. Meanwhile* DORIS, *recovering from her fear, is beginning to simmer with rage, she remains still, however, watching.*

Now then. I'm going to start, quite quietly, explaining a few things to you.

DORIS: Enjoying yourself, aren't you?

HENRY: You've said it.

DORIS [*gaining courage*]: You'll grin on the other side of

your face before I've done with you.

HENRY [*politely*]: Very likely, Dorrie, very likely indeed!

DORIS: And don't you Dorrie me, either! Coming home here drunk, hitting poor mother and frightening Elsie out of her wits.

HENRY: Maybe it'll do her good, do 'em both good, a little excitement in the home. God knows, it's dull enough as a rule.

DORIS [*with biting sarcasm*]: Very clever, oh, very clever, I'm sure.

HENRY: Fifteen, no sixteen years ago to-night, Dorrie, you and me had a little rough and tumble in your Aunt Daisy's house in Stansfield Road, do you remember?

DORIS: Henry——

HENRY [*ignoring her*]: We had the house to ourselves, it being a Sunday, your Aunt had popped over to the Golden Calf with Mr. Simmonds, the lodger, which, as the writers say, was her wont——

MRS. ROCKETT: This is disgusting, I won't listen to another word.

HENRY [*rounding on her*]: You will! Shut up!

DORIS: Pay no attention, Mother, he's gone mad.

HENRY: Let me see now, where was I? Oh yes, Stansfield Road. You had been after me for a long while, Dorrie, I didn't know it then, but I realised it soon after. You had to have a husband, what with Nora married and Phyllis engaged, both of them younger than you, you had to have a husband, and quick, so you fixed on me. You were pretty enough and I fell for it hook, line and sinker; then, a couple of months later you'd told me you'd clicked, you cried a hell of a lot, I remember, said the disgrace would kill your mother if she ever found out. I didn't know then that it'd take a sight more than that to kill that leathery old mare——

MRS. ROCKETT [*bursting into tears*]: I won't stand it, I won't! I won't!

HENRY [*rising above her sobs*]: I expect you were in on the whole business, in a refined way of course, you knew what was going on all right, you knew that Dorrie was no more in the family way than I was, but we got married; you both saw to that, and I chucked up all the plans I had for getting on, perhaps being a steward in a ship and seeing a bit of the world. Oh yes, all that had to go and we settled down in rooms and I went into Ferguson's Hosiery.

DORIS: I've given you the best years of my life and don't you forget it.

HENRY: You've never given me the best of anything, not even yourself. You didn't even have Elsie willingly.

DORIS [*wildly*]: It's not true—stop up your ears, Elsie, don't listen to him, he's wicked—he's wicked——

HENRY [*grimly*]: It's true all right, and you know it as well as I do.

DORIS [*shrilly*]: It was only right that you married me. It was only fair! You took advantage of me, didn't you? You took away my innocence. It was only right that you paid for it.

HENRY: Come off it, Dorrie, don't talk so silly. I was the innocent one, not you. I found out you'd cheated me a long, long time ago, and when I found out, realised it for certain, I started cheating you. Prepare yourself, Dorrie, my girl, you're going to be really upset this time. I've been saving! Every week for over ten years I've been earning a little bit more than you thought I was. I've managed, by hook and by crook, to put by five hundred and seventy-two pounds—d'you hear me?—five hundred and seventy-two pounds!

MRS. ROCKETT [*jumping to her feet*]: Henry! You never have—it's not true——

DORIS [*also jumping up*]: You couldn't have—you'd have given it away—I should have found out——

HENRY: I thought that'd rouse you, but don't get excited, don't get worked up. I haven't got it on me, it's in the bank. And it's not for you, it's for me—all but fifty pounds of it, that much is for you, just fifty pounds, the last you'll ever get from me——

DORIS: Henry! You couldn't be so cruel! You couldn't be

so mean!

HENRY: I've done what I think's fair and what I think's fair is damn sight more than you deserve. I've transferred the freehold of this house into your name, so you'll always have a roof over your head—you can take in lodgers at a pinch, though God help the poor bastards if you do!

DORIS: Five hundred and seventy-two pounds! You've got all that and you're going to leave me to starve!

HENRY: Cut out the drama, Dorrie, and have a look at your mother's savings bank book—I bet you'll find she's got enough to keep you in comfort till the day you die. She soaked her old man plenty, I'm sure—before he took to soaking himself!

MRS. ROCKETT: It's a lie!

HENRY: Now listen to me, Mother Machree—you've 'ad one sock in the jaw this evening and you're not just asking for another, you're sitting up and begging for it.

MRS. ROCKETT: I'll have you up for assault. I'll have the police on you, my fine fellow!

HENRY: They'll have to be pretty nippy—my boat sails first thing in the morning.

DORIS [*horrified*]: Boat!

HENRY: I'm going away. I've got my ticket here in my pocket, and my passport. My passport photo's a fair scream, I wish I could show it to you, but I don't want you to see the nice new name I've got.

DORIS: You can't do it, I can have you stopped by law. It's desertion.

HENRY: That's right, Dorrie, you've said it. Desertion's just exactly what it is.

DORIS [*breathlessly*]: Where are you going, you've got to tell me. Where are you going?

HENRY: Wouldn't you like to know? Maybe Africa, maybe China, maybe Australia. There are lots of places in the world you know nothing about, Dorrie. You've often laughed at me for reading books, but I've found out a hell of a lot from books. There are islands in the South Seas for instance with cocoa palms and turtles and sunshine all the year round—you can live there for practically nothing, then there's Australia or New Zealand, with a little bit of capital I might start in a small way sheep-farming. Think of it; miles and miles of open country stretching as far as the eye can see—good food and fresh air—that might be very nice, that might suit me beautifully. Then there's South America. There are coffee plantations, there, and sugar plantations, and banana plantations. If I go to South America I'll send you a whole crate. 'Ave a banana, Dorrie! 'Ave a banana!

DORIS: Henry, listen to me, you can't do this dreadful thing, you can't! If you don't love me any more, think of Elsie.

HENRY [*still in his dream*]: Then there's the sea, not the sea we know at Worthing with the tide going in and out regular and the band playing on the pier. The real sea's what I mean. The sea that Joseph Conrad wrote about, and Rudyard Kipling and lots of other people, too, a sea with whacking great waves and water spouts and typhoons and flying-fish and phosphorus making the foam look as if it was lit up. Those people knew a thing or two I can tell you. They knew what life could be like if you give it a chance. They knew there was a bit more to it than refinement and fumed oak and lace curtains and getting old and miserable with nothing to show for it. I'm a middle-aged man, but my health's not too bad taken all round. There's still time for me to see a little bit of real life before I conk out. I'm still fit enough to do a job of work—real work, mind you—not bowing and scraping and wearing myself out showing fussy old cows the way to the lace and the china ware and the bargain basement.

DORIS [*hysterically*]: God will punish you, you just see if He doesn't, you just see——

HENRY: God's been punishing me for fifteen years, it's high time He laid off me now. He's been punishing me good and proper for being damn fool enough to let you get your claws into me in the first place——

DORIS [*changing tactics*]: Henry, have pity, please don't

be so cruel, please—please——

HENRY: And don't start weeping and wailing either, that won't cut any ice with me, I know what you're like, I know you through and through. You're frightened now, scared out of your wits, but give you half a chance and you'd be worse than ever you were. You're a bad lot, Dorrie, not what the world would call a bad lot, but what I call a bad lot. Mean and cold and respectable. Good-bye, Dorrie——

DORIS [*flinging her arms round him and bursting into tears*]: Listen to me, Henry, you've got to listen—you must. You can't leave us to starve, you can't throw us on to the streets—if I've been a bad wife to you, I'm sorry—I'll try to be better, really I will, I swear to God I will—— You can't do this, if you won't forgive me, think of Elsie, think of poor little Elsie——

HENRY: Poor little Elsie, my eye! I think Elsie's awful. I always have ever since she was little. She's never done anything but whine and snivel and try to get something for nothing——

ELSIE [*wailing*]: Oh, Mum, did you hear what he said? Oh, Dad, oh dear——

MRS. ROCKETT [*comforting her*]: There, there, dear, don't listen to him——

HENRY: Elsie can go to work in a year or so, in the meantime, Dorrie, you can go to work yourself, you're quite a young woman still and strong as an ox.—Here's your fifty pounds——

He takes an envelope out of his pocket and throws it on to the table. Then he goes towards the door. DORIS *rushes after him and hangs on to his arm.*

DORIS: Henry, Henry, you shan't go, you shan't——

HENRY [*struggling with her*]: Leave hold of me.

DORIS: Mother, mother—help—help me, don't let him go——

HENRY *frees himself from her and, taking her by the shoulders, forces her back into a chair, then he unlocks the door and opens it.*

HENRY: I'm taking my last look at you, Dorrie. I shall never see you again as long as I live——

DORIS: Mother! Oh God!—oh, my God!——

She buries her head in her arms and starts to sob loudly. ELSIE *runs and joins her, yelling.* MRS. ROCKETT *sits transfixed, staring at him murderously.*

HENRY [*quietly*]: Three generations. Grandmother, Mother and Kid. Made of the same bones and sinews and muscles and glands, millions of you, millions just like you. You're past it now, Mother, you're past the thick of the fray, you're nothing but a music-hall joke, a mother-in-law with a bit of money put by. Dorrie, the next few years will show whether you've got guts or not. Maybe what I'm doing to you will save your immortal soul in the long run, that'd be a bit of all right, wouldn't it? I doubt it, though, your immortal soul's too measly. You're a natural bully and a cheat, and I'm sick of the sight of you; I should also like to take this opportunity of saying that I hate that bloody awful slave bangle and I always have. As for you, Elsie, you've got a chance, it's a slim one, I grant you, but still it's a chance. If you learn to work and be independent and, when the time comes, give what you have to give freely and without demanding life-long payment for it, there's just a bit of hope that you'll turn into a decent human being. At all events, if you'll take one parting piece of advice from your cruel, ungrateful father, you'll spend the first money you ever earn on having your adenoids out. Good-bye, one and all. Nice to have known you!

The wails of DORIS *and* ELSIE *rise in volume as he goes jauntily out, slamming the door behind him.*

CURTAIN

SONGS

with introductory notes by
NOEL COWARD

SOME DAY I'LL FIND YOU

from *Private Lives*, 1931

'Some Day I'll Find You' was written as a theme song for 'Private Lives.' Gertrude Lawrence sang a refrain of it alone in the first act and in the second we sang it together. For me the memory of her standing on that moonlit stage balcony in a dead-white Molyneux dress will never fade. She was the epitome of grace and charm and imperishable glamour. I have seen many actresses play Amanda in 'Private Lives'—some brilliantly, some moderately and one or two abominably. But the part was written for Gertie and, as I conceived it and wrote it, I can say with authority that no actress in the world ever could or ever will come within a mile of her performance of it. 'Some Day I'll Find You,' among my sentimental songs, ranks next in popularity to 'I'll See You Again' and, now that Gertie is no longer alive, I find the nostalgia of it almost unbearable.

When one is lonely, the days are long;
You seem so near, but never appear.
Each night I sing you a lover's song;
Please try to hear, my dear, my sweet.

Can't you remember the fun we had?
Time is so fleet, why shouldn't we meet?
When you're away from me days are sad;
Life's not complete, my sweet, my sweet.

Some day I'll find you, moonlight behind you,
True to the dream I am dreaming.

As I draw near you you'll smile a little smile;
For a little while we shall stand hand in hand.
I'll leave you never, love you forever,
All our past sorrow redeeming; try to make it true,
Say you love me too.
Some day I'll find you again.

MRS. WORTHINGTON
1935

This song has achieved considerable fame and has been
a staunch and reliable friend to me. Throughout my concert tour in the Dominions and at troop shows from
Scapa Flow to the jungles of Burma it has never failed
me. It has never formed part of any score or been performed in any stage production; it has seldom been sung
by anyone but me and I have only made one rather
scurried recording of it. Its universal appeal lies, I believe, in its passionate sincerity. It is a genuine *cri de
coeur* and as such cannot fail to ring true. Unhappily, its
effectiveness, from the point of view of propaganda, has
been negligible. I had hoped, by writing it, to discour-
age misguided maternal ambition, to deter those dreadful eager mothers from making beasts of themselves,
boring the hell out of me and wasting their own and my
time, but I have not succeeded. On the contrary, the song
seems to have given them extra impetus and ninety-nine
out of a hundred of the letters they write to me refer to
it with roguish indulgence, obviously secure in the conviction that it could not in any circumstances apply to
them. This is saddening, of course, but realizing that the
road of the social reformer is paved with disillusion I
have determined to rise above it.

Don't put your daughter on the stage, Mrs. Worthington;
Don't put your daughter on the stage.
The profession is overcrowded and the struggle's pretty
    tough,
And admitting the fact,

She's burning to act,
That isn't quite enough.
She has nice hands, to give the wretched girl her due,
But don't you think her bust is too developed for her age?
I repeat, Mrs. Worthington,
Sweet Mrs. Worthington,
Don't put your daughter on the stage.

Regarding yours, dear Mrs. Worthington,
Of Wednesday the twenty-third;
Although your baby
May be
Keen on a stage career,
How can I make it clear
That this is not a good idea?
For her to hope,
Dear Mrs. Worthington,
Is on the face of it absurd.
Her personality
Is not in reality
Inviting enough,
Exciting enough
For this particular sphere.

Don't put your daughter on the stage, Mrs. Worthington;
Don't put your daughter on the stage.
She's a bit of an ugly duckling you must honestly confess,
And the width of her seat would surely defeat
Her chances of success.
It's a loud voice, and tho' it's not exactly flat
She'll need a little more than that
To earn a living wage.
On my knees, Mrs. Worthington;
Please, Mrs. Worthington,
Don't put your daughter on the stage.

Don't put your daughter on the stage, Mrs. Worthington;
Don't put your daughter on the stage,
Tho' they said at the School of Acting she was lovely as
    Peer Gynt
I'm afraid on the whole an ingénue role
Would emphasize her squint.
She's a big girl and tho' her teeth are fairly good
She's not the type I even would
Be eager to engage.
No more buts, Mrs. Worthington:
NUTS, Mrs. Worthington,
Don't put your daughter on the stage.

A ROOM WITH A VIEW

from *This Year of Grace*, 1928

'A Room with a View' was originally conceived on a lonely beach in Honolulu where I was convalescing after a nervous breakdown. The title, unblushingly pinched from E. M. Forster's novel, came into my mind together with a musical phrase to fit it and I splashed up and down in the shallows, searching for shells and rhymes at the same time. When I was singing it in the American production of 'This Year of Grace' the late Alexander Woollcott took a black hatred to it. The last couplet:

> 'Maybe a stork will bring, this that and t'other thing to
> Our room with a view'

sent him into transports of vituperation. He implored me to banish the number from the show or at least promise not to sing it myself, and when I refused to pander to his wicked prejudices he decided to make a more public protest. One evening he came to the Selwyn Theatre and sat in a stage box with a group of ramshackle companions, including Harpo Marx, and when I began to sing the verse they all, with one accord, ostentatiously opened newspapers and read them. My voice faltered and stopped and I broke down in helpless giggles. After a while I rallied and, with what I still consider to be great presence of mind, sang the last couplet in baby talk, whereupon Woollcott gave a dreadful scream and, making sounds only too indicative of rising nausea, staggered from the box. The audience, I fear, was a trifle bewildered.

★

I've been cherishing through the perishing winter nights
    and days,
A funny little phrase that means
Such a lot to me that you've got to be with me heart and
    soul
For on you the whole thing leans.
Won't you kindly tell me what you're driving at,
What conclusions you're arriving at?
Please don't turn away or my dream will stay hidden out
    of sight
Among a lot of might-have-beens.

A Room with a View, and you, and no one to worry us,
No one to hurry us through this dream we've found,
We'll gaze at the sky, and try to guess what it's all about,
Then we will figure out why the world is round.
We'll be as happy and contented as birds upon a tree
High above the mountains and sea.
We'll bill and we'll coo-ooo-oo
And sorrow will never come,
Oh, will it ever come true
Our room with a view?

I'm so practical I'd make tactical errors as your wife,
I'd try to set your life to rights.
I'm upset a bit for I get a bit dizzy now and then
Following the mental flights.
Come with me and leave behind the noisy crowds,
Sunlight shines for us above the clouds.
My eyes glistened while I listened to all the things you said;
I'm glad I've got a head for heights.

A Room with a View, and you, and no one to give advice,
That sounds a paradise few could fail to choose.

With fingers entwined we'll find relief from the preachers
   who
Always beseech us to mind our P's and Q's.
We'll watch the whole world pass before us while we are
   sitting still,
Leaning on our own window sill.
We'll bill and we'll coo-oo-oo
And maybe a stork will bring this, that and t'other thing to
Our room with a view.

MAD ABOUT THE BOY

from *Words and Music*, 1932

'Mad About the Boy' was presented in a composite vocal scene. A society lady, a streetwalker, a schoolgirl and a scullery maid in turn sang their impression of a famous film star. The singers were Joyce Barbour, Steffi Duna, Norah Howard and Doris Hare. The film star, who appeared briefly at the end, was played by Edward Underdown. I have always been very attached to this number. The refrain remains constant, with different lyrics, but the verses vary and are, I think, musically interesting, particularly the 'schoolgirl' verse which is begun against an accompaniment of five-finger exercises.

(Society lady)

I met him at a party just a couple of years ago;
He was rather over hearty, and ridiculous,
But as I'd seen him on the Screen
He cast a certain spell.
I bask'd in his attraction for a couple of hours or so,
His manners were a fraction too meticulous.
If he was real or not I couldn't tell,
But like a silly fool, I fell.

Mad about the boy,
I know it's stupid to be mad about the boy;
I'm so ashamed of it
But must admit
The sleepless nights I've had about the boy.

On the Silver Screen
He melts my foolish heart in every single scene,
Although I'm quite aware
That here and there
Are traces of the cad about the boy.
Lord knows I'm not a fool girl,
I really shouldn't care,
Lord knows I'm not a schoolgirl,
In the flurry of her first affair.
Will it ever cloy?
This odd diversity of misery and joy
I'm feeling quite insane
And young again
And all because I'm mad about the boy.

(Streetwalker)

It seems a little silly
For a girl of my age and weight
To walk down Piccadilly
In a haze of love.
It ought to take a good deal more to get a bad girl down;
I should have been exempt, for
My particular kind of Fate
Has taught me such contempt for
Ev'ry phase of love,
And now I've been and spent my last half-crown
To weep about a painted clown.

Mad about the boy,
It's pretty funny but I'm mad about the boy.
He has a gay appeal
That makes me feel
There's maybe something sad about the boy.
Walking down the street,

His eyes look out at me from people that I meet;
I can't believe it's true,
But when I'm blue,
In some strange way I'm glad about the boy.
I'm hardly sentimental,
Love isn't so sublime,
I have to pay my rental
And I can't afford to waste much time.
If I could employ
A little magic that would finally destroy
This dream that pains me
And enchains me,
But I can't, because I'm mad about the boy.

(Maid)

Every Wednesday afternoon
I get a little time off from three to eleven.
Then I go to the picture 'ouse
And taste a little of my particular 'eaven.
'e appears in a little while;
Through a mist of tears
I can see 'im smiling above me.
Every picture I see 'im in,
Every lover's caress
Makes me wonderful dreams begin
Makes me long to confess—
Yes—
That if ever 'e looked at me
And thought perhaps I was worth the trouble to love me
I'd give in and wouldn't care
'owever far from the path of virtue 'e'd shove me.
Just supposing our love was brief,
If 'e treated me rough,

I'd be 'appy beyond belief,
Once would be enough.

Mad about the boy
I know I'm potty but I'm mad about the boy.
'e sets me 'eart on fire
With love's desire;
In fact, I've got it bad about the boy.
When I do the rooms
I see 'is face in all the brushes and the brooms.
Last week I strained me back
And got the sack
And 'ad a row with Dad about the boy.
'e thrills me to the marrow,
I see through all 'is tricks.
I'm pierced by Cupid's arrow
Every Wednesday from four to six.
'ow I should enjoy
To 'ave 'im treat me like a plaything or a toy.
I'd give me all to 'im
And crawl to 'im,
So help me God, I'm mad about the boy.

(Schoolgirl)

Homework, homework,
Every night there's homework.
While Elsie practices the gas goes pop!
I wish, I wish she'd stop.
Oh dear, oh dear,
Here it's always "No, dear,
You can't go out again,
You must stay home,
You waste your money
On that common picture drome.

Don't shirk,
Stay home and do your work."
Yearning, yearning,
How my heart is burning.
I see him on Saturday in "Strong Man's Pain,"
Then on Monday and on Friday week again.
To me he is the sole man
Who can kiss as well as Coleman.
I could faint whenever there's a closeup of his lips.
Though John Barrymore is larger,
When my hero's on his charger
Even Douglas Fairbanks hasn't smaller hips.
If he would only know
That I adore him so.

Mad about the boy,
It's simply scrumptous to be mad about the boy.
I know that quite sincerely
Housman really
Wrote "The Shropshire Lad" about the boy.
In my English prose
I've done a tracing of his forehead and his nose,
And there is, honor bright,
A certain slight
Effect of Galahad about the boy.
I spoke to Rosie Hooper,
She feels the same as me,
She says that Gary Cooper
Doesn't thrill her to the same degree.
In "Can Love Destroy?"
When he meets Garbo in a suit of corduroy,
He gives a little frown and knocks her down,
Oh dear, oh dear, I'm mad about the boy.

I'LL FOLLOW MY SECRET HEART

from *Conversation Piece*, 1934

I was working on 'Conversation Piece' at Goldenhurst, my home in Kent. I had completed some odd musical phrases here and there but no main waltz theme, and I was firmly and miserably stuck. I had sat at the piano daily for hours, repeatedly trying to hammer out an original tune or even an arresting first phrase, and nothing had resulted from my concentrated efforts but banality. I knew that I could never complete the score without my main theme as a pivot and finally, after ten days' increasing despair, I decided to give up and, rather than go on flogging myself any further, postpone the whole project for at least six months. This would entail telegraphing to Yvonne Printemps who was in Paris waiting eagerly for news and telling Cochran who had already announced the forthcoming production in the Press. I felt fairly wretched but at least relieved that I had had the sense to admit failure while there was still time. I poured myself a large whisky and soda, dined in grey solitude, poured myself another, even larger, whisky and soda, and sat gloomily envisaging everybody's disappointment and facing the fact that my talent had withered and that I should never write any more music until the day I died. The whisky did little to banish my gloom, but there was no more work to be done and I didn't care if I became fried as a coot, so I gave myself another drink and decided to go to bed. I switched off the lights at the door and noticed that there was one lamp left on by the piano. I walked automatically to turn it off, sat down and played 'I'll Follow My Secret Heart,' straight through in G flat, a key I had never played in before.

★

(Melanie)   When may I love somebody, please?

(Paul)   Not until you are safely married and then
only with greatest discretion.

(Melanie)   I see.

(Paul)   What's the matter?

(Melanie)   It doesn't feel like my birthday any more.
A cloud has pass'd across the sun
The morning seems no longer gay.
With so much bus'ness to be done
Even the sea looks grey.
C'est vrai!
C'est vrai!
It seems that all the joy has faded for the day
As though the foolish world no longer wants
to play.

You ask me to have a discreet heart
Until marriage is out of the way,
But what if I meet with a sweetheart so sweet
That my wayward heart cannot obey
A single word that you may say?
Then we shall have to go away.
No, for there is nowhere we could go
Where we could hide from what we know
Is true.

Don't be afraid I'll betray you
And destroy all the plans you have made,
But even your schemes must leave room for
my dreams,
So when all I owe to you is paid
I'll still have something of my own,
A little prize that's mine alone.

I'll follow my secret heart my whole life
    through,
I'll keep all my dreams apart till one comes
    true.
No matter what price is paid,
What stars may fade above
I'll follow my secret heart till I find love.

THE STATELY HOMES OF ENGLAND

from Operette, 1938

'The Stately Homes of England' was what is colloquially known as a 'show stopper.' It was performed by Hugh French, John Gatrell, Angus Menzies and Ross Landon. They were all nice looking, their diction was clear and they never went off without resounding applause. Since then I have recorded it and sung it all over the world and it has been popular with everyone with the exception of a Mayoress in New Zealand who said it let down the British Empire.

Lord Elderley, Lord Borrowmere, Lord Sickert
And Lord Camp
With ev'ry virtue, ev'ry grace,
Are what avails the sceptred race.

Here you see the four of us,
And there are so many more of us
Eldest sons that must succeed;
We know how Caesar conquer'd Gaul
And how to whack a cricket ball,
Apart from this, our education
Lacks co-ordination.
Tho' we're young and tentative
And rather representative,
Scions of a noble breed,
We are the products of those homes serene and stately
Which only lately
Seem to have run to seed!

The Stately Homes of England
How beautiful they stand,
To prove the upper classes
Have still the upper hand;
Tho' the fact that they have to be rebuilt
And frequently mortgag'd to the hilt
Is inclined to take the gilt
Off the gingerbread,
And certainly damps the fun,
Of the eldest son,
But still we won't be beaten,
We'll scrimp and screw and save;
The playing fields of Eton
Have made us frightfully brave
And tho' if the Van Dycks have to go
And we pawn the Bechstein Grand,
We'll stand by the Stately Homes of England.

Here you see
The pick of us.
You may be heartily sick of us
Still with sense
We're all imbued,
We waste no time on vain regrets
And when we're forced to pay our debts
We're always able to dispose of
Rows and rows and rows of
Gainsboroughs and Lawrences
Some sporting prints of Aunt Florence's
Some of which were rather rude.
Altho' we sometimes flaunt our family conventions
Our good intentions
Mustn't be misconstrued.

The Stately Homes of England
We proudly represent,
We only keep them up for Americans to rent.
Tho' the pipes that supply the bathroom burst
And the lavat'ry makes you fear the worst
It was used by Charles the First
Quite informally,
And later by George the Fourth
On a journey north,
The State Apartments keep their historical renown,
It's wiser not to sleep there
In case they tumble down;
But still if they ever catch on fire
Which with any luck, they might,
We'll fight for the Stately Homes of England.

The Stately Homes of England,
Tho' rather in the lurch,
Provide a lot of chances
For Psychical Research.
There's the ghost of a crazy younger son
Who murder'd in Thirteen Fifty One,
An extremely rowdy Nun
Who resented it,
And people who come to call
Meet her in the hall.
The baby in the guest wing
Who crouches by the grate,
Was wall'd up in the west wing
In Fourteen Twenty Eight.
If anyone spots The Queen of Scots
In a hand embroider'd shroud,
We're proud of the Stately Homes of England.

WORLD WEARY

from *This Year of Grace*, 1928

'World Weary' was sung by Beatrice Lillie in the American production of 'This Year of Grace.' She sang it dressed as an office boy, sitting on a high stool while munching an apple realistically, sometimes at the expense of the lyric. Recently I sang it myself at the Café de Paris wearing an alpaca dinner jacket and not munching an apple. The penultimate couplet had to be changed for the published edition. 'Gosh darned' was substituted for 'God-damned.' This compromise, while soothing outraged public opinion, weakened the song considerably.'

When I'm feeling dreary and blue
I'm only too glad to be left alone,
Dreaming of a place in the sun when day is done,
Far from the telephone;
Bustle and the weary crowd,
Make me want to cry out loud.
Give me something peaceful and grand
Where all the land slumbers in monotone.

I'm world weary, world weary,
Living in a great big town;
I find it so dreary, so dreary,
Everything looks grey or brown.
I want an ocean blue, great big trees,
A bird's eye view of the Pyrenees;

I want to watch the moon rise up
And see the great red sun go down.
Watching clouds go by through a wintry sky fascinates
        me,
But if I'm standing in the street
Everyone I meet simply hates me,
Because I'm world weary, world weary;
I could kiss the railroad tracks,
I want to get right back to nature and relax.

Get up in the morning at eight,
Relentless fate
Drives me to work at nine;
Toiling like a bee in a hive
From four to five,
Whether it's wet or fine.
Hardly ever see the sky,
Buildings seem to grow so high.
Maybe in the future I will
Perhaps fulfil
This little dream of mine.

I'm world weary, world weary,
Living in a great big town;
I find it so dreary, so dreary,
Everything looks grey or brown
I want a horse and plow, chickens too,
Just one cow with a wistful moo.
A country where the verb "to work"
Becomes a most improper noun.
I can hardly wait
'Til I see the great open spaces,
My loving friends will not be there

I'm so sick of their God-damned faces,
Because I'm world weary, world weary,
Tired of all these jumping jacks;
I want to get right back to nature and relax.

DON'T LET'S BE BEASTLY
TO THE GERMANS
1943

'Don't Let's Be Beastly to the Germans' I think is a very good satirical song indeed. It was also, quite unwittingly, scathingly prophetic. When it was first written in the spring of 1943 Mr. Winston Churchill liked it so much that I had to sing it to him seven times in one evening. On the other hand, certain rather obtuse members of the general public objected to it on the grounds that it was pro-German! This odd misconception flung both the B.B.C. and His Master's Voice Gramophone Company into a panic. The former organization refused to allow it to be broadcast and the latter suppressed for three months the record I had made of it. I was away at the time, entertaining troops in the Middle East, and knew nothing of this rumpus until my return. Later on, the song became absorbed into the public consciousness in its correct perspective and now 'Don't let's be beastly . . .' has become a catch phrase. I shall never cease to be surprised at the sublime silliness of some of those protesting letters. After all, 'Let's help the dirty swine again to occupy the Rhine again' and 'Let's give them full air parity and treat the rats with charity' are not, as phrases, exactly oozing with brotherly love. International circumstances have by now set the seal of irony on the whole thing. I must really be more careful what I write about in the future.

We must be kind
And with an open mind
We must endeavor to find a way
To let the Germans know that when the war is over
They are not the ones who'll have to pay.
We must be sweet
And tactful and discreet
And when they've suffer'd defeat
We mustn't let them feel upset
Or ever get the feeling that we're cross with them or hate
    them;
Our future policy must be to reinstate them.

Don't let's be beastly to the Germans
When our Victory is ultimately won.
It was just those nasty Nazis who persuaded them to fight
And their Beethoven and Bach are really far worse than
    their bite.
Let's be meek to them
And turn the other cheek to them
And try to bring out their latent sense of fun;
Let's give them full air parity
And treat the rats with charity
But don't let's be beastly to the Hun.

We must be just
And win their love and trust
And in addition we must be wise
And ask the conquered lands to join our hands to aid
    them.
That would be a wonderful surprise.
For many years
They've been in floods of tears

Because the poor little dears
Have been so wrong'd and only long'd
To cheat the world, deplete the world and beat the world
    to blazes.
This is the moment when we ought to sing their praises.

Don't let's be beastly to the Germans;
When we've definitely got them on the run
Let us treat them very kindly as we would a valued friend;
We might send them out some Bishops as a form of lease
    and lend.
Let's be sweet to them
And day by day repeat to them
That 'sterilization' simply isn't done.
Let's help the dirty swine again
To occupy the Rhine again
But don't let's be beastly to the Hun.

Don't let's be beastly to the Germans;
When the age of peace and plenty has begun
We must send them steel and oil and coal and ev'rything
    they need
For their peaceable intentions can be always guaranteed.
Let's employ with them
A sort of 'Strength thro' joy' with them;
They're better than us at honest manly fun.
Let's let them feel they're swell again
And bomb us all to hell again,
But don't let's be beastly to the Hun.

Don't let's be beastly to the Germans,
For you can't deprive a gangster of his gun;
Tho' they've been a little naughty to the Czechs and Poles
    and Dutch
But I don't suppose those countries really minded very

much.
Let's be free with them
And share the B.B.C. with them;
We mustn't prevent them basking in the sun.
Let's soften their defeat again
And build their bloody fleet again,
But don't let's be beastly to the Hun.

MAD DOGS AND ENGLISHMEN

from *Words and Music*, 1932

Oddly enough, one of the few songs I ever wrote that came to me in a setting appropriate to its content was 'Mad Dogs and Englishmen.' This was conceived and executed during a two-thousand-mile car drive from Hanoi in Tonkin to the Siamese border. True, the only white people to be seen were French, but one can't have everything.

'Mad Dogs and Englishmen' was originally sung in America by Beatrice Lillie in 'The Little Show.' In 'Words and Music' Romney Brent sang it as a missionary in one of Britain's tropical colonies. Since then I have sung it myself *ad nauseam*. On one occasion it achieved international significance. This was a dinner party given by Mr. Winston Churchill on board H.M.S. *Prince of Wales* in honor of President Roosevelt on the evening following the signing of the Atlantic Charter. From an eye-witness description of the scene it appears that the two world leaders became involved in a heated argument as to whether 'In Bankok at twelve o'clock they foam at the mouth and run' came at the end of the first refrain or at the end of the second. President Roosevelt held firmly to the latter view and refused to budge even under the impact of Churchillian rhetoric. In this he was right and when, a little while later, I asked Mr. Churchill about the incident he admitted defeat like a man.

In tropical climes there are certain times of day
When all the citizens retire
To tear their clothes off and perspire.
It's one of those rules that the greatest fools obey,

Because the sun is much too sultry
And one must avoid its ultry-violet ray.

Papalaka papalaka papalaka boo,
Papalaka papalaka papalaka boo,
Digariga digariga digariga doo,
Digariga digariga digariga doo.

The natives grieve when the white men leave their huts,
Because they're obviously definitely Nuts!

Mad dogs and Englishmen
Go out in the midday sun.
The Japanese don't care to,
The Chinese wouldn't dare to,
Hindoos and Argentines sleep firmly from twelve to one.
But Englishmen detest a siesta.
In the Philippines there are lovely screens
To protect you from the glare.
In the Malay States there are hats like plates
Which the Britishers won't wear.
At twelve noon the natives swoon
And no further work is done.
But mad dogs and Englishmen
Go out in the midday sun.

It's such a surprise for the Eastern eyes to see,
That though the English are effete,
They're quite impervious to heat.
When the white man rides ev'ry native hides in glee.
Because the simple creatures hope he
Will impale his solar topee on a tree.

Bolyboly bolyboly bolyboly baa,
Bolyboly bolyboly bolyboly baa.

Habaninny habaninnny habaninny baa,
Habaninny habaninnny habaninny baa.

It seems such a shame when the English claim the earth
That they give rise to such hilarity and mirth.

Mad dogs and Englishmen
Go out in the midday sun.
The toughest Burmese bandit
Can never understand it.
In Rangoon the heat of noon is just what the natives shun.
They put their Scotch or rye down and lie down.
In a jungle town where the sun beats down
To the rage of man or beast
The English garb of the English sahib
Merely gets a bit more creased.
In Bangkok at twelve o'clock
They foam at the mouth and run
But mad dogs and Englishmen
Go out in the midday sun.

Mad dogs and Englishmen
Go out in the midday sun.
The smallest Malay rabbit
Deplores this stupid habit.
In Hong Kong they strike a gong
And fire off a noon-day gun
To reprimand each inmate who's in late.
In the mangrove swamps where the python romps
There is peace from twelve till two.
Even caribous lie around and snooze,
For there's nothing else to do.
In Bengal, to move at all
Is seldom, if ever done.
But mad dogs and Englishmen
Go out in the midday sun.

I'LL SEE YOU AGAIN

from *Bitter Sweet*, 1929

The 'Bitter Sweet' waltz, 'I'll See You Again,' came to me whole and complete in a taxi when I was appearing in New York in 'This Year of Grace.' I was on my way home to my apartment after a matinee and had planned, as usual, to have an hour's rest and a light dinner before the evening performance. My taxi got stuck in a traffic block on the corner of Broadway and Seventh Avenue, klaxons were honking, cops were shouting, and suddenly in the general din there was the melody, clear and unmistakable. By the time I got home the words of the first phrase had emerged. I played it over and over again on the piano (key of E flat as usual) and tried to rest, but I was too excited to sleep.

'I'll See You Again,' I am happy to say, has been sung incessantly by everybody. It has proved over the years to be the greatest song hit I have ever had or am ever likely to have. I have heard it played in all parts of the world. Brass bands have blared it, string orchestras have swooned it, Palm Court quartettes have murdered it, barrel organs have ground it out in London squares and swing bands have tortured it beyond recognition. It is as popular today as when it was first heard, and I am still fond of it and very proud of it.

Now, Miss Sarah, if you please,
Sing a scale for me.
Ah————————
Take a breath and then reprise in a diff'rent key.
Ah————————

All my life I shall remember knowing you;
All the pleasure I have found in showing you
The diff'rent ways
That one may phrase,
The changing light and changing shade,
Happiness that must die,
Melodies that must fly
Memories that must fade
Dusty and forgotten by and by.
Learning scales will never seem so sweet again
Till our destiny shall let us meet again.
The will of fate,
May come too late.
When I'm recalling the hours we've had
Why will the foolish tears
Tremble across the years?
Why shall I feel so sad,
Treasuring the mem'ry of these days always?

I'll see you again
Whenever spring breaks through again.
Time may lie heavy between,
But what has been is past forgetting.
This sweet memory
Across the years will come to me;
Tho' my world may go awry,
In my heart will ever lie
Just the echo of a sigh, good-bye.

I WENT TO A MARVELLOUS PARTY

from Set to Music, 1939

During the summer of 1937 or 1938, I forget which, Elsa Maxwell gave a party in the south of France. It was a 'Beach' party and when she invited Grace Moore, Beatrice Lillie and me she explained that we were to 'come as we were' and that it would be 'just ourselves.' When we arrived (as we were) we discovered that 'just ourselves' meant about a hundred of us, all in the last stages of evening dress. We also discovered that one of the objects of the party was for us to entertain. As we were on holiday and had no accompanist and were not in any way prepared to perform, we refused. Elsa was perfectly understanding, but the other guests were a trifle disgruntled. I believe Beattie was persuaded to sing, but Grace and I held firm. This whole glittering episode was my original inspiration for 'I Went to a Marvellous Party.' Beattie eventually sang the song in 'Set to Music' wearing slacks, a fisherman's shirt, several ropes of pearls, a large sun-hat and dark glasses. She has sung it a great deal since.

Quite for no reason I'm here for the season,
And high as a kite.
Living in error
With Maude at Cap Ferrat
Which couldn't be right.
Everyone's here and frightf'lly gay,
Nobody cares what people say,
Tho' the Riviera
Seems really much queerer

Than Rome at its height.
Yesterday night

I went to a marvellous party
With Lulu and Nada and Nell.
It was in the fresh air and we went as we were
And we stayed as we were, which was hell.
Poor Grace started singing at midnight
And she didn't stop singing till four.
We knew the excitement was bound to begin
When Laura got blind on Dubonnet and gin
And scratched her brassière with a Cartier pin
I couldn't have liked it more.

I went to a marvellous party;
I must say the fun was intense,
We all had to do what the people we knew
Would be doing a hundred years hence.
Dear Cecil arrived wearing armour,
Some shells and a black feather boa.
Poor Millicent wore a surrealist comb
Made of bits of Mosaic from St. Peter's in Rome,
But the weight was so great that she had to go home;
I couldn't have liked it more!

I went to a marvellous party
We played *the* most wonderful games.
Maureen disappeared and came back in a beard
And we all had to guess at her name.
We talked about growing old gracefully
And Elsie, who's 74, said
"A. It's a question of being sincere,
And B. If you're supple you've nothing to fear."
Then she swung upside down from the glass
        chandelier.
I couldn't have liked it more.

People's behaviour away from Belgravia
Would make you aghast.
So much variety
Watching society scampering past.
If you had any mind at all
Gibbon's divine "Decline and Fall"
Seems pretty flimsy,
No more than a whimsy.
By way of contrast,
On Saturday last

I went to a marvellous party
We didn't start dinner till 10,
And young Bobby Carr did a stunt at the bar
With a lot of extraordinary men.
Poor Frieda arrived with a turtle,
Which shattered us all to the core.
The grand-duke was doing a rhumba with me
When suddenly Cyril cried "fiddle-de-dee"
And whipped off his trousers and jumped in the sea.
I couldn't have liked it more.

I went to a marvellous party
Elise made an entrance with May.
You'd never have guessed from her fisherman's vest
That her bust had been whittled away.
Poor Lulu got fried on Chianti
And talked about *esprit de corps*.
Maurice made a couple of passes at Gus,
And Freddie, who hates any kind of a fuss,
Did half the Big Apple and twisted his truss;
I couldn't have liked it more.

THE PARTY'S OVER NOW
From Words and Music, 1932

Night is over, dawn is breaking,
Everywhere the
Town is waking,
Just as we are on our way to sleep.
Lovers meet and dance a little,
Snatching from romance a little
Souvenir of happiness to keep.
The music of an hour ago
Was just a sort of Let's pretend,
The melodies that charmed us so
At last are ended.

The party's over now,
The dawn is drawing very nigh,
The candles gutter, the starlight leaves the sky;
It's time for little boys and girls
To hurry home to bed,
For there's a new day waiting just ahead.
Life is sweet
But time is fleet;
Beneath the magic of the moon
Dancing time
May seem sublime,
But it is ended all too soon.
The thrill has gone,
To linger on
Would spoil it anyhow:
Let's creep away from the day
For the party's over now.

THE FINEST ANTHOLOGY
OF POETRY AVAILABLE
ANYWHERE
IN A LOW-PRICED EDITION

....

SIX CENTURIES

....

OF GREAT

....

POETRY

....

(DELL NO. FE-69)

AN EXTENSIVE COLLECTION OF THE GREATEST ENGLISH LYRIC POETRY

FORM

CHAUCER TO YEATS

....

ITS 544 PAGES

CONTAIN A WIDE SELECTION

OF ENDURING WORK BY OVER

100 ACKNOWLEDGED MASTERS

....

SELECTED AND ARRANGED
(WITH AN INTRODUCTION)
BY
ROBERT PENN WARREN
AND
ALBERT ERSKINE
EDITORS
OF SHORT STORY MASTERPIECES

....

NOW AVAILABLE WHEREVER

POCKET-SIZED BOOKS ARE SOLD.

If this book cannot be obtained locally, send 50c
(plus 5c for postage and handling) for each copy to
Dell Publishing Company, Inc., 10 West 33rd
Street, New York 1, N. Y.